THREE ICELANDIC OUTLAW SAGAS

THREE ICELANDIC OUTLAW SAGAS

THE SAGA OF GISLI

THE SAGA OF GRETTIR

THE SAGA OF HORD

VIKING SOCIETY FOR NORTHERN RESEARCH
UNIVERSITY COLLEGE LONDON
2004

This edition first published by Everyman Paperbacks in 2001

Reissued by Viking Society for Northern Research in 2004

ISBN 0 903521 66 0

The maps are based on those in various volumes of *Íslensk fornrit*.
The cover illustration is of Grettir Ásmundarson from AM 426 fol., a late 17th-century Icelandic manuscript in Stofnun Árna Magnússonar á Íslandi, Reykjavík

Printed by Short Run Press Limited, Exeter

CONTENTS

Preface vii

Chronology viii

Introduction xi

Note on the Text xxvi

THE SAGA OF GISLI 1

THE SAGA OF GRETTIR 69

THE SAGA OF HORD 265

Text Summaries 329

Genealogical Tables 340

Bibliography 341

The Verses 343

Glossary of Icelandic Terms 351

Index of names 357

MAPS

Iceland .... xvi–xvii

Haukadal 2

North-West Iceland 20–1

Hvalfiord 266

Central West Iceland 276–7

South-West Iceland 328

PREFACE

The translation of *The Saga of Gisli* in this volume was made by George Johnston and first published in Everyman's University Library in 1963 with Notes and an Introductory Essay by Peter Foote. It is here reproduced with only minor changes. *The Saga of Grettir* was published in G. A. Hight's translation in Everyman's Library in 1914 and reissued with an Introduction and Notes by Peter Foote in 1965. This new translation is by Anthony Faulkes, as is that of *The Saga of Hord*, which has not appeared in Everyman's Library before. The Introduction, Notes and Index in this volume are also by Anthony Faulkes but use material from Peter Foote's Notes and Essay on *The Saga of Gisli* (including the account of the metre of *dróttkvætt* on p. 343), from his Introduction and Notes to *The Saga of Grettir* (the Glossary has also benefitted from several more recent suggestions made by him), and from Anthony Faulkes's Introduction to *The Saga of Hord and the Holm-Dwellers*, translated by Alan Boucher, published by Iceland Review, Reykjavík, Iceland in 1983.

CHRONOLOGY

In this chronology many dates are uncertain; some of the events recorded in the sagas are probably not historical, and the dates given for them here are those that fit in with other events in the sagas.

AD	Historical Events	Events in the Outlaw Sagas
*c.*725	*Beowulf* written	
793	First viking raid on Northumbria	
*c.*850	Beginning of viking settlement in England	
*c.*870	Beginning of viking settlement in Iceland	
871	Alfred the Great becomes king of England	
*c.*885	Battle of Hafrsfiord. Harald Finehair becomes king of all Norway	
*c.*900		Onund Wooden-leg comes to Iceland
930	Foundation of *Althing*	
*c.*945		Birth of Asmund Hærulang
949		Birth of Geir Grimsson
950		Birth of Hord Grimkelsson
952		Thorbiorn Sur goes to Iceland
960		Gisli's failed attempt at sworn brotherhood
962	Division of Iceland into Quarters	
964		Gisli made outlaw
965		Hord and Geir go abroad
969		Geir returns to Iceland
977/8		Gisli killed
980		Hord returns to Iceland Thorstein Dromund born
984		Hord outlawed
*c.*985	Beginning of settlement of Greenland	
989		Deaths of Hord and the Holm-dwellers

AD	Historical Events	Events in the Outlaw Sagas
995	Olaf Tryggvason becomes king of Norway	
996		Birth of Grettir Asmundarson
999–1000	Christianity accepted in Iceland	
*c.*1005	Fifth court established	
1010	Burning of Nial	
1011		Grettir kills Skeggi, is made outlaw and goes to Norway
1013		Grettir's brother Illugi born
1014	Battle of Clontarf	Grettir returns to Iceland The Battle of the Heath
1015	Battle of the Nesses	Grettir goes to Norway again
1016		Grettir made full outlaw at *Althing* and returns to Iceland
1024		Death of Biorn Hitdælakappi
1024–5		Grettir in Thorisdal
1027		Death of Thorstein Kuggason
1028		Grettir goes to Drangey
1030	Fall of St Olaf. Death of Lawspeaker Skapti	
1031	Death of Snorri Godi	Deaths of Grettir and Illugi
1033		Death of Thorbiorn Ongul
1047		Thorstein Dromund and Spes go to Rome
1056	First bishop at Skalholt. Sæmund the wise born	
1066	Fall of Harald Hardradi in England	
1067	Ari the wise born	
1096	Tithe laws introduced in Iceland	
1106	First bishop at Holar	
1117–18	Icelandic Laws first written down	
*c.*1130	*The Book of the Icelanders* compiled	
1133	First Icelandic monastery founded (at Thingeyrar)	
*c.*1150	Earliest Icelandic manuscript fragments	
1153	Archbishopric established at Nidaros in Norway	
1179	Birth of Snorri Sturluson	
1199	Bishop Thorlak declared saint	
1214	Birth of Sturla Thordarson	
1217	Hakon Hakonarson becomes king of Norway	

AD	Historical Events	Events in the Outlaw Sagas
*c.*1220	Snorri Sturluson's *Edda*	
1226	*Tristrams saga*	
*c.*1230		*The Saga of Gisli* written
1241	Snorri Sturluson killed	
1245	Death of Styrmir the Wise	
*c.*1250	Oldest surviving manuscript of a saga of Icelanders (*Egils saga*)	
1262	Iceland ceded to king of Norway	
1263	Death of King Hakon	
*c.*1275	Codex Regius of eddic poems	
*c.*1280	*Nials saga. Hrafnkels saga*	
1284	Sturla Thordarson dies	
*c.*1320		*The Saga of Grettir* written
*c.*1340	Birth of Chaucer	
*c.*1350	*Modruvallabok* written	
1350–1400		*The Saga of Hord* written
1382	*Flateyjarbok* begun	
*c.*1400		Oldest surviving manuscript fragments of *The Saga of Gisli* and *The Saga of Hord* written
*c.*1500		Principal manuscripts of *The Saga of Grettir*, *The Saga of Hord* and *The Saga of Gisli* written
1550	Reformation in Iceland	
1944	Iceland regains complete independence	

INTRODUCTION

The three sagas translated from Old Icelandic in this volume are all about Icelanders in the Middle Ages who lived and died as outlaws in the Icelandic countryside. Like all other sagas of Icelanders, these three are anonymous, but they were certainly written by Icelanders, probably in the west or north-west of Iceland. They are very difficult to date precisely, but it is likely that *The Saga of Gisli* was written in the first half of the thirteenth century, perhaps about 1230, and thus is part of the first flowering of 'classical' Icelandic sagas. *The Saga of Grettir* is quite a lot later, from the fourteenth century, probably from about 1320 and later than most other sagas of Icelanders. Indeed the most recent editor of the saga (Örnólfur Thorsson, 1994) suggests that it may be from as late as the end of the fourteenth century. *The Saga of Hord* (called Holmveria saga, 'the Saga of the Holm-dwellers', in the principal manuscript) is also a late saga, probably from the second half of the fourteenth century. These two sagas were therefore written quite a long time after the Icelandic Commonwealth was ceded to the Norwegian Crown in 1262–3, possibly even as late as the time of the union of the Norwegian, Swedish and Danish crowns (1397); and also after translated Romances and Heroic Sagas (*fornaldar sögur*, Sagas of Ancient Time or Legendary Sagas) may be regarded as having to a large extent superseded Sagas of Icelanders as the primary expression of Icelandic identity and values.

The three heroes of the outlaw sagas lived in the so-called 'Saga Age', the century from the time of the completion of the settlement of Iceland and the foundation of the Althing or General Assembly, when the Icelandic legal system was first formalised, traditionally dated AD 930, to the death of St Olaf, king of Norway, in 1030. To the extent that all three sagas contain some accurate information about that period of Icelandic history, they must be based on earlier sources such as *The Book of Settlements*, other Sagas of Icelanders like *Eyrbyggja saga*, *Laxdæla saga* and *Egils saga*; and oral sources such as poetry composed by Icelanders of the intermediate period and oral prose stories handed down from the time of the three heroes. *The Saga of Grettir* and *The Saga of Hord* refer to statements by Icelandic historians of the thirteenth century (Sturla Thordarson, 1214–84; Styrmir Karason, d. 1245) which are not found in their surviving writings, and this has led some people to think that Sturla and Styrmir might have composed the original sagas on which the surviving sagas of Grettir and Hord were based (Styrmir was for ten years prior at the monastery on Viðey, not far from Hvalfiord, in the area where the author of *The Saga of Hord* may be presumed to have lived); but it is perhaps more likely that they merely referred to these heroes in more general writings, or indeed that the extant statements, if they are accurately reported at all, were simply oral ones. Sturla Þórðarson, however, refers to *The Saga of Hord* in his version of *The Book of Settlements* (c. 1275; this is the earliest source to mention either Hord or his saga), so this saga must have existed in some form in the thirteenth century. The sword Greyflank is mentioned in Sturla's *Íslendinga saga*, but it may have been known about from oral tales independent of *The Saga of Gisli*. *The Saga of Gisli* itself makes use of few written sources, not even *The Book of Settlements*, being probably older than most of the other sagas (it has some overlap with *Kormaks saga*, though these two sagas seem to be independent of each other), but the author may have had written genealogies that were also used in *The Book of Settlements* and other sagas, and adapts episodes from *Droplaugarsona saga* and *Bjarnar saga Hítdælakappa*, which are among the earliest Sagas of Icelanders. It was itself used in the version of *The Book of Settlements* made by Sturla Þórðarson and in *Eyrbyggja saga*. *The Saga of Grettir* makes extensive use of Sturla Þórðarson's version of *The Book of Settlements* (from which it gets the reference to the otherwise unknown Saga of Bodmod and Grimolf, as well as much of the information on which the first thirteen chapters are based) and a large number of other sagas. These include *Heiðarvíga saga, Ljósvetninga saga, The Saga of Gisli, Fóstbræðra saga*—the episode in ch. 52, together with one of Grettir's verses, is also in one version of the last of these, though in this case *The Saga of Grettir* may have been the original source—some of which are named in the text (e.g. *Laxdæla saga, Bjarnar saga Hítdælakappa* and *Bandamanna saga*). The information said to be derived from the saga of Earl Eiríkr probably comes from the episode in *Fagrskinna* 163–7; an unknown *Eiríks saga* is also referred to in *Fagrskinna* 139 as a source. Grettir himself is referred to in a variety of other medieval writings in Iceland (e.g. in Haukr Valdísarson's catalogue poem *Íslendingadrápa*, *c.*1200; one of his verses is quoted in Snorri Sturluson's *Edda*, p. 119) and was clearly very well known. *The Saga of Hord* refers to an otherwise unknown *Álfgeirs þáttr* as a source.

For *The Saga of Gisli* and *The Saga of Hord*, besides the complete texts that survive in a manuscript of the last quarter of the fifteenth century, on which the present translations are based, which also contains a text of *The Saga of Grettir* (AM 556 a 4to), there are extant other versions: a fragmentary and shorter or more compact one in the case of *The Saga of Hord*, on a single leaf in AM 564 a 4to, written about the beginning of the fifteenth century, where it is entitled 'Harðar saga Grímkelssonar', and fragments of a slightly different, rather poorly copied version of *The Saga of Gisli* that were also written in the early fifteenth century. Two eighteenth-century copies also survive of a third version of *The Saga of Gisli* that was rather longer than the fifteenth-century versions, especially in the introductory parts. There is no likelihood that these are oral variants of the sagas; the fragmentary version of *The Saga of Hord*, although it is actually found in an earlier manuscript than that which contains the complete text, is almost certainly an abridgement of the original saga; reported speech is often used instead of direct speech, and it contains no verses. The text of the first eight chapters, which is all that is extant in this version, is almost twice as long in the longer version, and some of the characters have different names. The longer version of *The Saga of Gisli* is also now thought to be closer to the original than the shorter version, even though in its early chapters it seems to have been much influenced by the style of Heroic or Legendary Sagas, while the shorter version seems to have been abridged and altered in other ways. *The Saga of Grettir* survives in only one version of which there are four independent medieval manuscripts, all written in the late fifteenth or early sixteenth century, though some of these have been added to since the original saga was written (these additions include material probably derived from Sturla's account of Grettir, from which some contradictions arise, particularly in the chronology); there is a large number of later manuscripts.

All three outlaw sagas, though predominantly in vernacular prose, include a number of verses, many of which are attributed to the respective heroes. These verses contain little narrative; they are mostly represented as speeches of the characters in the sagas, and constitute comments on their experiences. In some cases the attributions may be correct, though there is no way of proving or disproving it. But it is also possible that some of the verses were composed by the authors of the prose narrative, or, more likely, were composed by story-tellers to embellish accounts of the three heroes in the centuries between their deaths and the composition of the extant written sagas. Such verses could then become primary sources for the reconstruction of events in the prose narrative. It is even possible that some verses were added to the sagas after they were first written. Many of the verses in *The Saga of Hord* are in a style characteristic of fourteenth-century heroic poems and sagas (those exchanged between the hero and the dead viking Soti, and those of the idol in ch. 38, are in the simple style of eddic verse, rather than the usual elaborate skaldic style), while the series of verses attributed to Gisli in his saga, which tell of his prophetic dreams, were clearly composed in the Christian period (i.e. after AD 1000, but very likely in the twelfth century) by someone who wished to represent the heathen hero as having some intimations of the coming of the new religion. Few of the many verses attributed to Grettir are thought to be really by him (about ten at most), and are likely to date from the twelfth or more likely the thirteenth century. Some of the verses also appear in other sources (in *The Saga of Grettir*, the first half of the second verse of ch. 72, which is also in Snorri Sturluson's *Edda*, and the first two pieces of verse in ch. 63, which are also in *The Book of Settlements*, one version of which has both of them as complete 8-line stanzas; and the verse attributed to Thormod in ch. 27 of *The Saga of Grettir* also appears in *Fóstbræðra saga*), and these are more likely to be genuine, and at least can be shown to be older than the prose of the saga. Sometimes verses conflict with the story as told in the prose, e.g. in *The Saga of Gisli* (chs 17, 34, 36), which means that they cannot have been written by the author of the prose.

A number of the verses in *The Saga of Grettir* form series which may have been composed as continuous poems by a later, perhaps much later, story-teller, such as his autobiographical series in chs 24 and 52; Lopt's (Hallmund's) verses in ch. 54 and his dying poem in ch. 62, which may be based on those of Hialmar and Odd in Örvar-Odds saga (these all in a simpler style than the usual court metre, though they contain examples of complex word-play); the Sodulkolla verses in ch. 47; Grettir's poem about Hallmund in ch. 57 (two lines of which also appear in the poem about Hallmund in *Bergbúa þáttr*); and his last verses in ch. 80, which refer to some events that are not related in the saga. The Torfi Vebrandsson mentioned in the second of these is not known from other sources, but the events in the fourth are referred to in *Ljósvetninga saga*. Four of the verses in ch. 80 are only in one of the early manuscripts and may have been composed after the saga was written. The dream-verses in *The Saga of Gisli* may also have been composed as a continuous poem.

Of the three outlaw heroes, only Grettir lived and died a Christian, and *The Saga of Grettir*, particularly the final chapters, has a distinct Christian slant. Grettir's misfortunes, however, are not attributed to his religion or to his sinfulness, but consistently to his *gæfuleysi*, his lack of 'good luck' (sometimes translated 'misfortune'). *Gæfa* was originally a pre-Christian concept, and meant a quality, sometimes embodied as a kind of guardian spirit, which attached itself to some individuals or families, but could be alienated. Lack of it predisposed an individual's undertakings to failure. The words *gæfa* and *gæfumaðr* are translated in various ways in this volume, according to the precise contexts in which they occur, sometimes as 'luck, lucky man' (*gæfusamligr* 'fortunate'), sometimes as 'success, successful man' (see, for example, *The Saga of Grettir*, chs 31, 34, 39, 41, 52, 62, 78, 90, 92; *The Saga of Gisli*, ch. 27, 36). It is lack of *gæfa* which in *The Saga of Grettir* is supposed to be the reason for everything Grettir tries to do turning out badly, although his actual motivation is almost invariably good (*ógæfa*, *ógæfumaðr* is translated 'disposition to failure', '[a man] prone to failure' or the like; *ógæfufullr* 'prone to disaster', *gæfulauss* (pl. *-lausir*) 'having forfeited one's good luck', *The Saga of Hord*, chs 12, 34). Thus his attempt to save his shipwrecked companions leads to his outlawry, one of his exploits designed to cleanse a neighbourhood of evil spirits has disastrous consequences for him, and he loses his opportunity of gaining St Olaf's help to clear his name because of an unfortunate encounter with a devil in a church. He is cursed by one of his evil opponents with fear of the dark, which leads to him being forced to rely on untrustworthy helpers, and his actual death, shortly before well-meaning men were due to release him from outlawry, is caused by black magic. He is contrasted with his half-brother Thorstein Dromund, who, besides being quite different in physique and character, and in spite of being in a Christian sense a rather conventional sinner, ends up as an almost saintly figure.

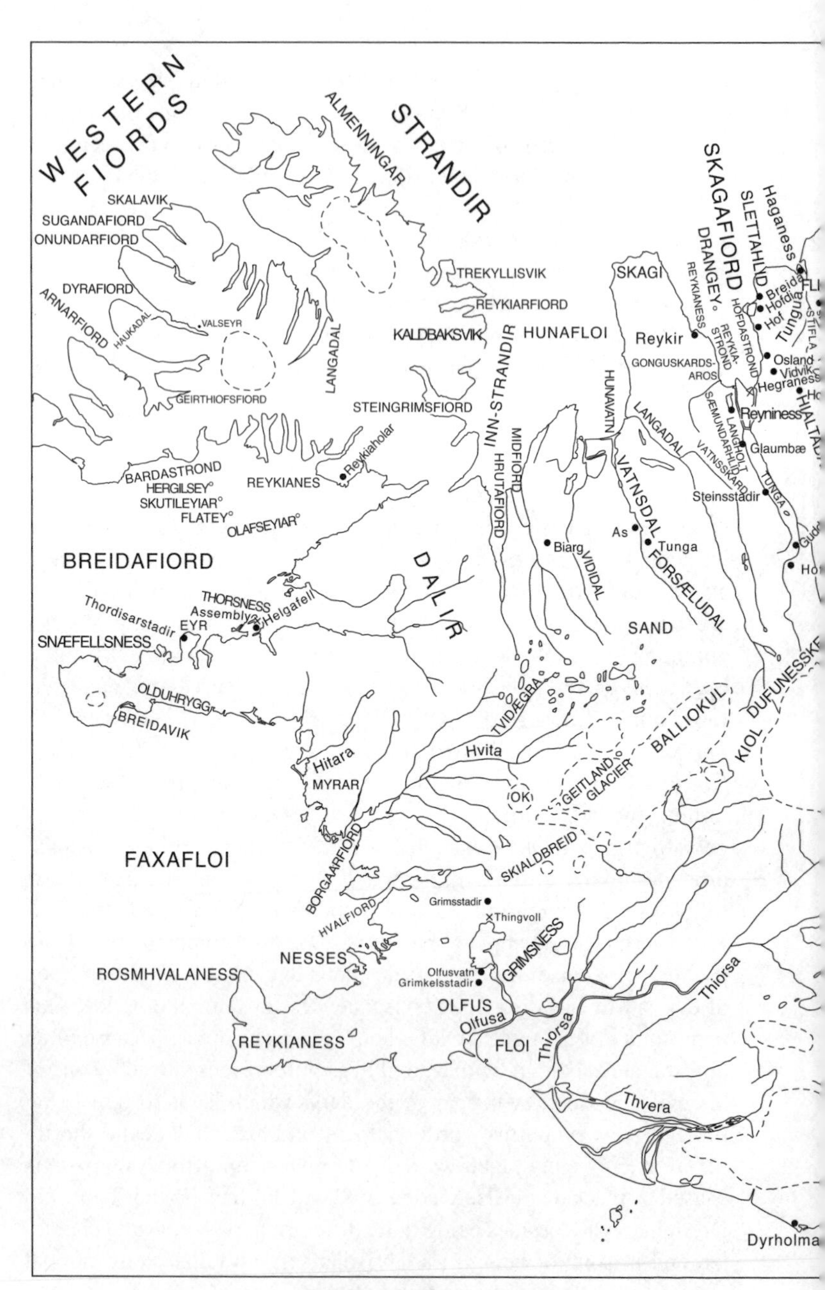

WEST ICELAND

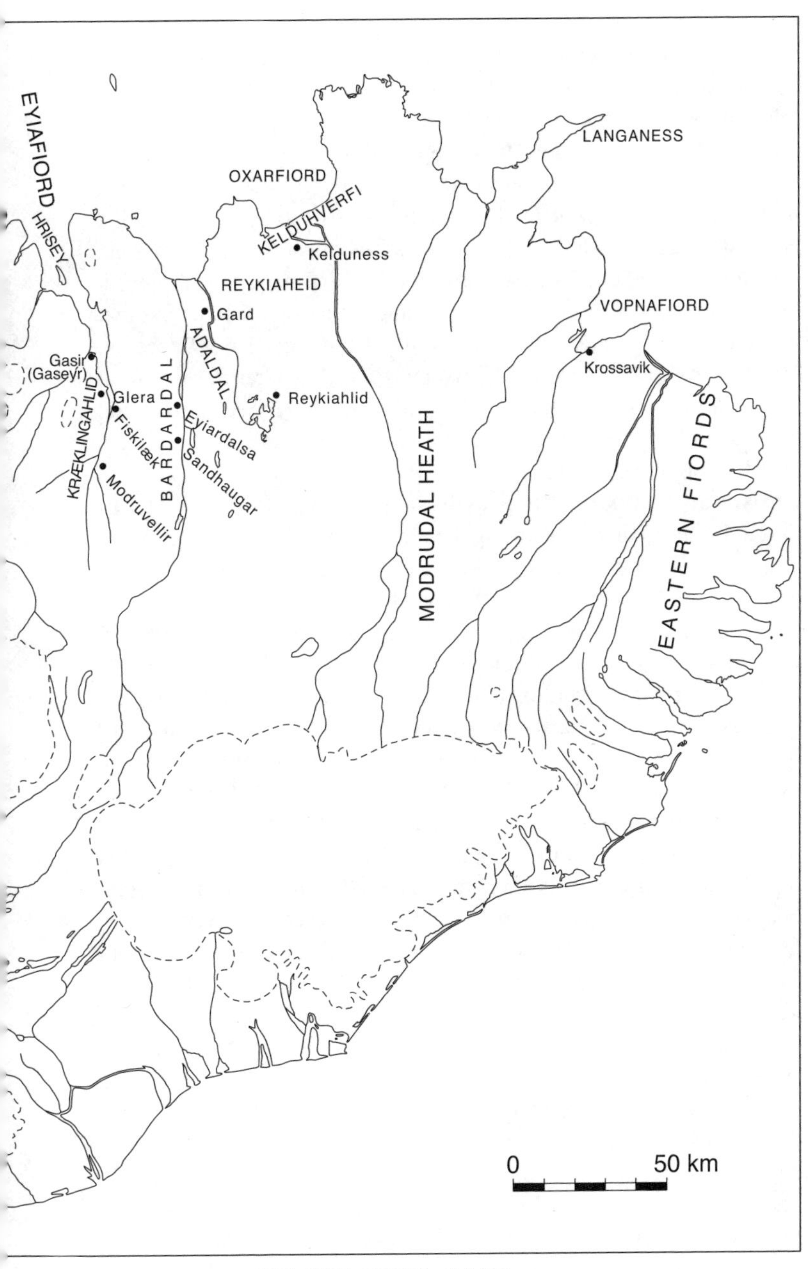

EAST ICELAND

Gisli is a well-meaning but tragic figure who tries to uphold his own and his family's honour and attempts to affirm his solidarity with his relations and in-laws, but he is drawn into a disastrous feud by envious and ill-motivated men. He is supported by his wife throughout his hard life, but betrayed by his sister and repeatedly let down by his brother and some of his friends, though others stand by him faithfully. His resistance to his enemies and particularly his last stand is heroic. The dreams and poems that are attributed to him in the saga represent him as torn between evil pagan values and the new Christian ones that will triumph soon after his death. In the prose narrative too (see ch. 10), he is represented as half-Christian. He is, like Grettir, said not to be a *gæfumaðr* (man of luck, successful man, ch. 36; see also the end of ch. 27, where the same contrast between success and ability is made as in the proverb quoted in *The Saga of Grettir*, ch. 34), but in his saga fate is more frequently invoked as the source of his misfortunes. Stories told in Eddic poems, concerning the relationships between Sigurd the Dragon-slayer, Gudrun, Brynhild, and Gudrun's brothers (Sigurd's oath-brothers), seem to have influenced the presentation of the story of Gisli and his wife and sister and brothers-in-law, and the verse in ch. 19 itself invokes the comparison.

Hord is a more conventional romantic hero who performs a number of stock viking exploits abroad and marries a foreign earl's daughter before, back in Iceland, allowing his temper to lead him to retaliate against a bad neighbour. This leads to his outlawry, and he too, in spite of his fundamental good-will and social commitment, is repeatedly let down by ill-disposed relatives and friends. During his outlawry he is represented as trying to avoid crime and to atone for his wrong-doing, but as being continually compromised by his associates, who are morally inferior to himself and whom he unsuccessfuly tries to restrain from excess and ill-advised actions. His death is achieved by trickery, and vengeance for it is brought about by his sister, his wife and his two young sons. His loyalty to his friends in spite of their faults and his attempts to save them from their own gullibility, his attachment to his wife, his ability to see clearly when all around him are blind, and his death to which he knowingly goes because of an appeal to his honour and heroism, all combine to make him an attractive and sympathetic character who seems more sinned against than sinning, and evoke the pity and admiration of the reader. The same sort of irony is employed in all three outlaw sagas, whose heroes come to be at odds with society in spite of good intentions and are portrayed as more honourable than their victorious enemies in spite of their faults.

The Sagas of Icelanders tell of many men who were outlawed, though only in the three sagas translated here can the hero's outlawry be regarded as the primary theme of the story. In all three the main structural basis is the hero's biography and his heroic death, though all three have substantial introductory sections giving the history of the respective families before the main story begins. These introductory sections can be regarded as establishing various themes that are significant later in the saga. *The Saga of Grettir* also has a substantial section after the hero's death which tells not only of the vengeance taken by his half-brother Thorstein Dromund in Constantinople, but also of Thorstein's subsequent adventures. These use motifs borrowed from European fabliau and romance, notably that of the ambiguous oath, well known from versions of the Romance of Tristram and Iseult. Another such episode is when the hero hides under the mattress on Hergilsey. Such elements occur also in *The Saga of Gisli*, for example in the episode in ch. 16 where the hero ties together all the cows' tails in the byre, clearly in order to make pursuit after he has killed his enemy difficult, though the expected comedy of his pursuers tripping over the obstacles does not materialise. These episodes were not necessarily taken direct from foreign models; the motif of the cows' tails is probably borrowed from *Droplaugarsona saga*, and Thorstein Dromund's release from prison by a woman, and the subsequent affair with her during which he has several lucky escapes from detection by her husband, seem actually to be based on stories told of Harald Hardradi in *Morkinskinna*. In *The Saga of Hord*, many of the hero's adventures abroad are characteristic of viking exploits in Heroic Sagas, though his marrying an earl's daughter is more like one of the Romance sagas. This saga has many links with other, earlier sagas, both sagas of Icelanders and Heroic sagas, as well as one or more versions of the *Book of Settlements*.

Under early Icelandic law, offences were regarded as injuries to individuals or families, whether they caused loss of property, limbs or life, or were perceived as damage to a person's or family's honour, and the injured parties could claim compensation or honour-payments. For this purpose all free men were regarded as having the same price.

Apart from fines (or rather, enforced compensation for physical or other injuries to members of other families), outlawry was the only sanction for misdemeanours available to courts in the Icelandic Commonwealth (on outlawry in Iceland see *Medieval Scandinavia: An Encyclopedia*, ed. Phillip Pulsiano (1993), under *Outlaw sagas*; *Outlawry*). This might be temporary, for three years ('lesser outlawry', *The Saga of Grettir*, chs 16, 78), or permanent in the case of serious uncompensatable injuries or killings ('full outlawry', *The Saga of Grettir*, ch. 84), in which case the guilty man lost all legal rights and status for the rest of his life. Thus the final solution to the problem of anti-social behaviour was social rejection. In either case, the guilty person would normally go abroad for the term of his outlawry, either to Norway and other parts of Europe, as raiders or traders or mercenaries or, in some cases, to Greenland, like Eirik the Red, who had had to leave Norway because of some killings and was subsequently outlawed from Iceland as well (Icelanders' attempts to colonise North America in the early eleventh century did not succeed), or the thirteenth-century Aron Hiorleifsson, who went to Norway (in other respects Arons's career was in some ways strikingly similar to Gisli's). If the person outlawed chose not to go abroad, like Gunnar in *Njáls saga*, he would usually be killed by his enemies, and if so they would incur no legal liability. It was presumably because of the difficulty of surviving in the geographical and climatic conditions of the uninhabited parts of Iceland that so few outlaws chose to try to live out their outlawry there, and anyone helping or sheltering an outlaw could incur a sentence of outlawry or other penalties himself (note, for instance, *The Saga of Gisli* chs 19, 20, 21, 23; *The Saga of Grettir*, chs 47, 54, 58). The landscape of Iceland is inhospitable, particularly inland away from the farming areas, and it is surprising that it was apparently possible for outlaws to survive in the wasteland there, and that some should apparently choose to try to do so. When they did, they provided material for story-tellers who celebrated the independence and heroism that the undertaking demanded. Besides the three heroes of the sagas in this volume, there were others in later times who became famous for surviving as outlaws in Iceland, notably Fjalla-Eyvindur in the eighteenth century. Some of these were celebrated in literary works of the nineteenth century or later, and many in folk-tales that survive from the eighteenth century to modern times.

Medieval Iceland before 1262 had an elaborate constituti
system, codified in manuscripts surviving from the thirtee
It was in various ways fundamentally different from wha
other parts of Europe. Not only did Iceland not have a kin
sequently no standing army or bureaucratic system; it had no officials to enforce the law and no professional lawyers. There were no authorities. All suits had to be brought by individuals before courts where decisions were made by a jury of men appointed by local chieftains (*goðar*). The chieftains themselves had no direct power over the courts, though they formed a legislature which could make new laws or alter existing ones. The courts' decisions had to be implemented by those who had brought the original suits, though a chieftain's help might be available to them. In many cases we are told that out-of-court settlements were brought about by agreed arbitrators or by direct negotiation between the parties. The lawspeaker or lawman was the only official in this system. He was elected from among the chieftains and presided over the legislature; his chief duty was to pronounce the law, both at sessions of the legislature and often privately at the request of the parties in a dispute (e.g. *The Saga of Grettir*, chs 27, 51, 77; *The Saga of Hord*, ch. 10).

This system meant that the law and its administrators were not perceived as opponents of ordinary people as they often are under other systems. The law was identified with the way of life of medieval Icelanders, the foundation of their social organisation, and there could be little possibility of alienation of individuals from it and consequently no idealisation of the outlaw life. The opponents of Gisli, Grettir and Hord were not 'authorities' or officials, corrupt or otherwise, but their opponents in local feuds to whom they were often related, at any rate by marriage. There is no equivalent of the Sheriff of Nottingham in the Icelandic sagas, unless it be Thorbiorn Ongul, who is appointed as a sort of unofficial representative of the farming establishment and deputed to get rid of Grettir, and Eyiolf the Grey, who is offered money to get rid of Gisli. Such payments, and the prices on the heads of Icelandic outlaws, were privately put up, not by the authorities. There is therefore no political or socio-economic element to these Icelandic outlaw stories (except for the concern of the farming establishment over the loss of their sheep that were being stolen by outlaws), even when, as in the case of *The Saga of Grettir* and *The Saga of Hord*, the story was written and probably constructed after the fall of the Icelandic Commonwealth when the government of the country and the administration of its legal system had come to be in the hands of the king of Norway's officials who were often perceived as foreigners exploiting the Icelandic peasantry. In the Iceland of their time, moreover, insofar as there was much stratification of society, the heroes of the outlaw sagas all had comparatively high social status, coming from the ranks of the wealthy landowners and being descended from leading settlers. They were the victims of feuds caused by social rivalry, not rebels against authority or society itself, or fighters for social justice against corrupt officials, though there is a good deal of unfairness both in their outlawry and in the ways in which they are killed. Moreover Icelandic geographical conditions were not conducive to the idealisation of outdoor life in the greenwood as an alternative to normal social life in the medieval town. In fact it is really only in the representation of the settlement of Iceland itself as due to noblemen's alienation from the newly imposed government of Harald Finehair in the ninth and early tenth centuries in the introductory chapters of many Sagas of Icelanders that Icelandic stories present any idealisation of rebellion against authority (perceived as corrupt) and the idea of the establishment of a more just society elsewhere; though the Icelandic constitution, like the organisation of life in the English greenwood, was not truly egalitarian.

Nevertheless there are some similarities between the outlaw sagas of Iceland and stories of English outlaws like Robin Hood (there is a reliable account of the development of the Robin Hood legends in R. B. Dobson and J. Taylor, *Rymes of Robyn Hood*, 1997). Although Gisli spends his outlawry in solitude or being sheltered by his wife, and Grettir on remote heathland or island with an occasional male companion, and they only occasionally attract other outlaws to themselves, Hord gathers together a band of outlaws and lives with his wife and children in a community with a hierarchy mirroring that of society in general. Both Gisli and Grettir employ tricks to escape their enemies, often disguising themselves or impersonating other people, and Grettir, like Robin Hood, attends assemblies of his enemies in disguise, obtaining safe-conduct from them, and competing in games (which he of course wins). Grettir, again like Robin Hood, manages to get on good terms with the king (in his case, of Norway), though he fails to become integrated back into society.

The three heroes of the Icelandic outlaw sagas, most members of their families and some at least of their chief opponents were historical persons in Iceland in the tenth and eleventh centuries, and some of their exploits and the outline of their lives are also historical, and often must have been derived from earlier written sources (though it has to be said that there is considerable doubt about Hord; it is possible that both he and his and Geir's deeds were entirely fabricated; the saga as a whole may contain little genuine historical tradition). Many of these persons and events are mentioned in other sagas or in historical sources like *The Book of Settlements* or Icelandic annals, though occasionally there are slips in the chronology and some of the people said to have been involved with the outlaws were not contemporary with them (Thorkel Moon, for instance, was lawspeaker at a much later time than the events, with which he is supposed to have been concerned in *The Saga of Grettir* ch. 12 and *The Saga of Hord* ch. 10, are supposed to have taken place; and Thorstein Thorskabit cannot have been still alive at the time claimed in *The Saga of Gisli*, ch. 5), and there are discrepancies in some of the relationships and names (e.g. Ingiald of Hergilsey in *The Saga of Gisli* was not really father of Geirmund and Gudrid; Asgeir of Asgeirsa and Asgeir Ædikoll in *The Saga of Grettir* are confused—in some other sources, e.g. *Laxdæla saga*, they are one and the same person—and Kalf Ageirsson and Thorvald Asgeirsson (ch. 15) were not actually brothers). The chronological summaries in *The Saga of Grettir*, chs 77, 82, and at the end of *The Saga of Hord* are inconsistent with the saga narratives and seem to be the result of attempts to combine discrepant sources (they may be additions or alterations to the original texts), though some of the errors in chronology, for instance those in chs 7 and 22 (where the figure should be 14 + 20) of *The Saga of Hord*, may be the result of mistakes in copying. Some of the less prominent characters also appear in other sagas and were certainly real people, for instance the Lawspeaker Skapti and Gest the Wise, as well, of course, as St Olaf and the kings Harald Finehair and Harald Hardradi of Norway. Snorri Godi is an important figure in *Eyrbyggja saga* and is the subject of the learned note known as *Ævi Snorra goða*, believed to be by the author of *The Book of the Icelanders*, Ari the Wise. Many of the minor episodes and most of the conversations, however, must be reconstructions, either by the authors of the sagas or by story-tellers intermediate between the events and the authors (sometimes episodes were modelled on those in earlier sagas; the stories of Grettir's childhood are of a conventional type, unlikely to be historical, and many of the episodes involving the supernatural in Grettir's life must be based on folk-stories). The background to these was real life in medieval Iceland, where the principal social events were the local assemblies, the Althing (the General Assembly held for a fortnight each summer) and the weddings and Yule-feasts, the games, wrestling matches and horse-fights (though the descriptions are never detailed enough to explain how these were organised and what the rules were), and everyone's normal occupation was farming. Only abroad were there towns which could provide larger communities as a setting for the action, or kings and noblemen with large followings. (Some of the details of procedures at Icelandic Assemblies, however, particularly in *The Saga of Grettir*, are inaccurate and belong to a later age, though versions of the long truce-formula in ch. 72 are found in *Heiðarvíga saga* and *Grágás*.) Some pre-christian rituals appear, such as the ceremony of blood-brotherhood and the burial rites in *The Saga of Gisli*, but although these are plausible and have links with some other accounts, it does not seem that any of the authors of the sagas had much detailed knowledge of heathen religion. The story in *The Saga of Hord* ch. 19, for instance, about the gods in Grimkel's temple, is more imaginative and sensational than plausible, and the heathen religious background in this saga is used more for sensational effect than for historical accuracy, like the folk-lore elements of *The Saga of Grettir*. The supernatural episodes in *The Saga of Hord* also seem more literary in conception than genuine folk-lore. Abroad, the background is the monarchical organisation of other European countries, the Church, and narrative elements such as the trial by ordeal (if Grettir had been allowed to undertake his ordeal in ch. 39, he would have had to carry a piece of red-hot iron in his bare hands a certain number of paces, and if the wounds did not go septic, he would be deemed innocent; such ordeals were banned in the thirteenth century), oaths with Christian sanctions and imprisonment in dungeons. Not all the episodes taking place abroad are legendary and literary: Icelanders did go and live in places as far removed as Greenland (where they farmed) and Constantinople (where they often joined Norwegians in the imperial guard and fought campaigns in the Mediterranean, as did Harald Hardradi, who fled there after the fall of his half-brother St Olaf in 1030 and later became king of Norway). Many of the episodes with supernatural elements must derive from Scandinavian folk-tales. Grettir, in particular, has several encounters with supernatural creatures and has links with cult figures that are able to pass into and out of another world, and have special powers to protect people from supernatural agencies. Some of these have similarities to episodes in the probably eighth-century Old English poem *Beowulf*, the hero of which also fights a male and female monster associated with water and invades a mound and kills the supernatural defender which is associated with death. It is possible that these episodes in *The Saga of Grettir* and the similar ones in *Beowulf* derive from poetic narratives about early kings of Denmark which also appear in *Hrólfs saga kraka* transformed into pseudo-historical prose. The supernatural elements in *The Saga of Hord* probably have closer links with Icelandic Heroic Sagas and folklore of a much later time.

The geographical settings of the three sagas are closely based on the real landscape of Iceland, even though natural features of the landscape are rarely described in detail; but the majority of the numerous place-names mentioned in these sagas can be identified on a map. The authors seem to have been well at home in the areas where their heroes lived. Only rarely does an author betray the fact that he does not have close knowledge of some of the saga sites. The island refuge of Hord and his companions in Hvalfiord, for instance, is a prominent sight visible from the route from Reykjavík to the north of Iceland, but is much too small for Hord and the large number of followers he is said to have had living there on it. Some places, like Thorisdal in *The Saga of Grettir*, have been identified, but the accounts of them in the sagas may in fact be legendary rather than real. The various huge rocks that Grettir is said at various times to have lifted can also be seen in Iceland where the saga-writer says they are, and three of these places are shown on the maps, though Grettir's actual feats of strength cannot all have been historical; some folk-tales about Grettir's feats were the subject of folk-tales later than the saga itself, and there are many modern place-names that relate to him and his exploits that probably originated after the saga was written. The account of events in Norway at the beginning of *The Saga of Gisli* betrays the author's limited knowledge of the geography of that country.

NOTE ON THE TEXT

In the first edition of the translation of *The Saga of Gisli* that is reprinted in the present volume, George Johnston included the following notes (here slightly modified):

> The translation of *The Saga of Gisli* is based on the edition in *Íslenzk fornrit*, which is largely based on AM 556 a 4to (Stofnun Árna Magnússonar, Reykjavík), which was written in the second half of the fifteenth century and also contains texts of *The Saga of Grettir* and *The Saga of Hord*. Occasionally the readings of other manuscripts have been preferred in the translation, or some slight rearrangements have been made, in places where there is such confusion in the Icelandic text that the flow of the narrative is disturbed.
>
> My first intention was to make a twentieth-century telling of the saga that would read as though it were a novel. After several attempts Peter Foote asked Ian Maxwell in Melbourne to read the version we then had, and because of his criticisms I decided to rewrite the translation from start to finish, following the Icelandic as closely as I could. The version that came out seemed livelier, subtler and more readable, slightly outlandish in tone, the style directly geared to the telling of the story. I wrote in twentieth-century words, however, and kept out archaisms, which would have seemed quaint or remote. It seemed to me that the 'otherness' of the Icelandic was best preserved by letting its word-order and idiom, especially in the shifting of tenses, play their part in the English too.
>
> The verses posed a more difficult problem. Their metre, diction and syntax are complex and artificial and their content is often slight: their value as poetry seems not very high. Yet they contain many of the keys of the story and, especially in this saga, their artificiality set in the stern spareness of the narrative gives the whole book a lyrical quality it would not otherwise have; many of them, in context, are true lyrics. They cannot be directly rendered in English, however; even a literal prose translation could rarely be faithful to their twisted syntax, and it would have to be heavily annotated on account of the allusiveness of the diction. So I decided to follow the metre closely, use as much of the imagery as could be fitted in, and give the sense of the original without attempting direct translation.
>
> The imagery is conventional. It is drawn from myths and legends and chiefly takes the form of kennings, a Germanic kind of poetic diction, which thc skalds used in their own elaborate way. Many of the kennings seem far-fetched to us, yet they have associations which may make them rich and suggestive even to our ears. For instance, there is a story behind the kenning in 'pour the dwarfs' liquor', meaning 'speak in poetry', which appears in two of Gisli's stanzas (ch. 26 and 34). It can be found in

Skáldskaparmál, 'The Diction of Poetry', in Snorri Sturluson's *Edda*, written about 1220 (pp. 61–4). (At one stage in its history, the mead of poetry was in the possession of dwarfs.)

A few minor changes have been made in this reprint of George Johnston's translation, mainly in the presentation of the proper names, which are now generally given in their original Old Icelandic form (though still in anglicised spelling); modifications have also been made to the punctuation. The translation of the verses has not been changed, but there is no attempt to reproduce the sound and rhythm of the verses in the translation of *The Saga of Grettir* and *The Saga of Hord*, and they are translated more literally than those in *The Saga of Gisli*; the translation of the prose in *The Saga of Grettir* and *The Saga of Hord* in general attempts to follow the principles underlying the translation of the prose in *The Saga of Gisli*.

The translation of *The Saga of Hord* is based on the edition in *Íslenzk fornrit*, following the longer version in AM 556 a 4to. The translation of *The Saga of Grettir* is based on the edition in *Íslenzk fornrit*, but follows the editions in *Íslendinga sögur* (Reykjavík: Svart á hvítu 1985, 1987) and *Sígildar sögur* 4 (1994) in keeping as close as possible to the text of the main manuscript, AM 551 a 4to. Words omitted in this manuscript that have been translated from one of the other manuscripts are enclosed in square brackets, as are also some words that are in the main manuscript but appear to be wrong (e.g. in chs 70 and 88 of *The Saga of Grettir*).

Explanations of the elaborate kennings in the verses are also given in square brackets and the mythological names which often feature in them are explained in the Index of Names (as are most of the nick-names or surnames in the prose of all three sagas). Spellings of Icelandic words and names in all three sagas have been anglicised, and Icelandic *j* has been replaced by *i*, *ð* by *d*, *þ* by *th*.

The translation of *The Saga of Grettir* and of *The Saga of Hord* aims to be as literal as possible, as in the translation of *The Saga of Gisli*, often retaining the use of the historic present, normally much more common in Icelandic narrative than in English, and other stylistic features such as abrupt transitions into direct speech. In relation to the alternation of present and past tense in narrative, however, it should be pointed out that what editors print as *segir* 'says' is often abbreviated *s.* in manuscripts of the sagas, though occasionally full forms *segir* or *sagði* 'said' are written; other verbs introducting direct speech (e.g. *svarar* 'answers', *mælti* 'spoke') are more often written in full. S. is also sometimes expanded to *svarar* 'answers' in editions. The choice of tense, and even of verb, must therefore frequently be attributed to the editors of the Icelandic texts, or perhaps to the scribes of individual manuscripts, rather than to the authors.

Nicknames are only translated when their meaning is uncontroversial; sometimes when the Icelandic word is retained, an English equivalent is added in brackets on the first occurrence and in the Index. Some technical Icelandic terms that have no English equivalent are not translated, and then explanations will be found in the Glossary. Words explained in the Glossary are italicised in the texts. Double inverted commas are used to identify proverbial statements, though some of these may only have become such after the saga was written.

THE SAGA OF GISLI

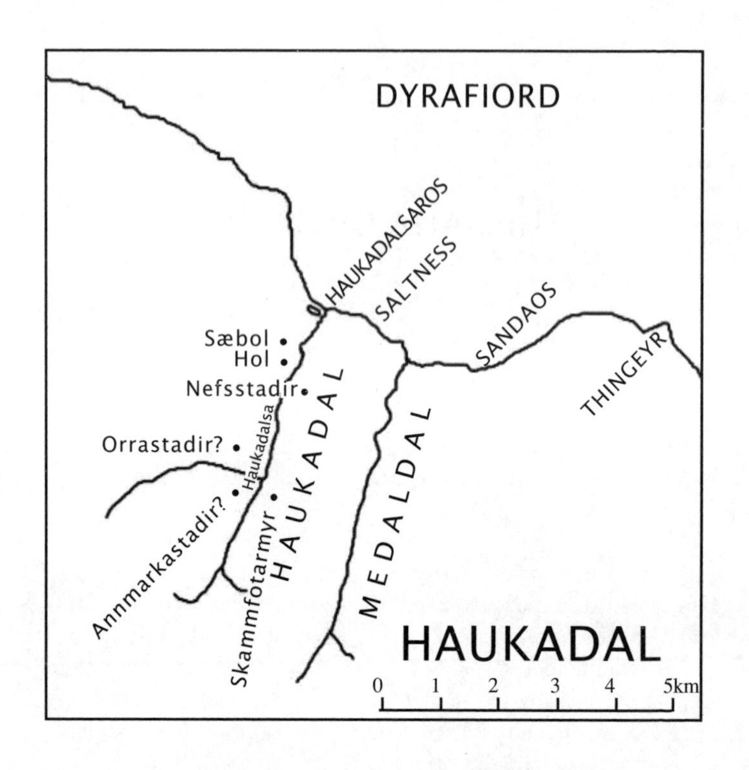
DYRAFIORD
HAUKADALSAROS
SALTNESS
SANDAOS
THINGEYR
Sæbol
Hol
Nefsstadir
Haukadalsa
Orrastadir?
Annmarkastadir?
Skammfotarmyr
HAUKADAL
MEDALDAL
HAUKADAL
0
1
2
3
4
5km

1

When this story begins, King Hakon, foster-son of Athelstan, was ruling over Norway, and it was near the end of his days. There was a man named Thorkel, who had the nickname Skerauki; he lived in Surnadal, and was a chieftain by title. He had a wife whose name was Isgerd, and three children, all sons. One was named Ari, another Gisli, and the third Thorbiorn—he was the youngest—and they all grew up at home. There was a man by the name of Isi; he lived in the fiord which is called Fibuli, in Nordmøre; his wife was named Ingigerd and his daughter Ingibiorg. Ari, the son of Thorkel of Surnadal, asks for Ingibiorg's hand in marriage, and she was given to him with a large *dowry*. A bondservant named Kol came with her.

There was a man known as Biorn the Pale, who was a berserk; he went about the country challenging men to fight if they would not give in to his demands. He came during the winter to Thorkel of Surnadal's place. Ari, his son, was then in charge of the farm. Biorn gives Ari two choices, whether he will rather fight with him on an island that lies near by in Surnadal, called Stokkaholm, or give over his wife to him. He chose at once, that he will rather fight than have shame come on him and his wife too. They were to meet after three days. Now the time comes round, they fight, and the outcome is that Ari falls and loses his life. It seems to Biorn that he has won land and woman. Gisli says that he will rather lose his own life than let this come about, and he is bent on fighting Biorn.

Then Ingibiorg had something to say: 'When I was married to Ari, it was not because I would not rather have been married to you. Kol, my bondservant, has a sword which is called Greyflank, and you must ask him to lend it to you; because with this sword it happens that whoever takes it into a fight wins.'

He asks the bondman for the sword, and the bondman made no small thing of lending it. Gisli got ready for the duel, they fight, and it turns out that Biorn falls. Now it seemed to Gisli that he had won a great victory; and the story tells that he asks for Ingibiorg, for he did not want to lose a good woman from the family, and marries her; and he takes over all the property and becomes an important man. Then his father dies, and Gisli takes over his property as well. He had them all killed, who had been with Biorn.

The bondman claimed back his sword, but Gisli will not give it up, and offers him money for it, but the bondman wants nothing but the sword itself; he gets it none the more for that. The bondman resents this and attacks Gisli and wounds him badly. Gisli hits back at the bondman's skull with Greyflank so hard that the sword broke, and the skull was broken, and both men die.

2

After this Thorbiorn takes over all the property which had belonged to his father and two brothers. He lives in Surnadal, at Stokkar. He asks for the woman who was called Thora, Raud's daughter of Fridarey, and marries her. Their life together was happy, and before long they had children. Their daughter was named Thordis; she was their eldest child. Thorkel was the name of their eldest son, Gisli the second and Ari the youngest, and they grew up at home. There were no more outstanding men to be found in the district of their age. Then Ari was taken as foster-son by Styrkar, his mother's brother, but Thorkel and Gisli stayed at home.

There was a man called Bard; he lived in Surnadal; he was a young man and had recently inherited his father's property. Another man called Kolbiorn lived at Hella in Surnadal; he was a young man and had newly come into his inheritance. Certain people said that Bard was seducing Thordis, Thorbiorn's daughter—she was both handsome and intelligent. This displeased Thorbiorn, and he said he thought that if Ari was at home things would not turn out well. Bard said that "the words of a weakling are worthless".

'And I shall go on as usual.'

Thorkel was friendly with Bard, and he was in with him in this, but the way his sister was going on with Bard angered Gisli as much as it did his father. One time, they say, Gisli joined Bard and Thorkel. He went as far as half-way to Grannaskeid—this is the name of the place where Bard lived—and then, when it was least expected, Gisli strikes

Bard his death-blow. Thorkel was angry, and said that Gisli had done wrong, but Gisli told his brother to be calm.

'And let us change swords, and you take the one that bites better.'

He began to joke with him. Thorkel grows calm then, and sits down beside Bard. Gisli goes home and tells his father, and he was pleased. There was never full friendliness between the brothers again and Thorkel did not accept the exchange of weapons, and he would not remain at home, but went to Holmgongu-Skeggi, who lived on Saxa Island—he was a close kinsman of Bard—and stayed there.

He egged on Holmgongu-Skeggi to avenge his kinsman, Bard, and marry Thordis. They went together to Stokkar in a party twenty strong; and when they came to the farmhouse Skeggi spoke to Thorbiorn of marriage ties.

'And having your daughter Thordis as my wife.'

But Thorbiorn would not let him have the girl. Kolbiorn was said to be courting Thordis. Skeggi thought that Kolbiorn was the cause of his not getting the marriage, and he goes to see him, and challenges him to fight on Saxa Island. Kolbiorn agrees that he will come, and said he would not be worthy of marrying Thordis if he had not the courage to fight Skeggi.

Thorkel and Skeggi went back to Saxa and awaited the meeting there with their twenty followers. And after three days Gisli went to see Kolbiorn, and asked if he was ready for the fight. Kolbiorn answers by asking if that is the way he must win her.

'Don't talk like that,' says Gisli.

Kolbiorn says, 'I feel as though I will not fight Skeggi to win her.'

Gisli calls him the worst kind of coward.

'And you can come to shame altogether, but I shall go anyhow.'

He takes eleven men and goes to the island. Meanwhile Skeggi had come to the place, and he sets forth the duelling rules and challenges Kolbiorn by marking out the ring, but he says he does not see him there, nor anyone to take his place. Skeggi had a carpenter called Ref. He told Ref to make wooden figures of Gisli and Kolbiorn.

'And have one stand close behind the other; and the nastiness of that will always be there to shame them.'[1]

[1] The making of such an image would have been equivalent to a charge of sodomy and hence of cowardice.

Gisli heard this as he came through the trees, and he answers: 'Your men will have something more useful than that to do; and you can look here at a man who is not afraid to fight you.'

They go into the ring and fight, and each holds a shield to guard himself. Skeggi has a sword called Warflame, and he swings it at Gisli so that it makes a loud whistle; then says Skeggi:

Warflame whistled,
Wild sport for Saxa.

Gisli struck back at him with a halberd and took off the point of his shield and one of his legs, and he said:

Hack went the halberd,
Hewed down Skeggi.

Skeggi bought himself off from the duel and from then on went on a wooden leg. Thorkel went home with Gisli, his brother, and they were on good brotherly terms again, and Gisli came out of this fight a much greater man.

3

The story mentions two brothers, one named Einar and the other Arni, the sons of Skeggi of Saxa. They lived at Flydruness, north of Trøndelag. They raised a troop of men in the spring and they went to Kolbiorn in Surnadal and offered him two choices, whether he would rather go with them and burn Thorbiorn and his sons in their house, or die right there. He decided that he would rather go.

They set out, sixty men in all, and came to Stokkar in the night and set fire to the buildings. All were asleep in one room, Thorbiorn and his sons and Thordis. There were two tubs of whey in the house.[2] Gisli and his brother and father take two goatskins and dip them in the whey-tubs and damp the fire with them, and they put down the flames three times this way; then they succeeded in breaking a way through the

[2] Whey was kept for drinking and pickling; cf. *Njáls saga* ch. 129.

wall and got out through it, ten of them together, and, under cover of the smoke, they got up the mountainside beyond dog's bark. Twelve men were burned in the house. The attackers thought they had burnt everybody.

Gisli and the others go on until they come to Styrkar's house on Fridarey, and there they call out men to help them, forty in all, and come without warning to Kolbiorn's house and burn him in it with eleven other men. They then sell their land and buy a ship—there were sixty of them in it—and sail away with all their belongings to the islands called Æsundir and lie up there waiting to put to sea. Meanwhile forty of them set out from there in two boats and go north to Flydruness. The brothers, Skeggi's two sons, had just started out with seven other men to collect their farm rents. Gisli's party turn on them and kill them all; Gisli killed three men and Thorkel two. After this they go to the farmstead and take away much booty. Gisli cut off Skeggi's head this time; he had been staying there with his sons.

4

They return to the ship and put to sea and are away from land for more than sixty days, and they come ashore in west Iceland on the south strand of Dyrafiord, in the estuary called Haukadalsos. There were two men who lived on opposite sides of the fiord, both named Thorkel. One of them lived at Saurar in Keldudal on the southern shore—this was Thorkel son of Eirik; the other lived on the north side, at Alvidra—he was called Thorkel the Rich. Thorkel son of Eirik was the first man of standing to go to the ship and greet Thorbiorn Sur (whey), who was called this after he had escaped by means of the whey. All land had been taken on both shores. Thorbiorn Sur bought land on the southern shore at Sæbol in Haukadal, and Gisli built a steading there, where they lived from then on.

A man called Biartmar lived in at the head of Arnarfiord; his wife was called Thurid and she was the daughter of Hrafn of Ketilseyr in Dyrafiord; this Hrafn was the son of Dyri, the first settler in the fiord. They had children: their daughter's name was Hild—she was the eldest; their sons were Helgi, Sigurd and Vestgeir. Vestein was the name of a Norwegian who came to Iceland at the time of the settlement and lodged with Biartmar. He married Hild, Biartmar's daughter. When they had been married not very long they had two children: Aud was the name of their daughter and Vestein of their son. Vestein, son of Vestein, became a good seafarer and trader. However, he had a farm called Hest in Onundarfiord at this time in the story. His wife was called Gunnhild; their sons were Berg and Helgi.

Now after this Thorbiorn Sur dies, and then his wife, Thora. Gisli and his brother Thorkel take over the farm; and Thorbiorn and Thora were buried in a mound.

5

There was a man, Thorbiorn, who was called Selagnup (seal's crag). He lived in Talknafiord at Kvigandafell. His wife was named Thordis and his daughter Asgerd. Thorkel, Gisli's brother, asks for this woman and marries her; and Gisli married Vestein's sister, Aud. Now the brothers farm together in Haukadal.

One spring Thorkel the Rich had to make the journey south to the *assembly* at Thorsness, and Gisli and Thorkel went with him. At Thorsness there lived then Thorstein Thorskabit (cod-biter), who was the son of Thorolf Mostrarskegg; he was married to Thora, the daughter of Olaf son of Thorstein: their children were a daughter, Thordis, and Thorgrim, and Bork the Stout. Thorkel finished his business at the *assembly*. And after the *assembly* Thorstein invited Thorkel the Rich and the brothers Gisli and Thorkel to his home and gave them good gifts at parting; and they invited Thorstein's sons to come west and visit them at their *assembly* the following spring. Then they journey home. Next spring Thorstein's sons make the journey west with ten companions to Hvalseyr *Assembly*, and there they meet Gisli and Thorkel, who invite them home from the *assembly*; but before that they were to go to a feast at the home of Thorkel the Rich. After that they visit the sons of Sur and are well feasted there.

Thorgrim finds the sister of Gisli and Thorkel handsome, and he asks for her hand, and she is betrothed to him and a bridal feast is held at once; the steading at Sæbol is given with her as a *dowry* and Thorgrim moves west to live; but Bork remains at Thorsness, and with him live his nephews, Saka-Stein and Thorodd. Now Thorgrim farms at Sæbol;

and the sons of Sur go to Hol and build a good steading there; and only a fence lies between the land of Hol and the land of Sæbol. They farm there side by side and are good friends. Thorgrim has the rank of a *godi*, and he is a great source of strength to the brothers. They go together to the local *assembly*, one spring, with forty men, and all of them were dressed in coloured clothes. Vestein, Gisli's brother-in-law, was in the party, and all the men who had come out from Surnadal.

6

There was a man called Gest, who was the son of Oddleif; he had come to the *assembly* and stayed in the *booth* of Thorkel the Rich. They sit and drink, the Surnadal men; but other men were in the court, for it was an *assembly* for hearing lawsuits. A man comes into the *booth* of the Haukadal men, a talkative fellow by the name of Arnor, and said:

'You are a fine lot, you Haukdalers—attending to nothing but the drink and will not come to the court where your *assembly-men* have cases to be heard—everyone thinks so, although I am the one to say it.'

Then Gisli said, 'Let us go to the court then; it may be that others are saying the same.'

They go to the court; and Thorgrim asks if any men need their support.

'And there will be no holding back, so long as we are standing, in any help we promise.'

But Thorkel the Rich replies, 'These cases amount to little that men have against each other here; we will tell you if we need you.'

Now word begins to go around about how showy these men are, and about their talk, how bold it is. Thorkel spoke to Gest:

'How long do you expect that the spirit and swagger of these Haukdalers will be so great?'

Gest answers, 'They will not all think alike in three summers, who are now in that party.'

Arnor was near by during this, and he bursts into the Haukdalers' *booth* and tells them what he has heard. Gisli says:

'These are somebody's real words he has told us, and let us see to it that his prophecy doesn't turn out right. I can think of a good thing to do, and that is to bind our friendship with stronger ties, and swear blood-brotherhood between the four of us.'

This seems a good answer. They go out to the spit of land called Eyrarhvalsoddi and cut and raise up a long sod in the turf, leaving the two ends fast, and they set a spear with a patterned blade under it, so long-shafted that a man could just reach the rivets of the head with outstretched hand.[3] All four should pass under, Thorgrim, Gisli, Thorkel and Vestein; and now they draw blood and let their blood run together in the earth which was scratched up under the sod, and mix it all together, earth and blood; and then they kneel and swear an oath, that each shall avenge the other as his brother, and they call all the gods to witness.[4] But when they came to shake hands Thorgrim said:

'There is burden enough in this for me if I do it with these two, Thorkel and Gisli, my brothers-in-law; but I have no ties with Vestein'—and he draws back his hand.

'Then more of us will do the same,' says Gisli, and he too draws back his hand, 'for I will not bind myself to the man who will not bind himself to Vestein, my wife's brother.'

People thought this a serious thing. Gisli said then to Thorkel, his brother:

'It has gone as I thought it would; what we have just done will be of no use, and I think that fate will have its way over this.'

Men go home, now, from the *assembly*.

7

During the summer it happened that a ship came to Dyrafiord, owned by two brothers, Norwegians; one was named Thorir and the other Thorarin, and they were men from Oslofiord. Thorgrim rode to the

[3] Rather than damascening, what is meant is probably pattern-welding; in this the body of the blade is made up of alternate strips of steel and iron welded together then split, twisted and rewelded, before having the cutting-edges added and the finishing treatment. A simpler and commoner process to produce the same surface effect was to hammer the pattern-bearing strips flat and then weld them to a core of plain iron.

[4] This ritual was presumably originally a symbolic rebirth from mother earth. Cf. *Fóstbræðra saga* ch. 2.

ship and bought four *hundred* of timber,[5] and paid some of the price down and left some to be paid later. The traders then laid up their ship in Sandaos and found lodgings for themselves. A man named Odd, the son of Orlyg, lived at Eyr in Skutilsfiord; he took in the two brothers.

Thorgrim sends his son Thorodd to look over and count his timber, because he intends to fetch it home soon. Thorodd comes and looks over the timber, but the lot they were buying looks to him rather different from what Thorgrim had told him. He used hard words to the Norwegians, but they would not stand for this and they attack him and kill him. Then the Norwegians go away from the ship after this work. They cross over Dyrafiord and take horse and make for their lodgings in Eyr; they journey all day and all night until they come to the dale which leads up out of Skutilsfiord and here they eat breakfast and go to sleep.

Thorgrim is told the news and he sets out at once. He has himself ferried across the fiord and goes after them alone. He reaches them, where they were lying, and wakes Thorarin; he prods him with his spear-shaft. Thorarin springs up and tries to draw his sword, because he recognised Thorgrim. But Thorgrim thrusts at him with his spear, and kills him. Now Thorir wakes, and he wants to avenge his companion. But Thorgrim thrusts his spear through him. The place is now called Breakfast Dale and Eastmen's Fall. Thorgrim returns home and becomes famous for this journey.

He stays on his farm over the winter. In the spring the brothers-in-law, Thorgrim and Thorkel, fit out the ship which had belonged to the Norwegians. These Norwegians had been great trouble-makers in Norway and the country was no longer safe for them. Now Thorgrim and Thorkel make this ship ready and put to sea in it. This summer Vestein and Gisli also sail out, from Skeliavik in Steingrimsfiord. Both ships sail out to sea. Onund of Medaldal looks after Thorkel and Gisli's farm, and Saka-Stein, along with Thordis, looks after Sæbol. At this time Harald Greycloak was ruling over Norway. Thorgrim and Thorkel bring their ship ashore in the north of Norway and they soon fall in with the king and present themselves to him and pay their respects. He

[5] This is taken to mean timber to the value of 480 (one *hundred* = 120) ells of homespun cloth (*vaðmál*); *c.*1000 eighteen ells of cloth were probably worth one ounce of silver, so the value of the timber would have been equal to about 27 ounces of silver.

received them well, and they joined his sworn retainers and won generous rewards and honours.

Gisli and Vestein were at sea more than sixty days, and they ran ashore in early winter in Hordland in a gale of wind and snow during the night, and they smashed their ship, but saved their goods and men.

8

A man named Beard-Bialfi had a trading-ship there. He was intending to sail south to Denmark. They ask him if they can buy a half share in his ship. He says he has heard that they are good men, and he gave them the half share, but they at once repay him with gifts worth more.

They voyage south to Denmark to the market town called Viborg and stay the winter there with the man called Sigrhadd. The three of them, Vestein, Gisli and Bialfi, were there; and they became good friends and exchanged gifts. Then early in the spring Bialfi readied his ship to go to Iceland. There was a man by the name of Sigurd, a trading partner of Vestein, Norwegian by birth, who was out west in England. He sent word to Vestein that he wanted to close the partnership because he no longer needed Vestein's money. So Vestein asks leave to go and settle up with him.

'Then you must promise that you will never go from Iceland, if you come safely back, unless I let you.'[6]

Vestein says yes to this.

One morning Gisli gets up and goes to the smithy. He was the handiest of men and skilled in everything. He made a coin which weighed not less than an ounce, and riveted it together with twenty studs in it, ten in each half, so that the coin seemed whole if it was put together, and yet it could be separated into two parts. The story goes that he takes the coin apart and puts one piece in Vestein's hand and tells him to keep it as a token between them.

'And we must each send his part to the other only if it is a matter of life and death. Yet my mind tells me that we will need to send them, though we may not meet again.'

Vestein sails west to England, and Gisli and Bialfi to Norway, and then in the summer to Iceland. They had got much money and reputa-

[6] It is presumably Gisli who speaks.

tion; they ended their partnership on good terms, and Bialfi bought the half share in the ship back from Gisli. Then Gisli journeys west to Dyrafiord in a merchant ship, with eleven men.

9

Thorgrim and Thorkel ready their ship in another place and return to Iceland, to Haukadalsaros in Dyrafiord, on the same day as Gisli had already sailed in on the merchant ship. They soon meet, and a joyful meeting it is; and then they go to their homes. Thorgrim and Thorkel had prospered on their voyage as well.

Thorkel was a vain man, and did not work on the farm, but Gisli worked night and day. So it happened on a day of good weather that Gisli sent all the men out haymaking, except Thorkel; he was the only man left at home at the farm, and he was lying down in the hall after his morning meal. The hall was a hundred and fifty feet long and sixty feet wide; on its south-west side stood the bower of Aud and Asgerd, and they were sitting there and sewing.[7] When Thorkel wakes up he goes toward the bower, because he heard voices coming from there, and he lies down on the nearest side. Now Asgerd speaks:

'Do something for me, Aud. Cut out a shirt for me, for my husband Thorkel.'

'I could not do it better than you,' says Aud, 'and you would not ask me if you had to make a shirt for my brother Vestein.'

'That is another story,' says Asgerd; 'and I shall feel like that for a while.'

'It is something I have known about for a long time,' says Aud. 'Let us not talk about it any more.'

'Nothing seems wrong to me,' says Asgerd, 'if I think well of Vestein; I have been told that you and Thorgrim often met before you were married to Gisli.'

'No blame came of that,' says Aud, 'because I have had nothing to do with a man since I married Gisli from which there might come blame; and now we will stop this talk.'

[7] *Dyngja*, here translated 'bower', was probably a separate building from the hall, used as a work-room for the women.

But Thorkel hears everything they had said, and he speaks up now that they have left off:

> Hear a great marvel,
> Hear of manslaughter,
> Hear a great matter,
> Hear of a man's death—

'of one man, or more.'

And he goes in. Then Aud speaks.

'"Trouble often comes from women's talk", and perhaps the trouble from ours will be the worst kind. We must decide what to do.'

'I have a plan for myself,' says Asgerd, 'which will work well enough; but I don't know the best thing for you.'

'What is your plan?' asked Aud.

'Put my arms round Thorkel's neck when we come to bed—and he will forgive me for this—and then tell him it is all a lie.'

'That will not be enough to count on, by itself,' said Aud.

'What will you do?' asked Asgerd.

'Tell my husband Gisli everything that I can't otherwise talk about or decide.'

In the evening Gisli comes in from work. Usually Thorkel would thank his brother for what he has done, but now he is glum and said not a word. Gisli asks him whether he is feeling all right.

'I am not ill,' says Thorkel; 'but this is worse than illness.'

'Have I done anything,' says Gisli, 'that has offended you?'

'Not in any way,' says Thorkel. 'You will know all about it, though perhaps not till later.'

They each go about their affairs, and there was no more talk between them.

Thorkel eats little food that evening, and he is the first man to go to bed. And when he had settled down Asgerd comes and lifts the blanket and makes to lie beside him. Then Thorkel broke his silence:

'I do not mean to have you lie here tonight, nor for many nights.'

Asgerd speaks, 'Why have you changed so suddenly? What is the matter here?' she asks.

Thorkel says, 'We both know now what the reason is, though it was kept from me for a long while; and your reputation will be no better if I speak plainer.'

She replies, 'You may think what you like about it, but I will not quarrel long over the bed with you; and you have two things to choose from. One is that you take me in and behave as though nothing has happened; otherwise I shall call witnesses at once, and declare my divorce from you, and I will have my father claim back my price and my *dowry*; and if this is your choice you will never have my bed company again.'[8]

Thorkel was quiet then, and after a while he said:

'I advise you to do whichever you like; but I will not keep you out of bed all night.'

She immediately showed what she most wanted and got straight into bed. They had not been side by side for long before they settled the matter between them as though nothing had happened.

Aud went into bed with Gisli, and she tells him of the talk she has had with Asgerd, and asks him not to be angry with her; and asked him to do something about it, if he could see anything good to be done.

'I can see nothing to be done about it,' he said, 'that will help; and yet I cannot blame you, for " Fate's words will be spoken by someone", and what is to follow, will follow.'

10

The year passes by and *moving-days* come round. Now Thorkel asks his brother Gisli to talk with him, and said:

'It has come about, brother,' he says, 'that I have something of a notion and a mood to change the way I live; and it goes this way, that I want us to divide our property, and I will set up house with Thorgrim, my brother-in-law.'

Gisli answers, ' "What belongs to brothers is best seen together"; it would certainly please me to leave things as they are, and not split anything up.'

'We cannot go on this way any longer,' says Thorkel, 'householding together, because a great wrong comes out of it, since you always have the work and trouble of seeing to the farm, and I never lift a hand to anything useful.'

[8] Divorce seems to have been a comparatively easy matter in pagan times in Iceland; cf. *Njáls saga* ch. 7. See *dowry* in Glossary.

'Do not find any fault with that,' says Gisli, 'as long as I have nothing to say about it. We have been through both sorts of times, when things were well between us and when things were bad.'

'"It does not matter what is said about it"; the property must certainly be divided, and because I am the one to ask for the division, you shall have the homestead and land and I shall have the cash.'

'If there is nothing else for it but to separate, then you do one or the other—for I do not mind which I do—either divide or choose.'[9]

It was settled that Gisli did the dividing, and Thorkel chose the cash and Gisli had the land. They also divided the dependants, who were two children; the boy was called Geirmund and the girl Gudrid, and she stayed with Gisli and Geirmund went with Thorkel. Thorkel went to Thorgrim, his brother-in-law, and lived with him; and Gisli then had the farm, and no such loss was suffered that the farm was any the worse for it.

The summer now passes in this way, and the *Winter Nights* come. It was the custom of many men to welcome winter in those days, and hold feasts and winter night sacrifices, but Gisli no longer sacrificed since his stay at Viborg in Denmark, though he still held feasts as before, and did everything with magnificence. Now he makes preparations for a great feast, when the time comes that was just spoken of, and he asks to the feast the two namesakes, Thorkel son of Eirik and Thorkel the Rich, and Aud's kinsmen, the sons of Biartmar, and many other friends and acquaintances. And on the day when the guests arrive Aud speaks:

'It is true to say that one man seems missing to me, who I wish might be here.'

'Who is that?' asked Gisli.

'It is my brother Vestein; I would like him to enjoy this feast here with us.'

Gisli said, 'I think differently about it, because I would willingly give money to have him not come here now.'

And with this their talk comes to an end.

[9] Under Icelandic law, brothers inherited their father's property in equal shares. If there were two of them, it was customary for one to have the land, the other the movable property. In order to ensure fair division, one would make the division and the other choose which share he had.

11

There was a man by the name of Thorgrim, who was called Thorgrim Nef (neb). He lived at Nefsstadir on the east side of Haukadalsa. He was full of sorcery and witchcraft, and he was as much a wizard as could be. Thorgrim and Thorkel invited him to come to their place because they too were having a feast. Thorgrim Nef was skilful with iron, and the story says that both Thorgrims and Thorkel go to the smithy and shut themselves in. The bits of Greyflank are brought out—they had fallen to Thorkel's lot when the brothers split up their property—and Thorgrim Nef makes a spear out of them, and the work was all done by evening; there was patterning in the blade, and a short handle fitted to it, about eight inches long. So much for them.

The story now goes that Onund of Medaldal came to the feast at Gisli's, and he took him aside and said that Vestein had come back to Iceland.

'And he can be expected here.'

Gisli moves at once and calls his housemen, Hallvard and Havard, and told them to go north to Onundarfiord and meet Vestein.

'And take him my greeting, and tell him at the same time that he is to stay at home until I visit him, and he is not to come to the feast in Haukadal.'

And he puts into their hands a knotted kerchief, and the half coin was in it as a token in case he should not believe their story. They go then, and take a boat from Haukadal and row to Lækiaros and come ashore and call on the farmer who lived there at Bersastadir; he was called Bersi. They give him a message from Gisli that he is to lend them two horses which he had, called the Bandvettir, the swiftest in the fiords. He lends them the horses, and they ride until they come to Mosvellir, and from there in towards Hest. Meanwhile Vestein sets out from home, and it happens that he rides below the sandhill at Mosvellir as the brothers are riding along the top, and so they pass by and miss each other.

12

There was a man named Thorvard, who lived at Holt. His housemen had fought over some work and struck each other with scythes, and both were wounded. Vestein comes by and stops the fight, and does it in such a way that the men become friends again and each is satisfied; then he rides out towards Dyrafiord with his two Norwegian companions.

But Hallvard and Havard come in to Hest and hear that in fact Vestein has already set out; they turn and ride after him at their hardest. And when they come to Mosvellir they see men riding in the middle of the valley, but there was a hill between them; they ride now into Biarnardal and come to Arnkelsbrekka; there both horses founder. They run from the horses then, and shout. Vestein and his men hear them now; they had come as far as Gemlufallsheid, and they wait there until they come up and give their message; they hand over the coin which Gisli has sent for him. He takes out the other half of the coin from his money-belt and turns very red as he looks at it.

'You speak the truth,' he says, 'and I would have turned back if you had met me sooner, but now the streams all run towards Dyrafiord and I shall ride there, and in any case I want to. The Norwegians shall turn back. But you get on by boat,' says Vestein, 'and tell Gisli and my sister of my coming.'

They go home and tell Gisli. He answers:

'That is how it must be, then.'

Vestein goes on to Gemlufall, to Luta, his kinswoman, and she has him ferried across the fiord and said to him:

'Vestein,' she said, 'be wary for yourself; there is need of it.'

He is taken over to Thingeyr; a man lived there then who was called Thorvald Spark. Vestein goes to his house, and Thorvald lends him his horse, but Vestein kept his own saddle-gear and he rides off with his bridle jingling. Thorvald rides with him to Sandaos and offers to stay with him all the way to Gisli's. He said there was no need for it.

'Much has changed in Haukadal,' said Thorvald; 'be wary for yourself.'

Then they part. Vestein rides now till he comes into Haukadal, and there was bright weather there, and moonlight. At Thorgrim's they were bringing in the cattle, Geirmund and a woman called Rannveig; she pens the cattle and he drives them in to her. Vestein rides up across the field and Geirmund comes over to him. Geirmund spoke.

'Do not come in here to Sæbol but go on to Gisli's, and be wary for yourself.'

Rannveig had come out of the cattle shed, and she looks at the man and thinks she knows him, and when the cattle have been brought in they argue about the man, who he was, and so go to the house. Thorgrim and the others are sitting by the fire, and Thorgrim asks if they have seen or met anybody, or what are they arguing about.

'I thought I recognised Vestein coming here,' said Rannveig, 'and he was in a *blue* cape and he had a spear in his hand, and he rode with a jingling bridle.'

'And what do you say, Geirmund?'

'I could hardly see him; but I thought he was one of Onund's housemen from Medaldal, and he was wearing Gisli's cape, and he was using Onund's saddle gear, and he had a fishing spear in his hand with a prong at the top.'

'One of you must be lying,' said Thorgrim. 'You go over to Hol, Rannveig, and see what is going on.'

She went over and came to the door when the men had arrived for the drinking. Gisli was standing in the doorway, and he spoke to her and asked her to come in. She said she should be going home.

'But I should like to speak to the girl, Gudrid.'

Gisli calls her, but nothing to any purpose came of it.

'Where is Aud, your wife?' she says.

'Here she is,' says Gisli.

She goes out and asked what she wanted. She replied that it was only a small matter, but nothing came of it. Gisli told her to do one or the other, come in or go home. She went home, and was somewhat foolisher than before, if that were possible, and had no news to tell.

In the morning Vestein had two bags brought to him with goods in them, which the brothers, Hallvard and Havard, had carried for him. He took out a tapestry ninety feet long, a head-dress made of a piece of stuff thirty feet long with three gold strands woven along its length, and three basins decorated with gold. He took these and offered them to his sister and Gisli and to Thorkel, his oath-brother, if he would accept. Gisli goes to Sæbol with the two Thorkels to his brother Thorkel. Gisli says that Vestein has come, and he has given them gifts to share, and he shows them to him and asks him to have whatever he chooses. Thorkel answers:

'It would be more fitting if you were to take all, and I will not accept the gifts; any return for them from me is not very likely.'

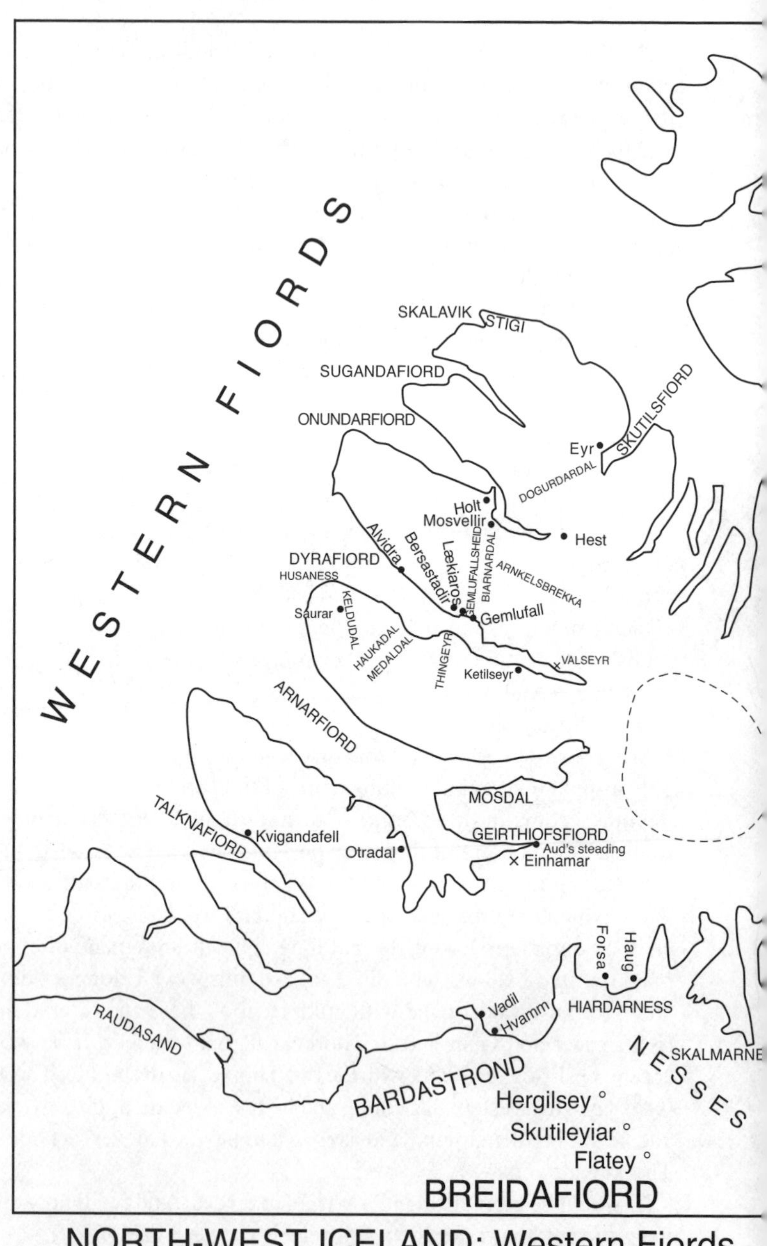

NORTH-WEST ICELAND: Western Fiords

NORTH-WEST ICELAND: Strandir

And he will not take them at all. Gisli goes home now, and it seems to him that everything is tending the same way.

13

Now a strange thing happens at Hol that Gisli sleeps badly two nights together, and they ask him what he has dreamed. He will not tell his dreams. Then comes the third night and they go to bed, and when they have been asleep, so hard a squall of wind hits the house that it takes all the thatch from one side. With this so much water fell from the sky that it was something unheard of, and the buildings let in the rain, as might be expected, when the thatch shifted. Gisli sprang up quickly and calls his men to save the hay.

Gisli had a thrall whose name was Thord, and he was nicknamed the Coward. The thrall stayed in the house, but Gisli and nearly all the other men went to see to the haystacks. Vestein offered to go with him, but Gisli will not have it. And now, when the roof started leaking worse, the sister and brother turn their beds lengthwise down the room; everyone else had left the room except only these two. Then someone comes in a little before dawn, quietly, and goes over to where Vestein is lying. He had woken up then. The first thing he knows is that a spear is thrust into his breast and right through him. When Vestein took the blow, then he spoke this:

'A heart thrust!' he said.

And then the man went out. Vestein tried to stand up; but he fell beside the bed, dead. Aud wakes up now, and calls to Thord the Coward and tells him to take the weapon from the wound. It was said then that whoever pulled the weapon from a wound would be bound to take revenge; it was called secret manslaughter and not murder when the weapon was left in a death-wound. Thord was so fearful of corpses that he did not dare go near one. Gisli came in then and saw what had happened, and he told Thord to be still. He took the spear from the wound himself and threw it, all bloody, into a chest, and let nobody see. Then he sat on the edge of the bed.

He had Vestein's body got ready for burial, as they used to do it in those times. Vestein's death brought great grief both to Gisli and to other men. Gisli spoke to Gudrid, his foster-daughter.

'You shall go to Sæbol and see what they are doing there; I am sending you on this errand because I have greatest faith in you in this as in other things, and be sure you can tell me what they are doing there.'

She goes, and comes to Sæbol. They were up and sitting armed, the two Thorgrims and Thorkel. When she came in she was not greeted quickly, for the people there mostly had little to say for themselves. However, Thorgrim asks her for her news. She told of Vestein's death, or murder. Thorkel answers:

'That would have seemed news to us at one time.'

'A man is there lost,' says Thorgrim, 'to whom we are all bound to show respect, and we are bound to give him burial with the greatest honour and build a mound for him; and it is true to say that such a man is a great loss. You may also tell Gisli that we shall come today.'

She goes home and tells Gisli that Thorgrim sat with his helmet and sword and fully armed, and Thorgrim Nef had a timber-axe in his hand, and Thorkel had his sword and it was drawn a hand's breadth.

'And all the men were up and some were armed.'

'That was to be expected,' says Gisli.

14

Gisli now prepares, with all his men, to bury Vestein in the sandhill that stands beside the rush-pond below Sæbol. And when Gisli was on his way, Thorgrim and Thorkel and Thorgrim Nef came with a large company of men to the mound-making. They did everything for Vestein as the ways then were, and then Thorgrim went to Gisli and spoke.

'It is a custom,' he says, 'to tie Hel-shoes on men which they should walk in to Valhall, and I shall do that for Vestein.'

And when he had done so he said, 'I do not know how to tie Hel-shoes, if these come loose.'

After this they sit down by the mound and talk, and they agree that it is unlikely that anyone will know who has done this crime. Thorkel asked Gisli:

'How does Aud take the death of her brother? Does she weep much?'

'You will be thinking you know the answer to that,' says Gisli. 'It is heavy for her, and she takes it as a great loss. I dreamt a dream,' says Gisli, 'the night before last and again last night, and I shall not say from the dreams who did the killing, although they point to that. I dreamt the night before last that out of a certain house slid a viper, and it stung Vestein to death. The next night I dreamt that a wolf ran out of the same house and bit Vestein to death. And I have not told either dream before now because I wanted nobody to interpret them.'[10]

Then he spoke a verse:

Fearful nor dark forethought
For Vestein oppressed me,
Now I ask no third such
Nightmare, come to fright me.
Sat we on the settles,
Sigrhadd's, mead-gladdened;
Menace of man's envy
Marred not then our heart joy.

Thorkel asked then, 'How does Aud take the death of her brother? Does she weep much?'

'You keep asking this, brother,' says Gisli, 'and you have a great curiosity to know.'

Gisli spoke a verse:

Carried under kerchief
Keeps she in sleep's cisterns
Surly drops of sorrow,
Storm of cheek in secret.
Oak of herbs from aching
Eyes, from grief's high places,
Has felt the salt dewfall,
For her brother mourning.

And again he spoke:

Sorrow, joy's dour slayer,
Sways her twigs of hazel—

[10] According to the beginning of ch. 13 Gisli's dreams were on the two nights before the night of Vestein's slaying, not on that night and the one before.

Eye-lashes, all heavy;
Utter they grief's nut fruits.
Picks the snake-plot goddess
Pity's fruit from bitter
Sight twigs, yet secretly
Summons this *skald*'s comfort.

The brothers go back to the house now, together. Thorkel spoke.

'These have been heavy tidings, and they will have been somewhat more grievous to you than to us; nevertheless, "a man is his own company for most of the way". I hope that you will not make so much of this that men become suspicious; I would like us to begin sports and be on as good terms as we ever have been before.'

'That is well spoken,' says Gisli, 'and I agree willingly, but on this condition, that if something happens to you in your lifetime that seems as much to you as this seems to me, then you will promise to carry on with the same understanding as you are now asking of me.'

Thorkel agrees. Then they go into the house and hold Vestein's funeral feast. And when that has been drunk, they each go home, and everything was quiet again.

15

They began the games as though nothing had happened. The brothers-in-law, Gisli and Thorgrim, played against each other oftenest, and the watchers could not decide which was stronger, though most of them thought that Gisli was. They played the ball-game on the ice of the rush-pond, and there was always a crowd. One day, when there was a very big crowd, Gisli called on them to divide up evenly for a game.

'An even division is what we want,' says Thorkel, 'and furthermore, we wish that you would not spare anything against Thorgrim; because word is going round that you are sparing yourself; but I should gladly see you win the full honour, if you are the stronger.'

'He and I have not fought it out yet,' says Gisli, 'but perhaps the time is coming when we shall.'

They play a game, and Thorgrim is outmatched; Gisli throws and the ball rolls out of bounds. Gisli tries to go after it, but Thorgrim holds him and does not let him get it. Then Gisli throws Thorgrim so hard that he can do nothing to save himself and his knuckles are skinned and the blood spurts from his nose and the flesh is torn from his knees. Thorgrim stood up slowly; he turned to Vestein's grave-mound and spoke:

Spear in the wound sharply
Sang. I feel no anguish.

Gisli picked up the ball on the run and pitched it between Thorgrim's shoulders so that he fell forward; then Gisli spoke:

Ball on the broad shoulder
Banged. I feel no anguish.

Thorkel sprang up and spoke, 'Now it can be seen who is strongest or the best in action, and let us stop now.'

And so they did. The games were not played any more and summer came on and there was some coldness now between Thorgrim and Gisli.

Thorgrim decided to give an autumn feast on the *Winter Nights* and to welcome winter and make a sacrifice to Frey, and he invites his brother Bork and Eyiolf son of Thord and many other important men. Gisli also makes ready a feast and invites his wife's kinsmen from Arnarfiord and the two Thorkels and no fewer than sixty men were expected at Gisli's. There was to be drinking at both houses and the floors at Sæbol were strewn with rushes from the rush-pond.

When Thorgrim and his people were making preparations and were ready to hang the hall with tapestries and the guests were expected that evening, then Thorgrim spoke to Thorkel:

'What we need here are the fine hangings that Vestein wanted to give you. It seems to me that there is a great difference between owning them outright and never using them at all; and now I want you to have them sent for.'

Thorkel answers, '"He knows all who knows when to stop", and I shall not send for them.'

'I shall do it, then,' said Thorgrim, and he told Geirmund to go. Geirmund answers:

'I will do some work, but I have no taste for this errand.'

Thorgrim goes to him and strikes him a hard blow and said:

'Go now, then, if it seems better to you.'

'I shall go now,' he said, 'though now it seems worse; but you can be sure that I shall be willing to give you the filly of the foal you have given me, and you will not be underpaid at that.'

Then he goes. And when he comes there, Gisli and Aud are getting ready to hang the tapestries. Geirmund gave them his message and told them everything that had happened.

'What is your wish, Aud? Shall we lend the tapestries?' said Gisli.

'You do not ask because you do not know, that I wish them neither this favour nor any other that might do them honour.'

'Was it my brother Thorkel's wish?' said Gisli.

'He thought well of my coming for them.'

'That is good enough,' said Gisli.

And he comes on the way with Geirmund and gives him the hangings. Gisli goes with him as far as the fence and speaks:

'Now it is this way: I think I have made good your errand, and I want you to be helpful in something that is important to me, for "a gift always looks to a return", you know, and I want you to slide back the bolts on three doors this evening; and you might remember how you were sent on this errand.'

Geirmund answers, 'Will your brother Thorkel be in danger?'

'In no danger,' says Gisli.

'It will be put on the right road, then,' says Geirmund.

And when he comes back home he throws down the hangings. Then Thorkel speaks:

'Gisli is not like other men for his patience, and he has bettered us.'

'This is what we need,' says Thorgrim.

And they put up the hangings. Then in the evening the guests come. And the weather thickens; after dark the snow falls in windless air and covers all the paths.

16

Bork and Eyiolf come in the evening with sixty men; there were a *hundred* men altogether at Sæbol, and half that number at Gisli's. They started the drinking during the evening, and then they went to bed and slept. Gisli spoke to Aud his wife:

'I have not fed his horse for Thorkel the Rich. Come with me and lock the door after me, and stay awake while I go out, and unlock the door for me again when I come back.'

He takes the spear Greyflank from the chest, and he is wearing a *blue* cape over his shirt and linen under-breeches, and he goes now to the stream which runs between the two steadings and from which water was taken for both. He goes by the path to the stream and then wades down the stream to the path which led to the other house. Gisli knew the lay-out at Sæbol because he had put up the buildings; there was a way in through the byre. This is where he goes; thirty cows were stalled on either side; he ties the cows' tails together and closes the byre and fixes the door in such a way that it may not be opened from the other side. Then he goes to the dwelling-house; and Geirmund had done his work, because the doors were not barred. He goes in and shuts the door after him, in the way it had been closed up during the evening.

Now he takes his time over everything. After shutting the door he stands and listens to hear if anyone is awake, and he finds that all are asleep. There were three lights in the room. He takes sedge from the floor and twists it together; then he throws it on one of the lights, and it goes out. He stands again and waits, in case anyone wakes up, but he hears nothing. He takes another twist of sedge and throws it on the nearest light and puts it out. Then he knows that not all are asleep, because he sees that a young man's hand reaches for the third light, and pulls the lamp down and snuffs it out. Now he goes farther into the room to the *bed-closet* where Thorgrim slept, and his sister, and the door was ajar, and they are both in bed. He goes up and gropes about inside and puts his hand on his sister's breast; she was sleeping next the outside. Then Thordis spoke:

'Why is your hand so cold, Thorgrim?'

And she wakes him. Thorgrim asked:

'Do you want me to turn your way?'

She thought he had put his arm over her. Gisli waits yet for a while and warms his hand in his shirt and they both go to sleep. Then he takes hold of Thorgrim gently, so that he wakes up. He thought that Thordis had roused him and he turned to her. Gisli pulls back the covers with one hand, and with the other he thrusts Greyflank into Thorgrim so that it goes through him and sticks in the bed. Then Thordis calls out and says:

'Wake up, men in the room. Thorgrim is killed, my husband!'

Gisli turns away quickly towards the byre and goes out as he had intended, and makes the door fast behind him; he goes home then by the same way as he had come, and his tracks could not be seen. Aud unlocks the door for him when he comes home, and he goes to bed and behaves as though nothing has happened and as though he has done nothing. But the men were still full of drink at Sæbol and did not know what ought to be done; this caught them unawares, and because of this nothing was done that was either fitting or useful.

17

Eyiolf spoke, 'Big and bad things have happened, and these people are stupid who are here. I think the thing to do is to light the lamps and guard the doors, so that the man who has done the killing cannot get away.'

And so it was done. People think, when they cannot find him, that it must perhaps be someone in the house who has done the work. Time passes on and daylight comes. They took Thorgrim's body and pulled the spear out and prepared him for burial, and sixty men stayed there, while the other sixty set out for Gisli's place at Hol. Thord the Coward was outside, and when he sees the crowd of men, he runs in and says that a whole army is coming to the house, and he is in quite a flurry.

'That is well, then,' says Gisli, and he speaks a verse:

> Fell I not nor failed at
> Fierce words, but my piercing
> Blade-mouth gave forth bloody
> Bane-speech, its harsh teaching.
> Sole, I watch in silence,
> Seeing this loud people:
> While the ship-tree welters
> Worried shouts bestir them.

Now they come to the house, Thorkel and Eyiolf; they go to the *bed-closet* which Gisli and his wife slept in, and Thorkel, Gisli's brother, goes ahead into the closet and sees where Gisli's shoes lie, frozen and all caked with snow; he pushes them under the foot-board so that other men will not see them. Then Gisli greets them and asks for their news. Big and bad news Thorkel tells him, and he asks Gisli if he knows what might lie behind it, and what should be done about it.

'Big and bad deeds follow one another closely,' says Gisli. 'We will offer to help bury Thorgrim, for you have a right to expect that of us, and it is fitting that we do it honourably.'

They accept this offer, and they all go together to Sæbol for the mound-making, and lay Thorgrim in a boat. Now they heap up the mound according to the old ways, and when it is ready to be closed, Gisli goes to the river-mouth and takes up a stone, so big as to be called a boulder, and puts it in the boat, and every timber seemed nearly to give way with it, and the boat creaked mightily, and he said:

'I cannot make fast a boat, if the weather moves this one.'

Some men said that this did not seem much unlike what Thorgrim had done with Vestein when he spoke about the Hel-shoes. Now they go home from the burial. Gisli spoke to his brother, Thorkel:

'I think you owe it to me, brother, to keep things as friendly between us now as they have been at their best; and let us start up the games.'

Thorkel readily agrees. And now each party go to their houses. Gisli has not a few men for company, but the feasting comes to an end, and Gisli sends off his guests with good gifts.

18

Now Thorgrim's wake is drunk, and Bork gives good gifts, for friendship's sake, to many men. The next thing that happens is that Bork pays Thorgrim Nef to work a spell, that there should be no help for the man who had killed Thorgrim, however much men might want to give it to him, and there should be no rest for him in the country. He was given a nine-year-old ox for the curse. He goes to work on it at once, and makes himself a scaffold and works this magic with all its obscenity and devilry.

There was something else that seemed to have a strange meaning, that snow never stayed on the south-west side of Thorgrim's mound and it did not freeze there; and men explained this by saying that he must have been so favoured by Frey for his sacrifices that the god was unwilling to have frost come between them. This went on through the winter while the brothers held their games there.

Bork moves into the house with Thordis and marries her. She was pregnant at the time, and she gives birth to a son, and he is sprinkled with water and named Thorgrim at first, after his father; but as he grew up they found that he was moody and unruly, so they changed his name and called him Snorri.

Bork lived there over the winter and joined in the games. A woman named Audbiorg lived in the upper part of the valley at Annmarkastadir. She was the sister of Thorgrim Nef. Her husband had been Thorkel, who was nicknamed Annmarki (blemish). Her son's name was Thorstein; he was one of the strongest at the games, after Gisli. Gisli and Thorstein were always together against Bork and Thorkel. One day a great many people came to see the games, because many were curious to watch the play and to find out who was the strongest or most skilful. And it happened, as in other places everywhere, that there was greater keenness among the players when there were more watchers. It is said that Bork had failed against Thorstein all day, and at last he grew angry and snapped Thorstein's bat for him, and Thorstein threw him and stretched him out on the ice. When Gisli sees this he told him to play with all his might against Bork.

'And I will change bats with you.'

And so they did. Gisli sits down and goes to work on the bat, facing Thorgrim's mound; there was snow on the ground, and the women were sitting up on the slope, his sister Thordis and many others. Gisli spoke a verse which he should have kept to himself:

Giant-bane Grim's grave mound,
Grows thin shoots, unfrozen;
God of war-blade gleaming
Gained, by me, pain's ending.
Wearer of grim war mask
Wields at last his field-plot;
Him, for land who hungered
Hauled earth made I swallow.

Thordis got the verse by heart from the one hearing and goes home, and by then she has worked out its meaning. They break up the games now, and Thorstein returns home. There was a man by the name of Thorgeir, who was called Orri (heath-cock); his farm was called Orrastadir. Another man, whose name was Berg, was called Skammfot (short-leg), and his farm was called Skammfotarmyr (Short-leg's marshland); it was east of the river. And now, as people are going home, Thorstein and Berg talk over the games and end by quarrelling; for Berg favours Bork and Thorstein argues against him, and Berg hits Thorstein a blow with the back of his axe-head. But Thorgeir comes between them and hinders Thorstein from avenging the blow.

Thorstein goes home to Audbiorg, his mother; she binds up his wound and grumbles about what has happened to him. The old woman gets no sleep that night, she is so fidgety. The weather was cold outside, and still and cloudless. She goes withershins about the house a few times and sniffs in all directions with her nostrils lifted. And as she was doing these things the weather began to change and there came a heavy, drifting snowstorm, and after that a thaw; a flood broke out on the mountainside and an avalanche rolled on to Berg's steading, and twelve men were killed there. The marks of the rock-fall may be seen to this day.

19

Thorstein goes to Gisli and Gisli gives him shelter, and he gets away southward to Borgarfiord and goes abroad from there. And when Bork heard of the disaster at Berg's, he goes up to Annmarkastadir and has Audbiorg seized and he takes her out to Saltness and stones her to death. And when this has happened Gisli sets out and comes to Nefsstadir and catches Thorgrim Nef and takes him out to Saltness, where a bag is put over his head[11] and he is stoned to death, and then buried under a heap of stones beside his sister Audbiorg, on the ridge between Haukadal and Medaldal.

Things are quiet now, and the spring passes on. Bork goes south to Thorsness, meaning to live there, and it seems to him that his move westward has brought him no honour; he had lost such a man as Thorgrim was and had got no redress. He makes ready for his move and sets his house in order and fixes his plans, for he means to make a

[11] So that the sorcerer's evil eye could do no harm as he died.

second trip after his goods and his wife. Thorkel, Gisli's brother, also made up his mind to move, and sets out with Bork, his brother-in-law.

The story tells now that Thordis, daughter of Sur, Bork's wife and Gisli's sister, went some distance on the way with her husband. Bork spoke:

'Now I want you to tell me why you were so moody last fall when we broke up the games, for you promised to tell me before I went away.'

They have now come to Thorgrim's grave-mound when they begin this talk. She puts her foot in front of her and says she will go no farther; then she tells him what Gisli said when he looked at Thorgrim's mound and she recites the verse to him.

'And I think,' she says, 'that you need search no farther over Thorgrim's death, and a case against him will be rightly brought.'

At this Bork becomes very angry and said:

'I will turn back now and kill Gisli, and there is no sense in lingering.'

But Thorkel says he cannot agree to that.

'I am not sure how much truth there is in what Thordis has told us; it seems to me just as likely there may be nothing in it at all, and "women's counsels are often cold".'

So they ride on their way, as Thorkel has persuaded them, until they come to Sandaos, and there they dismount and bait their horses. Bork was in a silent mood, and Thorkel said that he wanted to see his friend Onund. He rides off straightway, so hard that he is quickly out of sight. Then he swings round and goes to Hol and tells Gisli what has happened, that Thordis has now opened up the case, and found the meaning of his verse.

'And you must now make up your mind that it has come out into the open.'

Gisli was silent, and then he spoke a verse:

> Wife veil-hearted wavering[12]
> Warped to miss, my sister,
> Giuki's daughter's great heart,
> Gudrun's soul, stern moody.

[12] *wife veil-hearted wavering:* the Icelandic talks of 'my sister, heedful of marriage head-dress'. Thordis heeds her ties with her husband more than her ties with her brother, Gisli, and he compares her unfavourably with Gudrun,

Brooding wrath for brothers
Bent her mood to vengeance;
Heart's cause for her husband
Held she not, but felled him.

'I did not think I had deserved this from her, because I think I have shown more than once that her honour was as important to me as my own; sometimes I have put my life in danger for her sake, and now she has given me death's word. And I should like to know, brother, what I can look for from you, in your position, seeing what I have done.'

'Warning, if men are trying to kill you, but I will not give you protection that may bring a case against me.[13] I think it a great wrong done to me that my kinsman Thorgrim has been killed, my partner and my good friend.'

'Was it to be expected that such a man as Vestein would be left unavenged? And I would not answer you as you have now answered me, nor act as you say you will.'

They part. Thorkel returns to Bork and they go on south to Thorsness, and Bork puts his house in order; and Thorkel buys land on Bardastrond, the farm that is called Hvamm. Then the *summoning-days* come round and Bork rides west with forty men, intending to summon Gisli to the *assembly* at Thorsness,[14] and Thorkel, son of Sur, goes with him, and Bork's nephews Thorodd and Saka-Stein; there was also a Norwegian in the party called Thorgrim.

---

the wife of Sigurd the Dragon-slayer (now known to most people through Wagner and William Morris), the Kriemhilt of the *Nibelungenlied*. Sigurd was slain by her brothers, on whom she could not take vengeance. Her second marriage was to Atli, king of the Huns, who treacherously killed her brothers in order to win the treasure they had obtained on Sigurd's death. For this Gudrun slew Atli after first feasting him on the flesh of his dead sons.

[13] It was an offence to give aid or shelter to an outlaw. See Introduction, p. xx.

[14] About the same time as Gisli was outlawed a reform in the Icelandic constitution was made. Before then a case had to be brought at the *Assembly* in the locality of the man prosecuted, no matter where the prosecutor came from. After the reform, however, cases in which the prosecutor came from a different district were to go to the more neutral ground of newly established *Quarter Assemblies* (one for each quarter of the country). Cf. *The Saga of Grettir*, ch. 25.

They ride to Sandaos. Then Thorkel spoke:

'I have a debt to collect at a small farm near here'—and he named the farm—'and I shall ride there and collect the debt while you come after me at your own pace.'

He goes ahead; and when he got to the place he had spoken of, he asks the housewife to change horses with him and let his stand by the door.

'And throw some *homespun* over the saddle,[15] and when my friends come along, tell them that I am sitting in the living-room and counting money.'

She gives him another horse and he rides quickly and comes into the woods and meets Gisli and tells him what is going on, that Bork has come from the west.

20

Gisli asks his brother what he thinks is best to do, and he wants to know what Thorkel will do to help him, and whether he will give him shelter. He answers as before, that he will give him warning if any attacks are to be made, but he will keep himself clear of a law-case. Thorkel then rides off and takes a way that brings him up behind Bork and the others, and slows down their pace somewhat.

Gisli then hitches up two oxen and drives a cart with his valuables in it to the woods, and with him goes his thrall, Thord the Coward. Then Gisli spoke:

'You have often been obedient to me, and done as I have asked you, and I ought to give you some good reward.'

It was Gisli's way to be well dressed, and in a *blue* cape; he takes the cape from his back then and said:

'I will give you this cape, friend, and I want you to have the good of it at once and put it on, and sit in the sledge behind, and I will lead the oxen and be dressed in your cloak.'

They do as he says. Then Gisli spoke.

'If it happens that anyone calls out to you, then you must be sure not to answer at all, and if anybody wants to hurt you, then you run to the woods.'

[15] Presumably this is to suggest that this cloth is part of the debt he is collecting. See *homespun* in the Glossary.

This fellow had as much sense as he had spirit, for he had none of either. Gisli now leads the oxen. Thord was a man of big build and he sat high in the sledge; also he plumed himself rather, and thought himself splendidly dressed.

Now Bork and his company see them as they go towards the woods and ride after them fast. And when Thord sees this he jumps off the sledge and runs as hard as he can to the trees. They think it is Gisli and ride their fastest after him, and shout at him loudly. But he keeps quiet and runs his hardest. Thorgrim the Norwegian throws a spear after him, and it hits him between the shoulders so hard that it throws him forward, and this was his death-wound. Then Bork speaks:

'Well shot! It couldn't have been better!'

The brothers say that they will go after the thrall and see if there is any fight in him; so they go into the woods. The next thing is that Bork and the others come up to the *blue*-caped man and pull back his hood, and now it seems that their luck is less than they had thought, for they find Thord the Coward where they had expected to find Gisli. And the story says now that the brothers come among the trees where Gisli is, and he sees them and they him. One of them throws his spear at him, and Gisli catches it in flight and throws it back at Thorodd and it hits him in the middle and goes right through him. Stein turns back to his fellows and says the going is rather heavy in the woods. Bork, however, wants to carry on the chase, and so they do. And when they are among the trees Thorgrim the Norwegian sees where the branches move in a certain place, and he throws a spear there which hits Gisli in the calf of the leg. Gisli throws the spear back and it goes through Thorgrim, and he is killed.

They search the woods but they do not find Gisli, and they turn back then, leaving things as they are, to Gisli's house, and there they speak the summons against him for the slaying of Thorgrim. They take nothing from the house in the way of valuables and ride home. Gisli goes up the mountainside behind the farm and binds up his wound while Bork and the others are at the steading. When they were gone Gisli went back to his house and got ready to move.

When Bork first got the case ready against him for hearing at the Thorsness Assembly, Gisli sold his land to Thorkel son of Eirik and took payment in cash; this was much easier for him to handle. He takes a boat now, and puts his valuables in it, which were worth a large sum, and takes his wife Aud with him and his foster-daughter Gudrid, and goes out to Husaness and comes ashore there. Gisli goes up to the house there and meets a man, and the man asks him who he is, and Gisli told him what he thought fit, but not the whole truth. Gisli takes up a stone and throws it out to an island, which lay off shore there, and told the farmer to have his son do the same when he came home, and said that he would know then what man had come his way. For this was what no other man could do, and it showed, once more, that Gisli was better at such feats than most other men.

Gisli goes to his boat and rows out around the headland and across Arnarfiord and up into the fiord that runs in from Arnarfiord, which is called Geirthiofsfiord, and there he settles down, and he builds a full steading and stays there for the winter.

21

The next thing that happens is that Gisli sends word to Aud's uncles, Helgi and Sigurd and Vestgeir, asking them to go to the *assembly* and offer to pay a settlement for him so that he should not be outlawed. So these sons of Biartmar go to the *assembly*, but they bring about no kind of settlement, and men say that they behaved badly and they were almost in tears before it was over. They tell Thorkel the Rich what has happened, and said that they did not dare tell Gisli that he had been outlawed. Nothing else of note happened at the *assembly* besides Gisli's sentence.

Thorkel the Rich goes to Gisli and told him that he had been outlawed. Then Gisli spoke this verse:

They would not
At Thorsness
Have quailed thus
In my case
If Biartmar's
Sons' breasts
Had harboured
Vestein's heart.

Glum they were
Who should be glad,
Brothers of my
Wife's mother:
These gold-spenders
Desponded
As though sprayed
By a bad egg.

Word has come from northward
To warn me, from Thorsness;
Thing-men, unthewed,[16] wronged me,
Thorkel, in the court there.
Bork and Stein will brook my
Bitter coin, in witness,
Well earned, of my ill will,
Weighed and fully paid them.

Gisli asks the two Thorkels what he can expect of them. They tell him that they will give him shelter, as long as they do not lose their property on account of it. Then they ride home.

It is told that Gisli was three years in Geirthiofsfiord, but now and again with Thorkel son of Eirik, and the next three years he goes all about Iceland and visits the chieftains and asks for their help, but because of the black power that Thorgrim Nef had put into his spell-casting and cursing, he did not succeed in getting a chieftain to take up with him, and although sometimes they seemed not unlikely to favour him, something always got in the way. He stayed for long stretches, however, with Thorkel son of Eirik, and he has now been an outlaw for six years.

After this he stays sometimes with Aud in the house in Geirthiofsfiord, and sometimes in a hiding-place north of the river which he had made for himself; he had another hiding-place by the cliffs south of the river, and sometimes he stayed there.

[16] *unthewed*: the word *thew* is used with its old meaning in mind, custom or habit, especially a good habit or virtue.

22

Now when Bork hears of all this he makes a trip to see Eyiolf the Grey, who lived then in Otradal on Arnarfiord, and asks him to hunt for Gisli and kill him as an outlaw, and he says that he will give him sixty ounces of the purest silver if he will make every effort to hunt for him. Eyiolf takes the money and agrees to carry out the hunt.

A man was with Eyiolf whose name was Helgi, and he was called Spying-Helgi; he was both quick on his feet and sharpsighted, and he knew all the country round the fiords. He is sent into Geirthiofsfiord to find out whether Gisli is there. He sees that there is a man, but does not know whether it is Gisli or someone else. He goes home and tells Eyiolf what he has found. Eyiolf says he is sure it must have been Gisli, and he acts quickly and goes off with six men into Geirthiofsfiord, but he sees no sign of Gisli, so he comes back home, having done nothing.

Gisli was a wise man, and one who dreamed dreams that had true meanings. It is agreed among all wise men that Gisli went longer as an outlaw than any other man, except Grettir son of Asmund. The story says that one autumn Gisli had a struggle in his sleep one night, when he was staying at Aud's steading; and when he awoke, she asked him what he had been dreaming. He answers:

'I have two women in my dreams,' he says, 'and one is good to me, but the other always tells me something that makes me feel worse than before, and she foresees nothing but bad for me. And this time in my dream I seemed to come to a house or a hall, and I seemed to go into the house, and there I recognised many of those who were inside, kinsmen of mine and friends. They were sitting by the fires and drinking, and there were seven fires; some were nearly burnt out and some were burning very brightly. Then came in my better dream-woman and said that these marked my life, what I had yet to live; and she counselled me that while I lived I should give up the old faith, and have nothing to do with magic or witchcraft, and deal kindly with the blind and the halt and the poor and the helpless. There was no more to the dream.'

Then Gisli spoke some verses:

> Wife, land of the wave fire,
> Where I came were flaming

Seven fires to my sorrow
Stern, in the hall burning;
Bench crews rose and bowed there
From board seats to greet me;
In return I answered
Old meet words of greeting.

Bend your eyes, band goddess
Bade me, glad spender,
Fires, your life foretelling,
Furnish the hall, burning.
Years are few of yearning
Yet, until a better
Time for you, storm tamer,
Treader of sword weather.

Let your heart from learning
Lightness, and in right wise,
Schooled by good *skalds*, said she,
Seek the best, unresting.
Worst lot for the waster
Of wave fire, brave spender,
Ever, to know evil
Is, men say, in wisdom.

Hold your blade from bloodshed,
Be not first to stir them
Nor press them, promise me,
The proud gods of slaughter.
Help the blind and handless,
And heed this, ring-speeder,
Low the mocker's fame lies
And lame-harmer's name, low.

23

Now is to be told how Bork keeps egging on Eyiolf and thinks the business not as well followed up as he would like it to be and thinks that he has not got much for the money he has paid over, and he says that he knows for certain that Gisli is in Geirthiofsfiord, and he tells Eyiolf's men that have been sent between the two of them that Eyiolf must hunt for Gisli or else, he says, he will go after him himself. Eyiolf then bestirs himself and again sends Spying-Helgi into Geirthiofsfiord, and this time he has food with him and is away for a week, and he keeps watch for a sight of Gisli. He sees him one day when he is going from his hiding-place, and recognises him; this is what he has been waiting for, and he goes back and tells Eyiolf what he has found out. Eyiolf gets ready and sets out for Geirthiofsfiord with eight men, and goes to Aud's farmhouse; they do not find Gisli there, and they range the woods all round, hunting for him and do not find him. They come back then to Aud's house and Eyiolf offers her much money to tell them where Gisli is, but it is far from her mind to do that. Then they threaten to hurt her, but this has no effect, and they must go home empty-handed.

People thought this trip could not have been more contemptible, and Eyiolf stays at home for the rest of the fall. Although Gisli was not found this time, he reasons that he is, nevertheless, bound to be taken when he is such a short distance from Eyiolf's farm. Gisli leaves home now and rides out to Strond and comes to see his brother Thorkel at Hvamm. He knocks at the door of the sleeping-quarters where Thorkel is, and Thorkel comes out and greets him.

'Now I want to know,' said Gisli, 'if you will give me some help; I expect good help from you, because I am hard pressed, and I have held off asking you for a long while.'

Thorkel answers as before and says that he will give him no help which might bring a case against him, and says that he will give him money, or a horse if he needed one, or anything else like this, as he had said before.

'I see now,' said Gisli, 'that you will give me no real help. Give me three *hundred* ells of *homespun*, and comfort yourself with the thought that I will not often trouble you for help again.'

Thorkel does so, gives him cloth and some silver as well. Gisli says that he will accept that too, and went on to say that he would not treat him so meanly, however, if he stood in his place. Gisli is moved when they part. He goes now to Vadil, to the mother of Gest son of Oddleif, and comes there before daylight and knocks. She answers the door. It was often her way to take in outlaws, and she had an underground room; one way into the underground room was by the river, and the other was in her kitchen, and traces of it can still be seen. Thorgerd welcomes Gisli.

'And I will let you stay here for a while, but I do not know whether I can give you anything but a woman's help here.'

Gisli says that he will accept, and says that men's help had not been so good that it would be unlikely that women's help would be better. Gisli is there over the winter, and nowhere was he better treated during his outlawry.

24

As soon as it is spring Gisli goes back to Geirthiofsfiord, and he cannot be away from his wife Aud any longer, so devoted are they to one another; he is hidden there over the summer and until fall. And then the dreams come on again, as soon as the nights grow long; and the worse dream-woman comes to him now, and he has hard dreams, and once he tells Aud what he has dreamed when she asked him, and then he spoke a verse:

If dreams true lines draw me
Dark for age they mark me;
Thread-work goddess through my
Thought-filled sleep has sought me.
Although the ale goddess
Invites no bright meaning,
Linker of strong letters
Not less soundly rests him.

Then Gisli says that the worse woman comes to him often, and is always wanting to smear him with gore and blood, and wash him in it, and she carries on hideously. Then he spoke another verse:

Not every dream avails me,
Albeit word not fails me;
She, goddess, has spoken,
So is my joy broken.

At sleep's edge she seeks me,
With slaughter's gilt freaks me;
This woman works bloody
Wound flood on me, ruddy.

And again he spoke:

Told have I the tall ones,
Trees of the spear's greeting,
My dream of death's coming,
Dear wealth goddess, clearly.
Seekers of sark's hatred,
Strife gods, who outlawed me,
Will feel my filed weapon's
Fang, if I grow angry.

And now things are quiet. Gisli goes to Thorgerd and stays another winter with her. The following summer he goes to Geirthiofsfiord and is there until the fall. Then he goes again to his brother Thorkel's place and knocks on the door. Thorkel will not come out, so Gisli takes up a stick and cuts runes on it and throws it in. Thorkel sees it and picks it up and looks at it, and then stands up and goes out and greets Gisli and asks for his news. He says that he has none to tell him.

'And I have come to see you for the last time, brother, and let your help now be worthier; and I shall pay you by never asking help from you again.'

Thorkel replies again the same as before; he offers him a horse or a boat but refuses to stand by him himself. Gisli accepts the boat and asks Thorkel to help him launch it. He does so, and brings him four *hundred* pounds of food and a *hundred* ells of *homespun*. And when Gisli has got into the boat, Thorkel stands on the shore. Then Gisli spoke.

'Now you think that you are in clover, and the friend of many chieftains, and you have nothing to fear; and I am an outlaw, and many men are my bitter enemies. But I can tell you this, that you will be killed before me. We must now part, and on worse terms than ought to be, and we shall never see each other again; and you must know that I would never deal with you like this.'

'I am not worried by your prophecies,' said Thorkel.

And they part like this. Gisli rows out to the island Hergilsey in Breidafiord. He takes out of the boat the decking and thwarts and oars and everything not fixed in, and he overturns the boat and lets it wash ashore in the Nesses. And men guess, when they see the boat, that Gisli has been drowned, since the boat is wrecked and washed up, and that he must have taken it from his brother Thorkel.

Now Gisli goes up on Hergilsey, to the house. A man lives there whose name was Ingiald; his wife's name was Thorgerd; Ingiald was Gisli's cousin, and had come out to Iceland with him. When they meet he offers Gisli shelter and any help he can give him; and Gisli accepts and stays there in quiet for a while.

25

There was a thrall with Ingiald, and a bondwoman; the thrall was named Svart and the bondwoman was named Bothild. Helgi was the name of Ingiald's son, and he was as simple as could be, and a fool; a tether was made for him, a stone with a hole in it was tied to his neck and he browsed the grass out of doors like the cattle, and he was called Ingiald's fool. He was a big man, almost a giant. Gisli is there over the winter, and he builds a boat for Ingiald and many other things. And whatever he made was easy to recognise because he was handier than most other men. Men began to wonder why so many things were well made that Ingiald had, for he was not good with his hands. Gisli is always in Geirthiofsfiord over the summer; three years have now passed from the time he had begun to dream, and this is the best shelter he has had, which Ingiald gives him.

It seems to men, now, that all these things taken together are suspicious, and they begin to think that Gisli must be alive, and that he must have been living with Ingiald and not drowned, as had been said. Men begin to talk about the fact that Ingiald now has three boats, and all well made. These rumours come to the ears of Eyiolf the Grey, and it falls to Helgi's lot to set out again, and he comes to Hergilsey.

Gisli is always in an underground room when anyone comes to the island. But Ingiald was a hospitable man, and he offers Helgi a bed, so he was there for the night. Ingiald was a hard-working man; he rowed out to fish every day that the weather was fit. And in the morning, when he was ready to set out, he asks whether Helgi is not keen to get on with his journey, and why is he still in bed. He said that he was not quite well, and he breathed heavily and rubbed his head. Ingiald told him to lie still then, and he rows out to sea; and Helgi takes to groaning hard. Now the story says that Thorgerd goes to the underground room and means to give Gisli his breakfast; and there is a partition between the pantry and the room Helgi was lying in. Thorgerd goes out of the pantry; Helgi climbs up on the partition and sees that somebody's food has been set out; and at this Thorgerd comes back in, and Helgi moves fast, and he falls down from the partition. Thorgerd asks why he is doing this, climbing up in the rafters, and not lying still. He says that he is so frantic with the pains in his limbs that he cannot lie still.

'And I wish,' he says, 'that you would help me back to bed.'

She does so. Then she goes out with the food. But Helgi gets straight out of bed and follows her, and sees now what is going on; he goes back and lies down after this and stays there for the day.

Ingiald comes home in the evening and goes to Helgi's bed and asks whether he is any better. He says he has taken a turn for the better, and he asks to be ferried off the island in the morning. So he is taken south to Flatey, and from there he makes his way to Thorsness; and he tells them that he has found out that Gisli is with Ingiald. Bork sets out then by ship with fourteen men, and sails north across Breidafiord. This day Ingiald has rowed out to fish and Gisli with him, and the thrall and the bondwoman in another boat, and they were lying off some islands that are called Skutileyiar.

26

Now Ingiald sees the ship sailing from the south, and he said:

'A ship is sailing there, and I think it will be Bork the Stout.'

'What should we do now?' asked Gisli. 'I want to find out if you are a clever man, as much as you are a stout fellow.'

'I can decide quickly,' said Ingiald, 'though I may not be clever; let us row as hard as we can to the island and then climb up on Vadsteinaberg and fight as long as we can stand.'

'That is what I expected,' said Gisli, 'that you would offer a plan that calls for the best courage; but I make a worse payment for your help than I intended if you lose your life for my sake. That must never be, and we shall follow another plan. You shall row to the island with the thrall and go up on the hill and make a stand to defend yourselves, and they will think I am the other man with you when they sail north around the headland. And I shall change clothes with the thrall, as I have done once before now, and I shall go in the boat with Bothild.'

Ingiald did as Gisli advised; and one thing was apparent, that he was very angry. And as the boats separate the bondwoman spoke:

'What is to be done now?'

Gisli answered in a verse:

> Woman, this wight, deeming
> His wing turned from Ingiald,
> Plans, and plies his cunning
> —I pour the dwarfs' liquor.
> Whether ill or well fare
> Awaits me, I mate it
> Boldly, splendid bond-wife,
> Bright tree of the sea's fire.

Now they row south towards Bork and his men and look as though they expected no trouble. Then Gisli tells her what he wants her to do.

'You shall say,' he says, 'that this is the fool in the boat, and I shall sit in the bows and mimic him, and tangle myself in the lines and hang overboard sometimes and carry on as foolishly as I know how; and if we get past them a little, I shall row my hardest and try to put distance between us as fast as possible.'

She rows on towards them and yet not too close, and makes it look as though she is going to another fishing ground. Bork calls out to her and asks if Gisli is on the island.

'I do not know that,' says she, 'but I do know that there is a man there who is both bigger than other men, those who are on the island, and better with his hands.'

'Ay,' says Bork. 'And is farmer Ingiald at home?'

'A while ago he rowed to the island,' said she, 'and his thrall with him, or so I thought.'

'That will not have been a thrall,' says Bork; 'that must have been Gisli; and let us row after them as fast as we can.'

His men kept their eyes on Gisli and answered:

'We think there is some sport here with the half-wit: look at the fool things he is doing!'

They told Bothild that she was badly off, having to look after this idiot.

'I think so too,' she says. 'But it's my belief you are making a joke of it, and do not feel sorry for me at all.'

'No more of this foolishness,' says Bork. 'Let us get on our way.'

They leave her and row to the island and go ashore, and then they see the men up on Vadsteinaberg, and they go up after them and think that everything is going their way, for Ingiald and his thrall have taken their stand on the crag. Bork knows the men right away, and he spoke to Ingiald:

'You will be wise to give up Gisli, or else tell me where he is, and you are a son of a bitch to shelter my brother's murderer when you are my tenant, and it's bad treatment you deserve from me, and it would only be right if you were killed.'

Ingiald answers, 'My clothes are threadbare, and it will not grieve me not to make them more so; and I will rather lose my life than not do Gisli any good turn that I can, or keep him from trouble.'

And men have said that Ingiald gave Gisli most help, and that his help was the most useful to him; and the story says that when Thorgrim Nef worked his curse he spoke in this way, that Gisli should get no benefit even though men should help him here on the mainland; but it did not come into his head to say anything that covered the off-shore islands, and so this help lasted rather longer than any other, though it was bound to come to an end.

27

Bork does not think it proper to attack Ingiald, his tenant. They go away then to the house and hunt for Gisli there, and do not find him, as was to be expected. They go about the island and come to the place where the fool was, browsing grass in a little dale with a stone tied around his neck. Then Bork has something to say.

'Not only is Ingiald's fool much spoken of, but he is in rather more places than I thought, and it is no good staring at him here. We have been so careless that it is hard to believe, and I can hardly see how we shall put it right again. That will have been Gisli in the boat near us, making out that he was the idiot, for he has the wit for anything and he is a great mimic; but it will be most shameful if he slips through our fingers, so many of us as we are. We must go quick after him and not let him get out of range.'

Then they jump into their ship and row after them, and pull fast on the oars. Soon they see that Gisli and the bondwoman have gone far into the sound, and now both boats row hard. The larger boat, with the more men in it, goes faster, and comes up so near at last that Bork is within spear-shot of him, but by then Gisli has come to shore. Then Gisli speaks, and said to the bondwoman:

'We shall part now, and here is a gold ring that you shall take to Ingiald, and another for his wife, and tell them that they are to give you your freedom, and take these as tokens. I also want Svart to be given his freedom. You must surely be called the one who has saved my life, and I want you to be rewarded for it.'

They part, and Gisli climbs ashore and up to a rocky cleft; it is just off Hiardarness. The bondwoman rowed away, sweating from the exertion, and reeking of it.

The ship comes to shore and Saka-Stein is the first out of it, and he climbs up to look for Gisli; and when he reaches the cleft Gisli is standing there with his drawn sword, and he brings it right down on his head so that it splits him to the shoulder, and he fell dead to the ground. Bork and the rest now go up on the island; but Gisli jumps down into the sea, intending to swim to the mainland. Bork throws a spear after him, which takes him in the leg and cuts right through, and it makes a bad wound. He pulls the spear out, but he loses his sword because he was so weary that he could not keep his grip on it. It was dark by the time he reached the shore. He goes into the woods, for there was much bush land there then. Bork and the others row over to the mainland and hunt for Gisli, and they surround him in the woods, and he is so tired and stiff that he can hardly walk, and he is aware of men all around him. He tries to think of a way out, and he comes down to the water's edge and makes his way round to Haug in the darkness along the foreshore which was passable on the ebb, and he meets a certain farmer called Ref.

This farmer was a very cunning man. He greets Gisli and asks him for his news. He told him everything that had happened between him and Bork. Ref had a wife called Alfdis, handsome in looks but violent in temper, and altogether a shrew; she was a match for Ref. When he has told Ref his news, Gisli asks him for help.

'For they will be here soon,' said Gisli, 'and they are pressing me hard, and there are not many I can turn to for help.'

'I shall make one condition,' said Ref, 'that however I go about helping you, you will not interfere at all.'

'I agree to that,' said Gisli, 'and I shall not walk a step farther.'

'Go inside, then,' said Ref.

And so they did. Then Ref spoke to Alfdis:

'Now I am going to change men in bed with you.'

And he takes all the covers off the bed and said that Gisli was to lie down there in the straw, and he puts the covers back over him, and Alfdis gets back in bed on top of him.

'And you stay there,' said Ref, 'for the time being, whatever happens.'

He tells Alfdis now to be on her worst behaviour and as though she was out of her mind.

'And do not hold back,' said Ref. 'Say whatever bad thing comes into your head, curses and bad language; and I will go and do the talking with them, and pick my words to suit myself.'

And for the second time, when he comes out, he sees men approaching, and these are Bork's companions, eight of them together. Bork is behind, at Forsa. These men had been sent up there to hunt for Gisli and take him if he has come this way. Ref is outside, and he asks for their news.

'We can only tell you what you must have heard already. But do you know anything about where Gisli has gone?' they ask. 'Has he perhaps come here?'

'I will give you two answers,' said Ref. 'He has not come here and if he had tried it he would have met with swift disaster, and I do not know whether you think it is true or not that I am as ready as any one of you to kill Gisli; but I have enough wit to think that it would be no small gain to have the confidence of such a man as Bork is, and I want to be his friend.'

They ask, 'Will you mind if we search you and your home?'

'By all means,' says Ref. 'I shall be very glad of it, because I know that then you can search more surely in other places, if you know for certain first that he is not here. So go in and search the place inside out.'

They go in. And when Alfdis heard their noise she asks what thugs were on the move out there, or what kind of hooligans they were, bothering people in the night. Ref told her to quiet down. But she lets go a flood of bad language; she tells them a few things that they will not quickly forget. They carry out their search all the same, but not as thoroughly as they would have done if they had not first had to put up with such bad language from the housewife. They go away then, having found nothing, and wish the farmer a good life; and he wishes them good travelling. Then they come back to Bork, and they are all dissatisfied with this trip and they think that they have had a great and shameful loss in Saka-Stein without achieving anything they had set out for. The news goes about the district, and nobody can see any difference between this and their other failures against Gisli. Bork goes home now, and tells Eyiolf how things stand.

Gisli stays with Ref for a fortnight, then he goes away, and parts good friends with Ref and gives him a knife and belt, which were valuable things; they were all he had left on him. Afterwards he goes back to his wife in Geirthiofsfiord, and he has added a great deal to his fame by this adventure. And it is true to say that there has not been such a powerful man as Gisli, nor one so courageous, and yet he was not lucky. But it is time to speak of something else.

28

It is to be told now that in the spring Bork goes to the *assembly* in Thorskafiord with a large party of men, with the purpose of meeting his friends. Gest comes from the west, from Raudasand on Bardastrond, and also Thorkel, son of Sur, each sailing his own ship. And when Gest is ready to set out, two boys come to him, badly dressed and carrying staves in their hands. It becomes known for certain that Gest has a talk in private with the boys, and it is also certain that they ask for passage on his ship and he gives it to them. They go as far as Hallsteinsness with him, and there he puts them ashore east of the farm on the headland called Grenitresness. From here they make their own way to the *assembly*.

There was a man named Hallbiorn; he was a tramp who used to go about the country, never with fewer men than ten or twelve; and he had built himself a *booth* at the *assembly*. The boys go there and ask for shelter in his *booth*, and say they are tramps. He says he will give *booth*-room to anyone who will ask him for it.

'I have been here many springs,' he said, 'and I know all the noblemen and chiefs.'

The boys say that they will be glad of his protection, and want to learn from him.

'We are very curious to see the famous men that the big stories are about.'

Hallbiorn says that he will go down to the shore, and he said that he would recognise every ship as soon as it came in, and tell them. They thank him for being so friendly. Then they go down to the shore and across to the water's edge; and they see that some ships are sailing in. The older boy speaks:

'Whose is that ship, that is sailing this way first?'

Hallbiorn said that it was Bork the Stout's ship.

'And who is sailing next to him?'

'Gest the Wise,' he said.

'And who is sailing after him, and drawing up there in the creek mouth?'

'That is Thorkel, son of Sur,' he said.

They see now that Thorkel goes ashore and sits down on the ground while their gear is being carried off to a point above high-water mark. And Bork gets their *booth* ready. Thorkel had a Russian fur hat on his head, and a grey cloak fastened with a gold pin at the shoulder, and a sword in his hand. Then Hallbiorn goes over, and the two boys with him, to where Thorkel is sitting. Now one of the boys, the older one, speaks:

'Who is this lordly man sitting here? I have not seen such a handsome and noble-looking man.'

'Your words are well spoken, and I am called Thorkel.'

The boy says, 'That must be a valuable sword that you have in your hand; will you let me have a look at it?'

Thorkel answers, 'It is a very strange thing you ask, but I will let you see it.'

And he hands it to him. The boy took the sword and turned aside a little, and undoes the peace-straps[17] and draws the sword from the scabbard. When Thorkel saw this, he said:

'I did not give you leave to draw the sword.'

'I did not ask your leave,' said the boy.

And he swings the sword back and drives it into Thorkel's neck so that the blow took off his head. As soon as this has happened Hallbiorn the tramp jumps up; the boy throws the bloody sword down, and picks up his staff and the two of them run with Hallbiorn and his gang; and the tramps are nearly off their heads with panic. They run up by the *booth* which Bork is getting ready. Men crowd around Thorkel, and nobody seems to know who has done the deed.

Bork asks what this excitement and noise means that is going on around Thorkel. And when Hallbiorn and his gang run up by the *booth*—there were fifteen tramps—and when Bork asks this question, the younger boy answers him, whose name was Helgi—the one who had done the killing was called Berg:

'I do not know what they are meeting about; but I think they are trying to decide whether Vestein left only daughters or had sons too.'

Hallbiorn runs to his *booth*; and the boys go into the scrub that was round about and are not found again.

29

Men come running now to Hallbiorn's *booth* and ask what it all means. The tramps say that two young boys had come into their gang, and they say they had no inkling of this, and they say that they knew nothing at all about them; they tell something, however, about their looks, and what sort of things they had said. Bork thinks he knows now from the words Helgi had spoken that it must have been the sons of Vestein; and so he goes to see Gest and talk over with him how he should go about this business. Bork says:

'It is more my duty than anyone else's to take up Thorkel's case, since he was my brother-in-law. It seems not unlikely to us that this is how it happened, that Vestein's sons must have done the deed; because

[17] Peace-straps would have been fastenings round the sword-hilt to prevent the sword accidentally coming out of the sheath.

we do not know that any other man would be likely to have anything against Thorkel, except them. It may be that they have got away for now. Tell me what you think: how should the case be taken up?'

Gest answers, 'I would know what to do if I had done the killing; I would use the trick—so that the case would fail that might be brought against me—of calling myself by another name.'

And Gest puts many difficulties in the way of bringing a case forward. People have been sure that Gest was in the plot with the boys, because he was tied to them by kinship. They break off their talk, and the case is dropped. And Thorkel is buried with the old rites and men go home from the *assembly*; and nothing else of importance happens at this *assembly*. Bork was discontented with his trip, as he had often had cause to be, and he had furthermore brought on himself much disgrace and dishonour from this affair, the way things had been left.

The boys go on until they come to Geirthiofsfiord, spending five days and nights in the open country. Then they come to Aud's, and Gisli is there at the time; they come at night and knock on the door. Aud opens it and greets them and asks for their news. Gisli was in the *bed-closet* beneath which there was an underground passage, and she would raise her voice if he needed to be on guard. They tell her about the killing of Thorkel and about how they are managing; and they tell her also how long they have been without food.

'I am going to send you,' said Aud, 'across the ridge to Mosdal, to Biartmar's sons; I shall give you food and a token so that they will give you shelter; and I am doing this because I do not want to ask Gisli to help you.'

The boys go into the woods where they might not be found and eat the food, for they had gone hungry for a long time; and then they lie down to sleep when they had eaten their fill, because they were very tired.

30

Now it is to be said of Aud that she goes in to Gisli and spoke:

'It means much to me now how you will take this, so as to treat me more honourably than I deserve.'

He understood her at once and said:

'I know that you are going to tell me of the killing of my brother Thorkel.'

'It is as you have guessed,' said Aud, 'and the boys came here and they wanted to hide out with you, and they thought they could put their trust in nothing but this.'

He answers, 'I cannot bear to see my brother's killers, and be together with them.'

And he jumps up and goes to draw his sword, and he spoke a verse:

Guess not but that Gisli,
Given this cause, driven
By thought of slain Thorkel,
—*Thing* tidings men bring him—
Battle-ice but that he
Brandish may in answer.
Doubt not. I will dare till
Death has made me breathless.

Then Aud said that they were gone.

'For I had wit enough not to risk them here.'

Gisli said that this was the best way, that they should not meet; and he becomes calmer at once, and things are then quiet for a while. It is said that now there are no more than two years left of those that the dream-woman said he would live. And as the season wears on Gisli stays in Geirthiofsfiord, and the dreams all return and the hard struggles in his sleep, and now it is always the worse dream-woman who comes to him, except for odd times when it is the better. One night it happens that the better dream-woman again comes to him; she seemed to be riding a grey horse, and she invites him to ride with her to her home, and he goes with her. They come now to a house which is very like a nobleman's hall, and she leads him into it by the hand, and it seems to him that there are cushions along the raised benches, and all the furnishings are rich. She asked that they should stay there together and be happy.

'And you shall come here when you die,' she said, 'and enjoy riches and contentment.'

Then he wakes up, and he spoke some verses about what he had dreamt:

Goddess of threads gladly
On her grey steed prayed me
Rise up, praise-rune maker,
Ride away beside her.
Golden one, of seagull's
Ground, in weakness found me;
To help me and heal me
Her grave promise gave me.

Splendid sea-flame goddess
Showed me, ode-contriver,
Where, for my worn body
And will, lay a pillow.
Linen goddess led me
Lo, where sleep would know me;
No hilled pallet held me;
My head, sweetly bedded.

'Hither, when death's heavy
Hand-blow has unmanned you,'
Said then that sweet lady,
'Shall the *valkyr* bring you.
Adder's earth and other
Old rich treasure told here
And my self you solely
Sovereign shall govern.'

31

Then the story says that a time comes when Helgi was again sent spying into Geirthiofsfiord; and people think it likely that Gisli is there. A man goes with him whose name is Havard. He had come to Iceland that summer and he was a kinsman of Gest son of Oddleif. They were sent into the woods to cut timber, and so they made their business appear to be, but in fact they were meant to look for Gisli and see if they could find his hiding-place. And one day at twilight they see a fire in the cliffs to the south of the river. This was at nightfall, when it was already quite dark. Havard asks Helgi what they should do about this.

'For you,' he says, 'will be more used to this business than I.'

'There is one thing to do,' says Helgi. 'Build a cairn here on this hillock where we are standing, so that we can find it again when it is daylight; and we can take a sight across from the cairn to the cliffs, which are not far to see.'

They follow this plan. When they have built the cairn, Havard said that he was sleepy, so much so that he could no longer stay awake. He lies down and sleeps. But Helgi stays awake and does what is needed to finish the cairn. When he has done this, Havard wakes up and tells Helgi to sleep, and he says that he will watch. So Helgi sleeps for a while. And while he is sleeping Havard goes to work and takes the cairn all apart and scatters the stones in the darkness. And when he has done all this he takes a big stone and smashes it down on the rock-face near Helgi's head, so that the earth shook with it. Helgi springs up, and he is shaking and frightened, and he asked what was happening. Havard said:

'There is a man in the woods, and many stones like this have been coming down tonight.'

'It must have been Gisli,' says Helgi, 'and he must have found out that we are here; and you realise, man dear,' he says, 'that we will be smashed if such a stone hits us; and there is nothing else to do but get away as quickly as we can.'

Helgi runs off at his fastest; and Havard walks after him and asks Helgi not to leave him like that, but Helgi paid no attention and went as fast as his feet would go. At last they both come to their boat and jump into it and plunge the oars into the water and row hard, without letting up, until they come home to Otradal; and Helgi says he is sure now where Gisli is.

Eyiolf acts at once, and sets out with eleven men, and Helgi and Havard are in the party. They go on into Geirthiofsfiord and range through all the woods, hunting for the cairn and Gisli's hiding-place, but they found neither. Then Eyiolf asks Havard where they had built the cairn. He answers:

'I cannot be sure of that; because not only was I so tired that I hardly knew what was going on around me, but besides Helgi finished building the cairn while I was sleeping. I think it is not unlikely that Gisli knew we were there, and he carried away the cairn when it was daylight and we had left.'

Eyiolf said, 'We have had nothing but bad luck in this case, and we may as well turn back.'

And so they do, but Eyiolf says he will visit Aud first. They come to the steading and walk in, and Eyiolf settled down again to have a talk with Aud. He has this to say:

'I will make a bargain with you, Aud,' he says, 'that you tell me where Gisli is and I will give you the sixty ounces of silver which I have taken as the price on his head. You shall not be there when we take his life. It will also follow that I will arrange a marriage for you that will be better in every way than this one has been. You can see for yourself,' he says, 'how miserable it becomes for you, living in this deserted fiord, and having this happen to you because of Gisli's bad luck, and never seeing your kinsfolk or their families.'

She answers, 'I think the last thing,' she says, 'that we are likely to agree about is that you could arrange any marriage for me that I would think as good as this one. Even so, it is true, as they say, that "cash is the widow's best comfort"; and let me see whether this silver is as much or as fine as you say it is.'

He pours the silver into her lap then, and she puts her hand into it while he counts it and turns it over before her. Gudrid, her foster-daughter, begins to cry.

32

She goes out and finds Gisli, and she says to him:

'My foster-mother has gone out of her wits, and she is going to betray you.'

Gisli spoke, 'Put your mind at rest, for it will not be treachery from Aud that will be the cause of my death.'

And he spoke a verse:

Loud they tongue my lady,
Lords of masted fiord-elks;
Hoards she, say they, hard thoughts
Heart deep for her partner.

I have seen that single
Sorrow keeps she, mourning;
True drops, never traitor
Tears fall from my dear one.

Then the girl goes home again and says nothing of where she has been. Eyiolf has then counted the silver, and Aud spoke:

'In no way is the silver less or poorer than you have said, and you will think now that I have the right to do with it as I please.'

Eyiolf agrees with this gladly, and tells her certainly to do what she likes with it. Aud takes the silver and puts it in a big purse; she stands up and swings the purse with the silver in it at Eyiolf's nose, so that the blood spurts out all over him; then she spoke:

'Take that for your easy faith, and every harm with it! There was never any likelihood that I would give my husband over to you, scoundrel. Take your money, and shame and disgrace with it! You will remember, as long as you live, you miserable man, that a woman has struck you; and yet you will not get what you want for all that!'

Then Eyiolf said, 'Seize the bitch and kill her, woman or not!'

Havard has something to say: 'This errand has been poor enough, without this coward's work. Stand up, men, and do not let him get his way in this.'

Eyiolf said, 'The old saying is true, "A man's worst following comes from home". '

Havard was a well-liked man, and many of them were ready to back him up, besides wanting to turn Eyiolf from a bad act; and Eyiolf has to be satisfied to leave it at this and go. Before Havard went out Aud spoke to him:

'It would be wrong not to pay you the debt that Gisli owes you, and here is a gold finger-ring that I want you to have.'

'I would not have claimed it,' says Havard.

'I want to pay it, though,' says Aud.

She was really giving him the ring for the help he had given her.

Havard got himself a horse and rides south to Strond, to Gest son of Oddleif, and he refuses to stay with Eyiolf any longer. Eyiolf goes home to Otradal, discontented with what had been done; and indeed it was everywhere thought to have been most contemptible.

33

As the summer passes Gisli remains in his hiding-places, being wary for himself, and he has made up his mind not to go away again; it seems to him now that his burrows are all snowed in; and the years allotted to him in his dreams are all spent. Then comes a certain night in summer when Gisli has a bad sleep. And when he wakens Aud asks him what he has dreamt. He says that the worse dream-woman came to him and spoke:

'Now I shall overturn everything that the better woman has told you; and I shall see to it that no good will come to you of anything she has promised.'

Then he spoke a verse:

'Sorrow will you sever,
Such as deep love touches,
Turn your ways in torment,'
Told me the bowl goddess.
'Lord of life has led you
Lone, to unknown places,
Hills far from your hall roof,
Homeless, new world roamer.'

'I dreamt further,' he said, 'that this woman came to me and tied a bloody cap on my head, after she had washed my head in blood, and she spattered me all over so that I was all bloody.'

He spoke a verse:

I dreamt the dread goddess
Drenched my head in redness,
Froth of fires of Odin
That flows where the blows fall.
Goddess hands were hidden
Of hawk-track fire, brackish
Sword-loosed tides swept round them,
Stained them deep with wound rain.

And again he spoke:

I dreamt the doom goddess
Draped my bushy straight-cut
Hair with a dour head-piece,
Hat all blood bespattered;
Seared with smoking sword rain
Her soiled hands embroiled me;
Thread-work goddess thrust me
Then to my dream's ending.

Now the dreams become so much for Gisli, and he becomes so frightened of the dark, that he is afraid to be alone; and as soon as his eyelids close the same woman appears to him. It was on one of these nights that Gisli struggled very hard in his sleep. Aud asked what had appeared to him.

'I dreamt,' says Gisli, 'that men were attacking us, and Eyiolf was among them, and many other men, and we met, and I knew that there was fighting between us. One of them came in front, bellowing loud, and I seemed to cut him in two at the middle, and I thought he had a wolf's head. Then more of them attacked me. I seemed to have a shield in my hand, and I kept them off for a long while.'

Gisli spoke a verse:

I fought a lone fateful
Fight, this was my nightmare;
Single, not soon was I
Slain by their main power.
Good flesh by my gashing
Gave I mouths of ravens,
But in your white bosom
Bright blood drops fell ruddy.

And he spoke another:

My shield fenced my *skald*'s life
The sounding blades found my
Wooden bastion wide-hard
Towards them, loud sword points.
Metal dinned on meeting;
Much their power touched me,

Quelled me, though my called-for
Courage faced their murder.

And he spoke another:

Ill fared one crow feeder
Before the rest tore me;
I carved for the curved-bill
Corpse-stream hawk this morsel;
Hewed strong legs my hard edge
Unhurried, struck surely;
Mastered, he missed footing,
More to swell my glory.

The autumn was coming on and the dreams were not growing less but rather they came more often than before. It was one night when Gisli had again had a hard time in his sleep. Aud then asked him once more what had appeared to him. Gisli spoke a verse:

My both sides were bathed in
Blood, I dreamed so, flooded;
I dreamed harm descended
Of drawn wound flood on me.
Necklet goddess, nightly
Now, blood nightmares bow me;
A storm stirs, of weapons,
Strife of men against me.

He spoke another verse:

It seemed gods of slain net
Set with blades whetted,
Blood on my both shoulders,
Broad and straight, ring goddess.
Ire of corpse-stream eagle's
Eye-delight providers
Left me dwindled life hopes,
Less to come of blessing.

And again another:

Sheared they with their sword blades—
Shield troll-woman wielders—
My doomed arms; I dreamt they
Deeply harmed my sleep self.
I dreamt the helm-daunting
Downward sword teeth gored me,
Greedy mouths, thread goddess,
Gaped at me their fang shapes.

And he spoke still another verse:

Band goddess bent to me,
Bore for me dream sorrow,
Fresh dew on her eye-fringe
Felt that bright belt goddess.
Soft that sea-fire goddess
And soon, bound my wounds up:
Ministered or meant she
More, think you, than sorrow?

34

Gisli spends the whole summer at home, and all is quiet. Then comes the last day of the summer season. On that October night the story says that Gisli could not sleep, and neither could Aud and Gudrid. The weather was such that the air was very still and the frost, also, was heavy. Gisli says that he wants to go from the house to his hiding-place, which was southwards under the cliffs, and see if he might sleep there. All three of them go, and they are wearing long kirtles, and the kirtles trail in the white frost. Gisli is carrying a stick and cutting runes in it, and the chips fall to the ground. They come to the hiding-place. He lies down to see if he can get some sleep; and the women stay awake. Drowsiness comes on him, and he dreams that big birds come into the place, bigger than cock-ptarmigans; and they screeched horribly; and they had been wallowing in blood. Then Aud asked him what he had been dreaming.

'My dreams are no better than before.'

He spoke a verse:

> Loud in my mind, lady,
> Linen goddess, din came,
> Pierced me when we parted—
> I pour the dwarfs' liquor.
> Heard this tree of hard edge
> Hatred, fighting great birds,
> Beating wings. My bow's dew
> Will blight the hearts of fighters.

While he is talking they hear the sound of men's voices, and Eyiolf has come up with fourteen men, and they have been to the steading first and seen the trails over the frost, as if pointing the way. When Gisli and the two women become aware of the men they climb up on the cliffs to where the vantage is best, and the women each carry a big club. Eyiolf and his men come below. Eyiolf spoke then to Gisli:

'It will not be right now for you to run away, and let yourself be chased like a coward, because you are called a great hero. We have not had many meetings, and we would like it if this might be the last.'

Gisli answers, 'Come at me like a man, for I shall not run any farther away. And it is for you to attack me first, because you have more against me than the other men who are here in your party.'

'I shall not leave it to you,' says Eyiolf, 'to place my men for me.'

'It was more likely,' says Gisli, 'that your dog's heart would be afraid to cross weapons with me.'

Eyiolf spoke then to Spying-Helgi, 'You would make a great name for yourself if you were the first to go up the cliff at Gisli, and the fame of it would go about for a long while.'

'I have seen for myself,' says Helgi, 'that you will mostly have others in front of you, where there is some danger; but because you egg me on so hard I shall do as you say, but you must come right after me, and be next man up, if you are not all a coward.'

Helgi starts upwards where the way seems best to him, and he has a big axe in his hand. Gisli was equipped with an axe, which he held in his hand, and a girded sword and a shield by his side, and he was wearing a grey, cowled cloak which he had tied round himself with a cord. Helgi takes a run and springs up the cliff at Gisli. He turns to meet Helgi, swings back his sword and brings it down across his loins, so that he cuts the man in two, and the parts fall back off the cliff.

Eyiolf follows up by another way, but Aud was facing him, and she strikes his arm with her club so that all the strength goes out of it, and he falls back down. Then says Gisli:

'I knew long ago that I was well wived, but I did not know until now how well. And yet the help you have just given me is less than you hoped and expected to give me, even though your blow was good, because I would have sent both of those men the same way.'

35

Two men then go up to hold Aud and Gudrid, and they think they have as much as they can do. Twelve men attack Gisli up on the cliffs. But he holds them off with stones and weapons so well that his defence has become famous. One of Eyiolf's fellows jumps forward and says:

'Let me have those good weapons you are holding, and your wife Aud along with them.'

Gisli answers, 'You will have to win them hard; because you are not good enough for them, neither the weapons that have been mine nor my wife.'

This man thrusts at Gisli with his spear. But Gisli strikes the spear-head from the shaft, and the blow is so heavy that the axe comes down on the flat rock beneath him and a corner snaps off from its edge. He throws down the axe then and draws his sword and fights with it, guarding himself with his shield. Now they attack manfully and he defends himself well and with spirit; and they battled fiercely. Gisli killed another two men, and now four of them are dead. Eyiolf tells them to go at him like men.

'It is not easy for us,' says Eyiolf, 'but what does that matter if the reward is good?'

Then, when it is least expected, Gisli turns about and runs across to a lone bluff called Einhamar, away from the cliffs; and there he makes his stand to defend himself. This took them unawares; and it now seems to them that they are much worse off—four men dead and the rest wounded and tired. There comes a lull in the attacking. Then Eyiolf eggs on his men harder than ever, and promises them big rewards if they will close in on Gisli. These were picked men that he had with him, for their determination and toughness.

36

A man called Svein is the first to come at Gisli. Gisli strikes at him and splits him to the shoulders and flings him down over the bluff. They hardly seem to know where the slaughter inflicted by this man will stop. Gisli spoke then to Eyiolf:

'By my will, you would never earn anything more dearly than the sixty ounces of silver you have taken on my head; and what is more, I will make you wish that you could give another sixty ounces that we had never met, for you will be disgraced for losing so many men.'

Now they search for an opening, and they will not turn away after this, not for their lives. They attack him from two sides, and two are in front with Eyiolf, one called Thorir and the other Thord, kinsmen of Eyiolf. These were two hard-fighting kind of men; and the thrusting is now fierce and quick, and they succeed in wounding him in some places with their spears, but he fights back fearlessly and with great spirit. And they take so much from him by stones and great blows that not one of them was unwounded who attacked him, for Gisli's aim was sure when he struck. They attack him fiercely, Eyiolf and his kinsmen; they saw that their honour was at stake. They wound him then with their spears, so that his bowels begin to come out; and he gathers the bowels in with his shirt and ties them underneath with the cord. Then Gisli told them to wait a little.

'You will finish up the case as you want to.'

He spoke a verse:

Sheer goddess of shower
Of spear-shaft's hall, cheer-heart,
Brave, bids of her lover,
Bold one, the cold tidings.
Fain am I though finely
Forged bright edges bite me;
My sire's true sword temper
Shows in his son's life-close.

This is Gisli's last verse; and as soon as he had spoken the verse, he leaps down from the bluff and drives his sword into the skull of Thord, Eyiolf's kinsman, and splits him right down to the middle; with this Gisli falls over on top of him and is lifeless. And they were all badly wounded, Eyiolf's fellows.

Gisli died of so many great wounds that there seemed to be something strange about it. His attackers said that he never gave ground, and they could not see that his last blow was weaker than his first. Thus Gisli's life comes to an end, and it is everywhere agreed that he was the most valiant of men, and yet he was not in all things a lucky man. They drag his body down and take away his sword; they bury him there among the stones and go down to the sea. A sixth man died beside the water.

Eyiolf asked Aud if she wanted to go with him. But she did not want to. After this they go home to Otradal, and that same night the seventh man died. An eighth is laid up by his wounds for a year and then dies of them. The rest recover, those who had been wounded, but they have gained nothing but dishonour. And it is everywhere agreed that never in this country has one man put up a more famous defence, so far as such things can be known for certain.

37

Eyiolf goes away to the south with eleven men to visit Bork the Stout, and he told him his news, and how it all happened. This put Bork in high spirits, and he tells Thordis to give Eyiolf a good welcome.

'And remember how much you loved my brother Thorgrim, and do well for Eyiolf.'

'I must grieve for Gisli my brother,' says Thordis; 'and is it not enough for Gisli's killer if a pot of porridge is put before him?'

And in the evening, when she brought the food in, she lets fall the tray of spoons. Eyiolf had put between the bench and his legs the sword which had been Gisli's. Thordis recognises the sword, and when she bends down to pick up the spoons she takes it by the hilt and thrusts it at Eyiolf, meaning to strike him in the middle. She did not heed the turn-up of the guard, which caught against the table; the blade went in lower than she intended, and cut into his thigh and made a bad wound. Bork seizes Thordis and twists the sword from her hand.

They all spring up and turn over the tables and the food. Bork asked Eyiolf to make a *self-judgment* for this, and he demanded full *wergild*, and says he would have demanded more if Bork had not behaved so well.

Thordis names witnesses and declares herself divorced from Bork, and says that she will not come again in the same bed with him; and she kept her word. She went then to live at Thordisarstadir out on the headland called Eyr.

Bork stayed on at Helgafell until Snorri *Godi* got him out of there. Then he went to live at Glerarskogar.

Eyiolf rides home, not at all pleased with the way his visit has turned out.

38

The sons of Vestein make their way to Gest, their kinsman, and ask him if he can arrange to get them away from Iceland, and their mother Gunnhild, and Aud, who had been Gisli's wife, and Gudrid, Ingiald's daughter, and her brother Geirmund. They sail from Hvita. Gest got them away at his expense. They were a short while at sea and came to Norway. Berg goes up the road and tries to find them a place to lodge in the town, and two companions were with him. They meet two men, and one of them was dressed in fine clothes, a young man and of big build; this one asked Berg his name. He told him the truth about his name and kin because he expected that in most places he would be more likely to benefit by his father's name than suffer. But the one who was in the fine clothes drew his sword and struck Berg his death-blow. He was Ari, son of Sur and brother of Gisli and Thorkel.

Berg's companions went back to the ship and told what had happened. The skipper got them away, and had Helgi taken on a ship that was going to Greenland. Helgi got there, and prospered in the country, and was respected as a fine man, and men were sent to kill him, but he was not to die this way. He perished on a fishing expedition, and this was thought a great loss.

Aud and Gunnhild went to Denmark, to Hedeby, and they became Christians there and went on pilgrimage to Rome, and did not return. Geirmund stayed on in Norway, and he married, and did well. His sister Gudrid was married, and she was thought to be a clever woman, and many people are descended from her.

Ari, son of Sur, went to Iceland. He landed in Hvita and sold his ship and bought land at Hamar and lived there for some years. Then he lived on several farms in Myrar and there are men who trace their descent from him.

We close here the story of Gisli, son of Sur.

THE SAGA OF GRETTIR

1

There was a man called Onund; he was son of Ofeig Burlufot (clubfoot), son of Ivar Beytil. Onund was brother of Gudbiorg, mother of Gudbrand Kula (ball), father of Asta, mother of King Olaf the Saint. Onund's family on his mother's side was from Upplond, but his father's people were mostly from around Rogaland and Hordland. Onund was a great *viking* and used to go raiding in the *West*. With him on his raids used to go Balki Blæingsson from Sotaness and Orm the Wealthy; Hallvard was the name of a third partner of theirs. They had five ships and they were all well manned. Once, they were on a raid around the Hebrides and when they came to Barra, they found a king there whose name was Kiarval; he also had five ships. They joined battle with him and a violent fight took place. Onund's men were very fierce. Many men fell on both sides, but the outcome was that the king took to flight with only one ship; Onund and his men took possession both of the ships and of a great deal of property and they stayed the winter there. They spent three summers on viking raids around Ireland and Scotland; then they went to Norway.

2

At this time there was a great deal of unrest in Norway; Harald Lufa (unkempt), son of Halfdan the Black, was fighting his way to power. Before this he had been king in Upplond. Then he went to the north of the country and fought many battles there [and was victorious every time]. So he fought his way down the country to the south and made himself master wherever he went; but when he came up to Hordland he was met by a great mob of the common people. The leaders were Kiotvi the Wealthy and Thorir Haklang (long-chin); there were also the men from South Rogaland and their king Sulki. Geirmund Heliarskin (dark-skin) was at this time away in the *West* and he did not take part in this battle although he had lands in Hordland.

That autumn Onund and his comrades came back from the *West*; and when Thorir Haklang and King Kiotvi heard of this, they sent men to meet them and asked for their support and promised them honours. Then they joined forces with Thorir because they were very keen to prove themselves and they said they wanted to be where the battle would be toughest.

Their clash with Harald was in Rogaland, in the fiord called Hafrsfiord; both sides had a great army. The battle was one of the biggest there has ever been in Norway; and it comes into most sagas because there are the most stories told about the people who were involved in it. Reinforcements came from all over the country and quite a lot came from abroad, and there were many *vikings*.

Onund positioned his ship on one side of Thorir Haklang's ship; this was pretty well in the middle of the fleet. King Harald attacked Thorir Haklang's ship, for Thorir was a great *berserk* and a fearless man; there was the toughest fighting there on both sides. The king urged on his *berserks* to the attack; they were called wolf-skins and no weapons could penetrate them; and when they stormed forward nothing could withstand them. Thorir fought very bravely and fell on board his ship with great valour; the ship was then cleared from stem to stern and its moorings cut. It then drifted back among the other ships. The king's men then attacked Onund's ship; he stood in the fore-part of the ship and fought bravely. Then the king's men said:

'This man in the bows is attacking hard; let's give him some remembrance of us to show that he has been in some danger.'

Onund was standing with one foot on the gunwale and striking at someone, and at the same time someone struck at him; and as he parried the blow he leaned backwards. Then one of the king's fo'c's'le men struck at Onund's leg below the knee and cut off his foot; Onund was immediately disabled. Then the greater part of his followers fell. Onund was got onto a ship belonging to a man called Thrand; he was son of Biorn and brother of Eyvind the *Easterner*. He was on the side opposing King Harald and was positioned on the other side of Onund's ship. Soon after, the whole army broke into flight. Thrand and other *vikings* then got themselves away each as best they could and sailed away to the *West*. Onund went with him and so did Balki and Hallvard Sugandi (sucker). Onund recovered and walked all his remaining life with the help of a wooden leg; because of this he was called Onund Wooden-leg as long as he lived.

3

In the *West* at this time there were many fine men who had fled from their ancestral lands in Norway because of King Harald, for he made everyone outlaws who had fought against him and confiscated their property. When Onund was healed of his wounds, he went in a party of ten kinsmen to see Geirmund Heliarskin, for at this time he was the most famous of the *vikings* in the *West*, and they asked whether he didn't want to try to win back the lands he owned in Hordland, and they offered him their support; they considered that they had their own property to look after as well, for Onund was a man of noble family and very wealthy. Geirmund said that Harald's power had now become so great that he thought there was little likelihood that they would get anything but humiliation from petty raiding, considering that men had been defeated when they had drawn an army from the whole population; and he said he had no intention of turning into a king's lackey and begging for what was already his own. He said he would rather go and find somewhere else where he could be lord; and besides he was now no longer in the prime of life. Then Onund and his companions returned to the Hebrides and there found many of their friends.

There was a man called Ofeig and he was nicknamed Grettir (grimacer); he was son of Einar, son of Olvir Barnakarl (children's friend), and also brother of Oleif Breid (broad), father of Thormod Skapti (shaft). Steinolf was another of Olvir Barnakarl's sons and he was father of Una whom Thorbiorn Laxakarl (salmon-man) married. Steinmod was yet another of Olvir Barnakarl's sons and he was father of Konal, father of Alfdis of Barra. Konal's son was Steinmod, father of Halldora whom Eilif, son of Ketil the One-handed, married. Ofeig Grettir married Asny, daughter of Vestar, son of Hæng. Ofeig Grettir's sons were Asmund Beardless and Asbiorn and his daughters were Aldis, Æsa and Asvor.

Ofeig had fled to the *West* because of the hostility of King Harald and so had his kinsman Thormod Skapti, and they had taken their families with them; they raided [around Scotland and] in many places in the *West*. Thrand and Onund Wooden-leg were going to go west to Ireland to see Thrand's brother Eyvind the *Easterner*; he was responsible for the defence of Ireland. Eyvind's mother was Hlif, daughter of

Hrolf, son of Ingiald, son of King Frodi, but Thrand's mother was Helga, daughter of Ondott Kraka (crow). The father of Thrand and Eyvind was Biorn, son of Hrolf of Ar. He fled from Gautland because he had burned Sigfast, the relative by marriage of King Solvi, to death in his house. Then he had gone to Norway in the summer and stayed the winter with *Hersir* Grim, son of Kolbiorn Sneypir (bringer of dishonour); he was going to murder Biorn for a reward. From there Biorn went to Ondott Kraka who was living in Hvinisfiord in Agder. He welcomed Biorn and he stayed with him during the winters and raided during the summers until his wife Hlif died. After that Ondott gave Biorn the hand of his daughter Helga and then Biorn again gave up warfare. Eyvind had then taken over his father's warships and had now become a very influential man in the *West*. He was married to Rafarta, daughter of Kiarval, king of the Irish; [their sons were Helgi the Lean and Snæbiorn].

When Thrand and Onund came to the Hebrides, they met Ofeig Grettir and Thormod Skapti and great friendship developed between them because those who had remained behind in Norway when the troubles were at their height seemed to have been reclaimed from the dead. Onund was very untalkative; and when Thrand noticed this, he asked him what was on his mind. Onund replied in a verse:

> I am no longer happy since I took part
> in shield-fire-clash [battle].
> Much afflicts one, at too early an age.
> The troll of storm-clashing [battle-axe] caused me great loss.
> I think that most men think very little of me.
> This is the greatest cause of my sorrow.

Thrand said he would be considered a valiant man wherever he went.

'The best thing for you to do is to settle down and get married; and you shall have my voice and support if I know where your inclinations lie.'

Onund said he was acting with the noblest of intentions, but that there had been better prospects of matches that were advantageous.

Thrand replied, 'Ofeig has a daughter whose name is Æsa; we can try in that direction if you wish.'

Onund said he was quite willing. Afterwards they discussed this with Ofeig; his reply was encouraging and he said he realised that the man was of noble family and very rich in money.

'But his lands I reckon of little value; and I think one could also call him a cripple, and besides, my daughter is only a child.'

Thrand said that Onund was more valiant than many men who had both their legs; and as a result of Thrand's persuasion the match was agreed on and Ofeig was to give his daughter a dowry consisting only of money, for neither of them was willing to bargain for land in Norway. A little later Thrand became engaged to Thormod Skapti's daughter; both engagements were to last for three years. After this they spent the summers in raids and the winters on Barra.

4

There were two *vikings* called Vigbiod and Vestmar; they came from the Hebrides and spent both summer and winter at sea; they had eight ships and raided around Ireland and used to commit many acts of violence until Eyvind the *Easterner* undertook the country's defence; then they fled to the Hebrides and raided there and went right up the Scottish firths. Thrand and Onund went against them and learned that they had sailed in to the Isle of Bute. So Onund and his companions went there with seven ships; and when the *vikings* saw their ships and found how many there were of them, they considered that they had sufficient numbers and took up their weapons and sailed towards them with their ships. Then Onund ordered his ships to be sailed between two cliffs; there was a narrow and deep channel there; it was possible to get ashore on one side and no more than five ships at a time could get in there. Onund was a clever person, and he got five of his ships to sail forward into the channel into such a position that they could easily row back when they wanted, for there was plenty of open sea behind them. There was also an island to one side; he got one of the ships to pull in there and the men from it carried a lot of stones to the edge of the cliff in a place that could not be seen from the ships.

The *vikings* attacked very boldly and thought their opponents had got themselves into a trap. Vigbiod asked who these people were who were all penned in like this. Thrand said he was Eyvind the *Easterner*'s brother, 'and there is also my comrade, Onund Wooden-leg, here.'

Then the *vikings* laughed and said:

> May trolls take Wooden-leg entire,
> may the trolls overthrow the lot.

'And it's not often we have seen men that cannot stand up go to battle.'

Onund said you could never tell until you had tried.

After this they sailed their ships up close to each other; a mighty battle began, and both sides fought well. And when battle had been joined, Onund let his ship drift towards the cliff; and when the *vikings* saw this, they thought that he must be trying to get away and they sailed towards his ship and went as close as they could get to the shore under the cliff. At this moment the men who had been given this job came to the edge of the cliff; they dropped such big stones on top of the *vikings* that nothing could withstand them; then a great number of the *vikings* fell and some were wounded so badly that they could no longer fight. Then the *vikings* tried to escape, but they could not because now their ships had got into the narrowest part of the channel; they were hampered both by the number of their ships and by the current, and Onund and his men were attacking vigorously at the point where Vigbiod's ship was, and Thrand was fighting against Vestmar but making little headway. When the men on Vigbiod's ship had been thinned out a bit, Onund's men, including Onund himself, began to board it. Vigbiod saw this and urged on his supporters excitedly; then he turned to meet Onund and at this most of the men gave way before him. Onund told his men to leave them both to it and see how they got on together, for Onund was a man of great strength; they put a log of wood under Onund's knee and he stood quite steady. The *viking* fought his way along the ship to the stern until he reached Onund and struck at him with his sword and it hit his shield and cut off the part it struck; then the sword carried on and hit the log that Onund had under his knee and the sword stuck fast there. Vigbiod leaned forward in tugging at the sword; at that moment Onund struck at his shoulder, taking off his arm; then the *viking* was disabled. When Vestmar found that his comrade had fallen, he leapt over onto the ship that was furthest from the shore and took to flight with everyone else who managed to get on to it. After this they searched the bodies of the slain. Vigbiod was now at the point of death; Onund went up to him and said:

Look and see whether your wounds are not really bleeding.
Did you see me give ground any?
The one-legged distributor of wealth [Onund]
got not even a scratch from you.
Many have more talk than sense.
The destroyer [Vigbiod] of the troll of battle [axe]
is not valiant when he is put to the test.

They took a great deal of booty there and went back to Barra in the autumn.

5

The next summer they prepared to go west to Ireland. Then Balki and Hallvard set out from the British Isles and went out to Iceland, for there was said to be good land to be had there. Balki took possession of some land in Hrutafiord; he lived at different times on both of the farms called Balkastadir. Hallvard took possession of Sugandafiord and Skalavik over as far as Stigi and lived there. Thrand and Onund went to see Eyvind the *Easterner* and he welcomed his brother, but when he found that Onund was there he got angry and wanted to make an attack on him. Thrand told him not to do that; he said it was not right to treat Norwegians with hostility, least of all those who did not go about doing mischief. Eyvind said he had done some in the past and had fought against King Kiarval; he said now he would have to pay for it. The brothers argued about this for a long time until Thrand declared that he and Onund would stand or fall together; then Eyvind let himself be appeased. They spent a long time there during the summer and they accompanied Eyvind on expeditions; he thought Onund a very valiant man. In the autumn they went to the Hebrides. Eyvind said that Thrand should inherit everything after their father if Biorn died before Thrand.[1] They stayed in the Hebrides until their marriages took place and for a few years afterwards.

[1] Normally brothers would share their inheritance from their father equally.

6

The next thing that happened was that Thrand's father Biorn died, and when *Hersir* Grim learned this he went to see Ondott Kraka and claimed the property Biorn had left, but Ondott said that Thrand was his father's heir. Grim said that Thrand was away in the *West* and that Biorn had been a Gautlander and maintained that the king was the legal heir of all foreigners. Ondott said he was going to keep charge of the property on behalf of his grandson[2] Thrand. Grim went away, having gained no more than this, and had no further success in his claim on the property.

Thrand now heard of his father's death and set out straight away from the Hebrides and Onund Wooden-leg with him, but Ofeig Grettir and Thormod Skapti went to Iceland with their families and landed at Eyrar in the south of the country and spent the first winter with Thorbiorn Laxakarl; afterwards they took possession of Gnupveriahrepp. Ofeig took the western part, between the River Thver and the River Kalf[3]; he lived at Ofeigsstadir near Steinsholt; but Thormod took the eastern part and he lived at Skaptaholt. Thormod's daughters were Thorvor, mother of Thorodd *Godi* from Hialli, and Thorvie, mother of Thorstein *Godi*, father of Biarni the Wise.

To return to Thrand and Onund, they sailed from the *West* to Norway and got such a favourable wind that no one knew of their coming until they reached Ondott Kraka. He welcomed Thrand and told him about the claim that *Hersir* Grim had made on the property Biorn had left.

'I think it is much better, kinsman, that you should inherit your father's property rather than the king's lackeys; and you have been very fortunate in that no one knows of your coming; but I suspect that Grim will go for one or the other of us if he gets the chance. I think you had better take possession of your inheritance and get yourself abroad.'

Thrand said he would do so; he took charge of the money and with all haste got ready to leave Norway. Before Thrand put out to sea, he asked Onund Wooden-leg if he would like to make for Iceland. Onund said he first wanted to go and see his relations and friends in the south of the country. Thrand said:

[2] Nephew according to *The Book of Settlements*, ch. 217.

[3] These two rivers were actually the boundaries of Thormod's land.

'Now we shall part, then; I would like you to look after my family, for it is on them that vengeance will fall, if I get away. I shall go out to Iceland; and I would like you to come too.'

Onund promised to do so; they parted on friendly terms. Thrand went out to Iceland. He was welcomed by Ofeig and Thormod Skapti. Thrand lived at Thrandarholt; this is to the west of Thiorsa

.

7

Onund went south to Rogaland and there met many of his relations and friends; he stayed there in secret with a man called Kolbein. He learned that King Harald had confiscated his lands and delegated the care of them to a man called Harek; he was one of the king's stewards. Onund visited him one night and surprised the house; Harek was beheaded. Onund took all the movable property that they could find there and they burned the farm; then he spent the winter in various places.

In the same autumn *Hersir* Grim killed Ondott Kraka because he had failed to get the property on behalf of the king; and Ondott's wife Signy loaded all their movable property the very same night onto a ship and went to her father Sighvat, taking her sons Asmund and Asgrim with her. A little later she sent her sons to her foster-father Hedin in Sokndal, but they couldn't stand it there for long and wanted to go back to their mother. So they left there and came to Ingiald Tryggvi (trusty) in Kvinesdal at Yule; he agreed to take them at the insistence of his wife Gyda; they stayed there during the winter.

In the spring Onund came to Agder in the north, for he had heard of Ondott's death and that he had been killed; and when he met Signy, he asked how he could help them. She said that they wanted very much to take vengeance on *Hersir* Grim for Ondott's killing; then Ondott's sons were sent for, and when they met Onund Wooden-leg, they all threw in their lot together and they kept themselves informed of Grim's movements.

In the summer there were preparations for a feast at Grim's, for he had invited Earl Audun to stay with him; and when Onund and Ondott's sons learned of this, they went to Grim's farm and set fire to the buildings, for they had come unexpectedly, and burned *Hersir* Grim and nearly thirty men to death in the house. They took possession of many fine treasures there. Onund went off into the forest, but the brothers took their foster-father Ingiald's boat and rowed away and lay low a little way away from the farm. Earl Audun arrived for the feast according to plan and soon found he was short of a friend; he got some men together and stayed there for a few nights and nothing was heard of Onund and his companions. The earl slept in an upstairs room with three men. Onund knew everything that was happening on the farm and sent for the brothers; and when they met, Onund asked whether they would rather guard the farm or attack the earl. They chose attacking the earl. They broke down the upstairs door with a battering ram; then Asmund took hold of the two who were with the earl and threw them down so violently that they were almost killed. Asgrim jumped on the earl and told him to pay him compensation for his father, for he had been in complicity with *Hersir* Grim and present in the attack when Ondott was killed. The earl said he had no money with him and asked for the payment to be deferred; then Asgrim placed the point of a spear against the earl's breast and told him to pay up on the spot. Then the earl took a neck-ring from his neck and three gold rings and a velvet cloak; Asgrim took this payment and gave the earl a nickname and called him Audun Geit (nanny-goat).

When the farmers and neighbours realised that there was a disturbance they went out and tried to help the earl; there was a tough battle, for Onund had a lot of men. Many noble farmers and earl's men fell there. Now the brothers came out and told what had happened between them and the earl; Onund said it was a bad thing that the earl had not been killed.

'That would have been a bit of our own back on King Harald for what we have lost because of him.'

They said that what they had done was a greater disgrace for the earl and afterwards they went away and went inland to Surnadal to Eirik Olfus (tippler) who was a *landed man*; he let them all stay with him during the winter.

They exchanged drinking-feasts over Christmas with a man called Hallstein, nicknamed Hest (horse), and Eirik did the first lot of entertaining and did it well and dutifully. Then Hallstein became the host, and they had a quarrel; he struck Eirik with a drinking-horn. Eirik was unable to get his own back and went home leaving matters where they stood. Ondott's sons were very annoyed at this and a little later Asgrim went to Hallstein's farm and went in on his own and dealt Hallstein a severe wound. The people who were in the house jumped up and attacked Asgrim; he defended himself well and escaped from them in the dark, but they thought they had killed him. Onund and Asmund heard of this and assumed that Asgrim was dead and it seemed to them that they could not do much about it; Eirik advised them to make for Iceland. He said it would be no good their staying in the country when the king would find it so easy to get at them. They did so and prepared to go to Iceland and they went on separate ships. Hallstein was kept to his bed by his wounds and died before Onund's party sailed. Kolbein, the one who was mentioned above, joined Onund's ship.

8

Onund and Asmund put out to sea when they were ready and sailed together. Then Onund uttered this:

> Men thought me once adequate
> in the storm-weather of Hrotti [battle]
> when the spear-storm destruction [battle] roared
> harshly, and Sugandi too.
> Now I must step out on to the shore-steed [ship]
> with one leg to visit Iceland.
> This poet is on the decline.

They had a hard voyage and a lot of cross-wind from the south; they were carried over the sea to the north. They made Iceland and found themselves to the north of Langaness when they recognised where they were. The ships were then so close together that they were talking together across the gap; Asmund suggested that they should sail to Eyiafiord, and they both agreed. Then they tacked along the coast. Then the wind began to freshen from the south-east; and when Onund and his men turned as close as possible into the wind, the yard broke. Then they lowered the sail and at that moment they were carried out to sea. Asmund managed to get round behind Hrisey and waited until the wind changed so that he could sail into Eyiafiord. Helgi the Lean gave him the whole of Kræklingahlid; he lived at the more southerly Glera. His brother Asgrim came to Iceland a few years later; he lived at the more northerly Glera. He was father of Ellida-Grim, father of Asgrim.

9

Now to return to Onund Wooden-leg, they drifted for several days. Then the wind turned round to come off the sea; they then sailed in to land. Then those who had been there before recognised that they had come to the west round Skagi; they sailed in up Strandafloi and went close to Sudur-Strandir. Then six men on a ten-oared boat rowed towards them and called out to the ship asking who was the captain. Onund gave his name and asked where they were from; they said they were workmen of Thorvald of Drangar. Onund asked whether all the land along the Strandir had been taken possession of; they said there was little vacant on the Inn-Strandir but none there to the north. Onund asked his crew whether they wanted to go and look on the west coast or to take this that had been shown them. They chose to have this land to begin with; then they sailed in along the side of the bay and went first to the bay by Arness, lowered a boat there and rowed to land. A wealthy man lived there at this time called Eirik Snara (snare), who had taken land between Ingolfsfiord and Ofæra in Veidileysa.

Now when Eirik knew that Onund had arrived there, he invited him to accept from him anything he wanted, but said there was little land that was not already taken. Onund said that first he would like to see what there was. Then they went in past the fiords and when they got up as far as Ofæra, Eirik said:

'Here you are; from here down as far as Biorn's property is vacant.'

A great mountain stretched out before them on that side of the fiords, and snow had fallen on it. Onund looked at the mountain and uttered this verse:

> Life is taking a crooked course
> for this shaft-sharpener
> with land and power
> and the sea-travelled rib-steed [ship] glides;
> I have fled lands and a multitude of kinsmen,

but this is the latest thing:
it is a mean bargain if I get Kaldbak
and I lose my cornfields.

Eirik replied, 'Many have suffered such great losses in Norway that nothing can make up for them; and anyway, I think that nearly all the lands in the best areas are taken; so I can't encourage you to go anywhere else. I am still willing for you to take what suits you of my lands.'

Onund said he would accept the offer, and afterwards took possession of the land from Ofæra and the three bays, Byrgisvik, Kolbeinsvik and Kaldbaksvik, right over to Kaldbakskleif. Then Eirik gave him the whole of Veidileysufiord and Reykiarfiord and the whole of that side of Reykianess; but there was no ruling made about driftage[4] because it was so plentiful that everyone took what he wanted. Onund built a farm at Kaldbak and had a large household; but when his livestock began to multiply he had another farm in Reykiarfiord. Kolbein lived in Kolbeinsvik and Onund lived an uneventful life for some years.

10

Onund was such a brave man that few could stand against him even though they had all their limbs; his name was also well known throughout the land because of his ancestry. The next thing that happened was that the quarrels between Ofeig Grettir and Thorbiorn Laxakappi (salmon-champion) began, and the end of it was that Ofeig fell at the hands of Thorbiorn in Grettisgeil near Hæl. Many men were got together to take part in the suit against the killer with Ofeig's sons; Onund Wooden-leg was sent for and he rode south in the spring and stayed at Hvamm at Aud the Deep-minded's. She gave him a great welcome, for he had stayed with her back in the British Isles. By this time her grandson Olaf Feilan was grown up; Aud was now very aged. She mentioned to Onund that she wanted to get her grandson Olaf married and wanted him to ask for Alfdis of Barra's hand for him; she was

[4] The most important kinds of driftage in Iceland were whales and timber (from North America). The laws made elaborate provisions about rights to driftage, but it often became a source of dispute.

Onund's wife Æsa's cousin. Onund thought this was a good idea, and Olaf rode to the south with him; and when Onund saw his friends and relatives-in-law, they invited him to stay. Then the lawsuit was discussed and it was brought to the Kialarness *Assembly*, because at this time the Althing had not been established; then the case was put to arbitration and very high damages were awarded for the killings and Thorbiorn Iarlakappi (earls' champion) was outlawed. His son was Solmund, father of Svidu-Kari; father and son stayed abroad for a long time afterwards. Thrand invited Onund and Olaf to stay with him, and so did Thormod Skapti. Then they made the proposal on Olaf's behalf; it was willingly accepted, for they knew what a fine lady Aud was. So the match was made. Onund and his companion rode home when this had been arranged. Aud thanked Onund for his help towards Olaf. That autumn Olaf Feilan married Alfdis of Barra; then Aud the deep-minded died, as is related in the Saga of the People of Laxardal.

11

Onund and Æsa had two sons; the elder was called Thorgeir and the younger Ofeig Grettir. Soon after Æsa died. Then Onund married a woman called Thordis; she was daughter of Thorgrim of Gnup in Midfiord, and was related to Midfiord-Skeggi; with her Onund had a son whose name was Thorgrim; he soon became a big, strong man and a very good farmer and sensible person. Onund lived at Kaldbak until his old age; he died of an illness and is buried in Wooden-leg's Mound; he has been the bravest man and the most agile one-legged man in Iceland. Thorgrim was the most outstanding of Onund's sons, although the others were older; and when he was twenty-five years old he had grey hair on his head. So he was nicknamed 'Hoary-top'. Thordis, his mother, afterwards married Audun Skokul north in Vididal; their son was Asgeir of Asgeirsa. Thorgrim Hoary-top and his brothers had considerable property in common and they did not divide it up. Eirik lived at Arness, as was mentioned before; he was married to Alof, daughter of Ingolf of Ingolfsfiord. Flosi was the name of their son; he was a promising man and had many relations.

Three brothers came out to Iceland, Ingolf, Ofeig and Eyvind, and they took possession of the three fiords that are named after them, and lived there from then on. Olaf was the name of Eyvind's son; first of all he lived in Eyvindarfiord, but later at Drangar, and he was a mighty man.

There were no quarrels between people of this district as long as the older generation was alive; but when Eirik was dead, it seemed to Flosi that the people of Kaldbak had no legal claims on the lands that Eirik had given Onund. Because of this there arose great discord between them, but Thorgrim still carried on as before; they were not able to go to the same entertainments any more. Thorgeir managed the household of the brothers in Reykiarfiord, and was always going fishing, for at that time the fiords were full of fish.

Now the men in the Vik hatched their plot. There was a man called Thorfinn; he was a workman of Flosi of Arness. Flosi sent this man after Thorgeir's life; he hid in the boat-shed. That morning Thorgeir prepared to go fishing and two men with him, and one was called [Hamund and the other] Brand. Thorgeir walked in front; he had a leather bottle on his back with drink in it. It was very dark, and when he was walking down from the boat-shed, Thorfinn leapt at him and hit him with an axe between the shoulders, and the axe sunk in and squelched; he let go the axe, because he thought there would be no need of dressings for that wound, and started to run away as quickly as he could. To complete the story as far as Thorfinn is concerned, he ran north to Arness and got there before it was fully light and announced the killing of Thorgeir and said he would need Flosi's help; he said the only thing to do was offer compensation.

'And that is the best way to put things straight for us in such an important matter as this.'

Flosi said he would first have to find out what had happened, 'and I think you are in a great fright after doing this great deed.'

Now to return to Thorgeir, he pulled himself round when he received the blow, and the axe hit the bottle, and he was not wounded. They didn't try to find the man because it was dark; they rowed out along the fiords and came to Kaldbak and said what had happened. They made a great joke of it and nicknamed him Thorgeir Bottle-back, and the name stuck; this was made up about what had happened:

Once renowned heroes washed
their shining shield-whitings

in roof-sharp house of wound-sea.[5]
Now this wretch, who is far and wide
renowned for lack of honour
has reddened both cheeks of the wound-harmer [axe]
in whey for his cowardice.

12

At this time there came a famine in Iceland so severe that there has never been another like it; the produce from sea-fishing and from things drifted ashore was reduced to almost nothing. This went on for many years. One autumn some merchants on an ocean-going vessel were driven off their course into this area and they were wrecked there in the Vik. Flosi put four or five of them up. Their captain was called Stein. The crew found lodgings in several places there around the Vik and they were intending to build themselves another ship out of the pieces of the old one, but they found this very difficult; the results were a ship very narrow at each end and broad amidships.

In the spring there came a very strong wind from the north; it lasted for nearly a week. When it had died down everyone went to see what had drifted ashore on their land. There was a man called Thorstein who lived at Reykianess. He found a whale blown ashore out on the south side of the ness at a place called Rifsker; it was a large fin-whale. He immediately sent a man to Flosi in the Vik and also to the neighbouring farms. Einar was the name of the man who lived at Giogr; he was a tenant of the people at Kaldbak and it was his job to attend to everything of theirs that drifted ashore on that side of the fiord. He found out that a whale had drifted ashore; he immediately took his boat and rowed across over the fiords to Byrgisvik. From there he sent a man in to Kaldbak; and when Thorgrim and his brothers heard the news, they got ready as quickly as they could and they went in a party of twelve in a ten-oared boat. Ivar and Leif, sons of Kolbein, went with them as well, in a party of six. All the farmers who could manage to get there went to the whale.

[5] Fish of shield = sword; wound-sea = blood; its house is a wound, whose sharp roof is the pointed cut made by a sword.

To return to Flosi, he sent word to relations north in Ingolfsfiord and Ofeigsfiord and also to Olaf Eyvindsson, who was at that time living at Drangar. Flosi got there first with the men from the Vik; they immediately set about cutting up the whale, and they dragged what was cut ashore; there were about twenty men there at first, but the crowd soon began to grow. Then the men of Kaldbak arrived with four ships. Thorgrim claimed possession of the whale and refused permission to the men of the Vik for the cutting and sharing out and carrying away of the whale. Flosi told him to produce some proof if Eirik had in so many words given Onund Wooden-leg the right to driftage there, otherwise he said he would defend his claim by force of arms. It seemed to Thorgrim that he was rather outnumbered, so he did not attempt to attack. Then a ship came rowing across the fiords from the south and they were pulling hard; they soon got there. It was Svan of Hol from Biarnarfiord and his men; when he got there he told Thorgrim not to let himself be robbed; they had previously become great friends and Svan offered his support. The brothers said they would accept it; they set to boldly. First of all Thorgeir Bottle-back charged up onto the whale against Flosi's men. Thorfinn, who has come into the story already, was cutting up the whale; he was up near the head and was standing on a shelf he had cut out for himself. Thorgeir said:

'Here, I am handing you your axe.'

Then he struck him on the neck, cutting off his head. Flosi was standing up on the shingle when he saw this; then he urged on his men to the counter-attack. Now they went on fighting for a long time, and the men of Kaldbak were getting the better of it; not many men there had any weapons except the axes they used for cutting up the whale, and knives. The men of the Vik fell back from the whale onto the beach. The *Easterner*s had weapons and were proving very dangerous; captain Stein cut off Ivar Kolbeinsson's leg and Leif, Ivar's brother, killed one of Stein's friends with a rib from the whale. Then they began to fight with anything they could lay their hands on, and men began to fall on both sides. Then Olaf and his men from Drangar arrived with many ships; they sided with Flosi. Then the men from Kaldbak were outnumbered; by this time they had loaded their ships. Svan told them to get aboard their ships; then they gave ground out to the ships. The men of the Vik pressed forward after them; and when Svan reached the sea, he struck at captain Stein and caused him a great injury. Then he jumped aboard his ship. Thorgrim dealt Flosi a great wound and so got away. Olaf struck at Ofeig Grettir and wounded him fatally. Thorgeir caught up Ofeig in his arms and ran with him to his ship; the men of Kaldbak rowed south across the fiords. So the battle was brought to an end. This verse was composed about the encounter:

> I have heard that rather tough
> war-weapons were used at Rifsker,
> for many unarmed men struck
> mainly with bits of whale;
> but metal-Gauts [warriors] have thrown
> lumps of whale-flab
> very hard in return;
> we find this fray unsavoury.

Afterwards a truce was arranged between them, and they took the case to the Althing. Thorodd *Godi* and Midfiord-Skeggi and many men from the south of the country sided with the men of Kaldbak. Flosi was outlawed and so were many of those who had been with him at the incident; and it was a drain on his resources, for he insisted on paying all the damages himself. Thorgrim and his supporters were unable to prove that they had given money for the lands and shore-rights that Flosi laid claim to. Thorkel Mani (moon) had at this time the office of *Law-speaker*; he was asked to give a verdict. He said he would have thought it more legal if some payment had been made, even if it had not been the full value.

'For Steinunn the Old did this with my grandfather Ingolf, and she received the whole of Rosmhvalaness from him and gave him a spotted cloak in return, and the bargain has remained valid ever since; and that involved property of greater value than we have to do with here. But it is my advice in this matter,' he said, 'that this bone of contention be apportioned out, and that each have an equal share; and then it must be made law that each man have shore-rights on his own property.'

This was done. It was arranged that Thorgrim and his supporters should lose Reykiarfiord and everything there on the northward side, but they should have Kamb. High compensation was awarded for Ofeig, nothing was paid for Thorfinn, and Thorgeir was compensated for the attack on his life; then they made peace together. Flosi arranged to go to Norway with captain Stein and sold his property in the Vik to Geirmund Hvikatimbr (swaying timber); he lived there afterwards. The ship the merchants had built was very broad in the beam; people called it Trekyllir and the bay there is named after it. Flosi sailed from the country on this ship but was driven back by the weather to Oxarfiord; that is when the saga of Bodmod and Grimolf and Gerpir began.

13

After this the brothers Thorgrim and Thorgeir divided their property between them; Thorgrim took the movable property and Thorgeir the lands. Then Thorgrim went down to Midfiord and with the consent of Skeggi bought land at Biarg. Thorgrim was married to Thordis, daughter of Asmund, who lived under Asmundargnup and who had taken possession of Thingeyrasveit. Thorgrim and Thordis had a son who was called Asmund; he was a big, strong man, intelligent, and had a fine head of hair. He had white hair on his head when he was still very young; for this reason he was nicknamed Hærulang (with long grey hair) or Hærulagd (grey-lock).

Thorgrim became a very keen farmer and kept everyone who lived there hard at work. Asmund did not like work much, and he and his father were not on very good terms; so things went until Asmund was grown up. Then Asmund asked his father for some goods to go abroad with. Thorgrim said it would not be much, but gave him a small amount of tradable ware; Asmund then went abroad and soon began to make money. He sailed to various countries and became a very great merchant and was rolling in wealth; he was a popular man, and very honest, and had many relations of high rank in Norway. One autumn Asmund was staying with a high-ranking man in the east in Oslofiord whose name was Thorstein; he came from Upplond and had a sister called Rannveig. She was a very good match. Asmund asked for this woman's hand and was accepted with her brother Thorstein's consent; Asmund settled down there for a while and was very highly thought of. He and Rannveig had a son who was called Thorstein, the most handsome of men and a strong man with a very fine voice, tall in stature but rather slow in his movements; because of this he was nicknamed Dromund. When Thorstein was a few years old his mother became ill and died;

after this Asmund found little pleasure in being in Norway. Then Thorstein's mother's family took charge of him and his property and Asmund took up trading voyages again and became a well-known man. Asmund brought his ship to Hunavatn. At this time Thorkel Krafla was the most influential of the men of Vatnsdal; he heard of Asmund's arrival in Iceland. Then Thorkel rode to the ship and invited Asmund to stay with him. Thorkel was living at Marsstadir in Vatnsdal; Asmund went to stay there. Thorkel was son of Thorgrim Karnsar*godi*; he was a very intelligent man. This was after Bishop Fridrek and Thorvald Kodransson had come to Iceland; at this time they were living at Lækiamot. They were the first to preach Christianity in the north of the country. Thorkel allowed the sign of the cross to be made over him, and so did many others with him.[6] Many things happened in connection with the dealings of the men of the northern part of the country and the bishop and his companion which do not concern this saga.

A woman had been brought up at Thorkel's whose name was Asdis; she was daughter of Bard, son of Iokul, son of Ingimund the Old, son of Thorstein, son of Ketil Raum. Asdis's mother was Aldis, who was daughter of Ofeig Grettir, as has been said already.[7] Asdis was unmarried and was thought a very good match both because of her family and her wealth. Asmund now became tired of trading voyages; now he wanted to settle down in Iceland. So he made a proposal and asked for this woman's hand. Thorkel knew everything about him, that he was a rich and thrifty man, and so the marriage of Asmund and Asdis took place; he then became the lifelong friend of Thorkel, a very keen farmer, learned in law, and ambitious. Soon after, Thorgrim Hoary-top died at Biarg; Asmund inherited his property and afterwards lived there.

14

Asmund Hærulang established a large and magnificent dwelling at Biarg and always had many people staying with him; he was a popular man. These were his and Asdis's children: Atli was the oldest; he

[6] *Prímsigning*, a sort of preliminary baptism, allowed a person to mix with Christians without committing himself to Christianity.

[7] Ch. 3.

was a straightforward and gentle person, friendly and kindly. Everyone liked him. They had a second son whose name was Grettir; he was very unmanageable in his youth, not very talkative and not a great mixer, but antagonistic both in words and deeds. He was not much loved by his father Asmund, but his mother was very fond of him. Grettir Asmundsson was a handsome person to look at, with a broad but not very long face and red hair and he was rather freckled. He was not at all precocious as a child. Thordis was the name of one of Asmund's daughters, who was later married to Glum, son of Ospak Kiallaksson from Skridinsenni. His other daughter was called Rannveig; her husband was Gamli son of Thorhall the Winelander. They lived at Melar in Hrutafiord. They had a son called Grim. The son of Glum and Thordis Asmund's daughter was Ospak, who was the one who quarrelled with Odd son of Ofeig as is told in the Saga of the Confederates.

Grettir grew up at Biarg until he was ten years old; then he began to come on rather. Asmund told him to get down to some work. Grettir said he didn't think that would be very good for him, but asked what he was to do. Asmund replied:

'You shall look after my farm-yard geese.'

Grettir replied and said, 'That is mean and miserable work.'

Asmund replied, 'You do this job well, and then we shall get on better together.'

Then Grettir took charge of the farm-yard geese; there were fifty of them besides many goslings. It wasn't long before he thought they were rather troublesome to shepherd around and the goslings he thought were slowcoaches. He got rather cross about this, for he wasn't a very self-restrained person. A little later some passers-by found goslings lying dead in the road and geese with their wings broken; this was in the autumn. Asmund was very displeased and asked if Grettir had killed the birds. He grinned and replied:

Indeed I do when winter comes,
the goslings' necks I wring.
Even if some are older ones,
unaided I can win.

'Well you won't be winning with them any more,' said Asmund.

'"That is a true friend who keeps you out of harm's way",' said Grettir.

'You must be found some other work,' said Asmund.

'"The more you experience, the more you learn",' said Grettir, 'and what am I to do now?'

'You shall massage my back by the fire, as I often get someone to do.'

'That will be rather hot on the hands,' said Grettir, 'but this is still miserable work.'

So it went on for a time, that Grettir carried on with this task. Now the autumn came; then Asmund became able to bear a lot of heat and used to urge Grettir to rub his back hard. It was the custom in those times for the *living-rooms* in farms to be very large; people sat there round the long open fire in the evenings. The tables would be put up in front of them and afterwards they would sleep round the sides away from the fire; and the women used to card wool there in the daytime. It happened one evening, when Grettir was to rub Asmund's back, that the old man said:

'You'd better buck yourself up a bit now, you useless creature.'

Grettir said, '"It's a bad thing to goad a stubborn person".'

Asmund said, 'There's never any good in you.'

Then Grettir noticed that there were some wool-combs standing on the bench, picked up one of them and scraped it down Asmund's back. He jumped up and was furious at this and was going to hit Grettir with his walking-stick, but he dodged; then the mistress of the house came and asked what they were up to. Grettir uttered this verse:

> The flinger of neck-rings [man] wants to burn my hands,
> O ground of hoards [woman], and I feel it greatly.
> That is a bad thing for both of us.
> Linen-Gerd [woman], I shall scratch
> the scatterer of rings [man] even harder
> with uncut nails.
> I can see blood from deep wounds.

The mistress of the house was annoyed that Grettir had played this trick, and said he would never learn to be careful of what he did.

He and Asmund didn't get on any better after this. A little while later Asmund suggested that Grettir should look after his horses. Grettir said he would prefer that to the hot back-massage.

'Then you must do this job as I tell you,' said Asmund. 'I have a chestnut mare with a stripe down its back that I call Kengala; she is so sensitive to the weather and the rain-fall that there will always be a storm without fail if she refuses to go out to pasture. If this happens you must shut the horses in the stable; but take them north up onto the ridge as soon as the winter frosts come. I should think it would be a good thing if you were to do this job better than the last two I gave you.'

Grettir replied, 'This is cold and manly work; but I think it's a bad thing to trust the mare, for I don't know that anyone else has ever done so.'

Now Grettir began looking after the horses, and so Christmas went by; then it got very cold and snowy and it was hard finding pasture. Grettir was not very well equipped with clothes and was not very hardened to the weather, so now he began to get very cold, but Kengala stood out in the most exposed places in all weathers; however early she went out to pasture, she would never go home before sunset. Then Grettir tried to think of some malicious trick to pay Kengala back for spending all this time out grazing. So early one morning Grettir went to the stable and opened it, and Kengala was standing in front of the manger, for even when the other horses with her were given fodder, she always ate it all herself. Now Grettir climbed up on her back; he had a sharp knife in his hand and he scraped it across Kengala's shoulders and so drew it back down both sides of her spine. The mare jumped very hard at this, for she was fat and very shy, and kicked out so that her hooves hit against the walls. Grettir fell off, and when he got up he tried to mount again. They had the hardest of struggles and the end of it was that he flayed all the skin off her back right down to her haunches and then drove the horses out and to the pasture. Kangala didn't want to nibble anything except her back; and soon after midday she set off and ran home to the stable. Then Grettir shut the stable up and went home. Asmund asked where the horses were. Grettir said he had seen to them in the stable as usual. Asmund said it wouldn't be long before there was a storm since the horses wouldn't stay out in such weather. Grettir said:

'"Many who have been more reliable have been wrong".'

So the night passed and the storm didn't come. Grettir drove the horses out, and Kengala couldn't stand it out in the fields. Asmund thought it was very strange that there was no change in the weather from what it had been before. The third morning Asmund went out to the horses and up to Kengala and said:

'The horses seem to have been reacting very badly to such a good winter, but your back will never let you down, Bleikala.'

' "Sometimes things turn out as you expect",' said Grettir, ' "and sometimes as you don't expect".'

Asmund stroked the mare's back, and the skin came away in his hand; he thought it very strange that this should happen and said it must be Grettir's doing. Grettir grinned and said nothing. The farmer went home cursing and swearing; he went into the *living-room* and heard his wife say:

'My son seems to have got on well with looking after the horses.'

Asmund uttered this verse:

> Grettir has now flayed the trusty Kengala;
> and has made a fool of me.
> These fine women are always garrulous.
> The clever child will soon make me tired
> of giving him work to do.
> May the fair ring-Hlin [woman, i.e. Asmund's wife] hear my poem.

His wife replied: 'I'm not sure which is worse, your always giving him work to do or his always doing it the same way.'

'Now we're going to settle accounts in this matter,' said Asmund, 'and he'll get the worst of it.'

'Then neither will have any reason to complain,' said Grettir; and so things stood for the time being. Asmund had Kengala killed.

Grettir played many boyish tricks that are not set down in the saga. He soon became very tall; no one knew exactly how strong he was because he wasn't very good at wrestling. He was always composing poetry and rhymes and people thought him rather insulting. He never spent much time in the *living-room* and didn't often say much.

15

At this time there were many up and coming young men in Midfiord. Poet-Torfa was living at Torfustadir. Her son was called Bersi; he was the ablest of men and a good poet. The brothers Kormak and Thorgils lived at Mel. A man called Odd grew up with them; he was a dependant of theirs and was nicknamed Odd Pauper-poet. There was a man called Audun. He grew up at Audunarstadir in Vididal; he was a straightforward and good-natured man and the strongest person there in the north of his age. Kalf Asgeirsson lived at Asgeirsa, and also his brother Thorvald. Grettir's brother Atli was also becoming a mature person and was the gentlest of men; everyone liked him.

These people used to hold ball games together on Midfiardarvatn. The men from Midfiord and Vididal used to come to them; and many people would come down there from Vestrhop and Vatnsness too, and also from Hrutafiord. Those who had come from further off would stay near by. They were matched together according to their strength and they would often enjoy themselves very much during the autumn.

Grettir went to the games at the request of his brother Atli, when he was fourteen years old. Then opponents were chosen for everyone. Grettir was to play against Audun, who has just been mentioned; he was the elder by a few years. Audun threw the ball over Grettir's head and he could not reach it; it flew a long way across the ice. Grettir was cross at this and thought Audun was trying to make a monkey out of him; but he fetched the ball, came back, and as soon as he got within reach of Audun he hit him right on the forehead with it, drawing blood. Audun hit Grettir with the bat he was holding but scarcely touched him because Grettir dodged; then they grabbed hold of each other and wrestled. Then everyone realised that Grettir was stronger than they thought, for Audun was a powerful person. They fought for a long time and in the end Grettir fell; then Audun put his knee on his stomach and knocked him about a good deal. Then Atli and Bersi and many others ran up and separated them. Grettir said there was no need to hold onto him like a mad dog and said:

'"Only a slave takes revenge straight away, but only a coward never does".'

They didn't let this lead to any quarrel, for the brothers Kalf and Thorvald wanted it to be made up; and Audun and Grettir were distantly related. So the game went on as before and there was no more quarrelling.

16

Thorkel Krafla was now getting very old; he had the Vatnsdal *godord* and was a very influential man. He was the lifelong friend of Asmund

Hærulang, as was only right seeing that they were relations. It was his custom to ride over to Biarg every spring to visit his relations and he did so again the next spring after the incident described above and went to Biarg. Asmund and Asdis welcomed him with open arms; he stayed there three nights and the kinsmen discussed many things together. Thorkel asked what Asmund thought about his sons, how industrious they would turn out to be. Asmund said he thought that Atli would be a good farmer, sensible and well off. Thorkel replied:

'Then he will be a useful man and will take after you; but what about Grettir?'

Asmund said, 'One can say this about him, that he will be a strong and ungovernable man; he has been a trial and a burden to me.'

Thorkel replied, 'That doesn't bode well, kinsman,' he said; 'now what are we going to arrange about our journey to the *assembly* this summer?'

Asmund replied, 'I'm finding it hard to get around now, and I would like to stay at home.'

'Would you like Atli to go for you?' said Thorkel.

'I don't think I can do without him,' said Asmund, 'because of the work he does and his management of the farm, but Grettir refuses to do any work; and he is intelligent enough, so that I should think he will be able to carry out my legal business with your guidance.'

'You please yourself, kinsman,' said Thorkel. He then rode home, as soon as he was ready, and Asmund sent him on his way with good gifts.

A little while afterwards Thorkel set out for the *assembly*; he rode with sixty men. Everyone who was in his *godord* went with him. He called at Biarg and Grettir rode on with him from there. They rode south over the moor which is called the Two-days moor. There were not very many places to feed the horses up on the hills and they rode hard down into the farmland; and when they got down to Fliotstunga they thought it was time to sleep and they took the bridles off their horses and let them wander around with their saddles on. They lay sleeping well on into the day and when they woke everyone looked around for their horses; they had gone off in different directions and some of them had rolled over on their backs. Grettir was the last to find his horse. It was then the custom for men to provide their own food for the journey to the *assembly*, and most people carried a knapsack on their saddles. Grettir's horse had got its saddle twisted round under its belly and the knapsack had gone, so he went to look for it, but couldn't find it. Then he saw a man walking by; he was in a hurry. Grettir asked who he was. He replied and said his name was Skeggi and that he was a farm-hand from As, up north in Vatnsdal.

'I am travelling with Thorkel,' he said, 'but I have been so careless as to lose my food-bag.'

Grettir replied, '"Unique misfortunes are the worst ones"; I've lost the bag I had as well, so let's look for them together.'

Skeggi was quite pleased with this idea. Now they walked round for a while and when it was least to be expected, Skeggi darted across the moor and picked up a knapsack. Grettir saw him bend down and asked what he had picked up.

'My knapsack,' said Skeggi.

'Whose word have I to take for it but yours?' said Grettir. 'Let me see, for "two things often look alike".'

Skeggi said no one was going to take from him what was his own. Grettir grabbed at the bag, and they both struggled over it and each was determined to get his own way.

'You are mistaken,' said the farm-hand, 'even if everyone isn't as high and mighty as you men from Midfiord,[8] if you think that people are not going to have the courage to defend their property from you.'

Grettir said it had nothing to do with questions of rank even if people were to have what belonged to them.

Skeggi said, 'It's a pity Audun isn't here to choke you, like at the ball game.'

'That is a good thing,' said Grettir, 'but you aren't going to choke me, whatever it was that happened then.'

Then Skeggi took hold of his axe and struck at Grettir; but when Grettir saw this, he grasped the shaft of the axe with his left hand above Skeggi's hands so that he let go straight away. Grettir then hit him with the same axe on the head so that it pierced straight to the brain; then the farm-hand fell to the ground dead. Grettir took the bag and threw it over his saddle. Then he rode after his companions. Thorkel had set off, for he didn't know that all this was going to happen. Then they missed Skeggi from the party; and when Grettir caught them up, they asked him what he knew about Skeggi. Then Grettir uttered a verse:

[8] Vatnsdal in the manuscript.

I think the hammer-troll [axe] came into
rather violent contact with Skeggi a little while ago.
The battle-giantess [axe] was greedy for blood.
She bent with cruel mouth over his head,
she did not hold back her warlike teeth
and she split his forehead.
I was present at their encounter.

Then Thorkel's companions ran up and said trolls wouldn't have taken a man in broad daylight. Thorkel was silent for a time and then said:

'There must be another meaning in the verse, and Grettir must have killed him; well, what was the reason?'

Grettir told him all about their quarrel. Thorkel said:

'This is very unfortunate, because Skeggi was put in my charge, and he was of a good family, and I will accept the blame in this way, I will pay such compensation as is adjudged, but I cannot prevent a sentence of outlawry. You have two choices, Grettir, either you can go to the *assembly* and take your chance on how things turn out, or else you can turn back here.'

Grettir chose to go to the *assembly*, and so it turned out that he went. The case was brought before the court by the heirs of the slain man; Thorkel arranged an agreement and he paid compensation, but Grettir was outlawed and was to stay abroad for three years.

When the leading men rode from the *assembly*, they stopped to graze their horses up below Sledaas, before they all went their several ways. Then Grettir lifted up the rock which lies there in the grass and is now called Grettir's Lift. Then many men went up to look at the rock and thought it was amazing that such a young man should lift such a big boulder.

Grettir rode home to Biarg and told his father all about it. Asmund was not very pleased and said he would grow up to be an unruly man.

17

There was a man called Haflidi who lived at Reydarfell on Hvitarsida. He was a merchant sailor and owned a trading ship; it was beached on the Hvita river. There was a man sailing with him whose name was Bard; he had a young and beautiful wife.

Asmund sent someone to Haflidi to ask him to take Grettir into his company and look after him. Haflidi said he had been told that this person had an unruly temper, but for the sake of his friendship with Asmund he took Grettir on. He then got ready to go abroad. Asmund wouldn't give him any goods to take with him on his journey except some food and a little cloth. Grettir asked him to give him some sort of weapon. Asmund says:

'You have not been a dutiful son to me; and I don't know whether the use you will put weapons to will be a good one, so I won't give you any.'

Grettir said, 'Then "there will be no need to repay what hasn't been done".'

Then father and son parted with little affection. Many wished him a good journey, but few said they hoped he would return. His mother accompanied him part of the way, and before they parted, she said:

'You are not being given the send-off, my son, that I would have wished for you, such a well-born man as you are; the worst thing seems to me to be that you have no weapon that is any good, but I have a feeling that you will have need of some.'

Then she took out from under her cloak an ornamented sword; it was a very fine piece of craftsmanship. Then she said:

'This sword belonged to my grandfather Iokul and to the former men of Vatnsdal, and it used to bring them victory; now I would like to give the sword to you, so make good use of it.'

Grettir thanked her very much for the gift and said this meant more to him than anything else even of greater value. Then he went his way and Asdis wished him all the best. Grettir rode south across the moor and didn't stop until he got over the moor to the south. Haflidi welcomed him. He went to speak to him and asked what he had brought with him for the journey. Grettir uttered a verse:

> Wind-cloth-horse-fir [sailor],
> I think that the somewhat wealthy
> winners of serpent's path [people]
> have provided me ill for my journey from home.
> But my good wealth-*norn* [lady, i.e. mother]
> has again proved to me
> by the gift of the wound-harmer [sword]
> that "a boy's best friend is his mother".

Haflidi said it was clear that she was the one who cared for him most.

They put out to sea as soon as they were ready and there was a favourable wind; and when they got beyond all the shallow water they hoisted the sail. Grettir made a nest for himself under the ship's boat and wouldn't stir from there at all, either to bale out or to help with trimming the sail, and wouldn't do the same share of the work he was supposed to do on the ship as the other men; nor would he pay to make up for it. They sailed south round Reykianess and then along the south coast; and when they got out of sight of land they began to be blown around a great deal. The ship was rather leaky and didn't stand up very well to the tossing about; they had a very wet time of it. Grettir then began to let fly with rhymes; the men got very annoyed at this. There was one day when the wind was both keen and cold; then the young men shouted out and told Grettir to make himself useful, 'because our paws are getting cold.'

Grettir looked up and said:

> I don't mind if all the fingers
> of you wretched men shrivel up from the cold.

They didn't get him to do any work and were even angrier than before, and said he would get what was coming to him for his insults[9] and lawlessness.

'You prefer,' they said, 'banging on captain Bard's wife's belly to doing your part on the ship, and things like this are intolerable.'

The weather got ever worse; then they had to bale for twelve hours at a time. Then they started shouting threats at Grettir. When Haflidi heard this he went to where Grettir was lying and said:

'You don't seem to be getting on very well with your fellow-sailors; you are refusing to do your duty by them and on top of that you insult them, and they are threatening to throw you overboard. Now we can't carry on after this fashion.'

'Why shouldn't they follow what fashion they like?' said Grettir. 'But I would like to have one or two of them alone to myself for a while before I go overboard.'

'You mustn't go on like this,' said Haflidi. 'Nothing will ever turn

[9] *níð:* a formal insult punishable by outlawry in medieval Iceland.

out right for us if you're thinking of doing things like that. I will tell you the best thing for you to do.'

'What is that?' said Grettir.

'They are complaining because you insult them; now I want you,' said Haflidi, 'to utter some verse insulting me, and then perhaps they will put up with you better.'

'I will never compose anything about you,' said Grettir, 'but what is complimentary; I will not treat you like one of these wretches.'

Haflidi said, 'A verse may be composed so that it is found to be nicer if you examine it closely, though at first sight it is not very nice.'

'I can easily do that,' said Grettir.

Haflidi went over to the crew [where they were bailing out] and said:

'You're having a hard time, and it's not surprising that you are annoyed with Grettir.'

'It's his rhymes that are worse than anything else,' they said. Then Haflidi said in a loud voice:

'He'll come to no good with those in the end.'

And when Grettir heard Haflidi finding fault with him, he uttered a verse:

> The times were different when, inside at Reydarfell,
> the clear voiced Haflidi ate curds.
> Then he seemed the master in his own house.
> But now the embellisher of spears' doom [warrior]
> eats a ness-grasp-reindeer Tveggi's [sailor's] breakfast
> twice on the same day.[10]

The sailors were very annoyed and said he wouldn't insult master Haflidi and get away with it. Then Haflidi said:

'Grettir has done enough to deserve some disgrace from you, but I won't have my honour put at stake against his malice and imprudence; so we will not avenge this at present while we are in such a dangerous position, but remember it when you get ashore if you wish.'

They replied, 'Can we not do the same as you? Why should we be more upset by insults than you?'

[10] ness-grasp = fiord, its reindeer = ship, whose Tveggi (Odin) is a seafarer.

Haflidi bade them do so. From then on the crew took much less notice of the rhymes than before.

They had a long and hard voyage. The ship started to spring leaks; they began to be exhausted from hard work. The captain's wife, the young one, always used to sew up Grettir's sleeves,[11] and the crew made great fun of him for this. Haflidi went to where Grettir was lying and uttered a verse:

> Stand up out of your hole, Grettir;
> the ship cuts a deep furrow.
> Remember most happy your
> words with the cheerful woman.
> The lady, linen-Nauma [Haflidi's wife], has sewn up your sleeves.
> The support wishes things to be right with you
> while land is beneath the horizon.

Grettir immediately stood up and said:

> Let's stand up, though the waves roll fast beneath the ship;
> I know the lady will not like it if I lie down in the boat.
> The good, fair woman will be most displeased
> if I always let others do my work for me.

Then he ran back to where they were bailing and asked what they wanted him to do. They said he wouldn't do much that was any good. He said:

' "There's a lot of difference between one man's help and another's".'

Haflidi told them not to refuse his help.

'Perhaps he thinks he will make up for what he hasn't done before if he offers his help.'

At that time there were no pumps on ocean-going ships for baling; they had what they called bucket-baling or tub-baling.[12] It was both

[11] Medieval shirts and tunics had wide sleeves but no buttons, so that it was necessary to sew them tight round the wrists to avoid them interfering with the movements of the hands.

[12] *dæla* means a mechanical pump in modern Icelandic, but in the Middle Ages ships would often have had bilge-troughs, which were ducts to convey water over the side when it was poured into them from buckets in the middle of the ship; see OED *dale*[3]. Without such contrivances the buckets had to be carried to the side of the ship to be emptied, making the work much harder.

uncomfortable and difficult. They used to have two buckets; when one went down the other went up. The men asked Grettir to go down and fill the buckets; they said they would now see what he could do. He said it would be best not to try him too far. He then went down and filled the buckets, and two of them were set to take them from him and empty them. They hadn't been doing this long before they were overcome with exhaustion. Then four men took over from them and the same happened to them. Some people say that there were eight men emptying for him before they had finished; by that time the ship was completely baled out. From then on the sailors spoke of Grettir quite differently, for they saw what strength he had at his disposal; and from then on he was the most untiring in helping, whatever was needed.

Then they were carried eastwards over the sea. The visibility became very bad; the first thing they found one night was that they had sailed the ship onto a rock so that the lower part of the stem was torn off. Then they launched the boat and took the women and everything that was movable off the ship. There was a small islet a short way from them and there they took as much as they could get of their things during the night. When it began to get light they discussed where it was they had come to; then those who had been abroad before recognised that they had some to Sunnmøre in Norway. There was an island a little way away towards the mainland which is called Haramarsey. There was a large settlement on the island and there was also a manor belonging to a *landed man*.

18

Thorfinn was the name of the *landed man* who lived there on the island; he was son of Kar the Old who had lived there for a long time. Thorfinn was an influential man.

Now when it had become full daylight, people saw from the island that some sailors were in difficulties. Then Thorfinn was told. He took action immediately and had a big rowing-boat of his launched; it had sixteen oarsmen each side. There were nearly thirty men on the rowing boat and they went as fast as they could and saved the sailors' property, but the ship sank; a great deal of valuable goods was lost there. Thorfinn took all the men from the ship back to his house; they were there for a week and dried their cargo. Then the sailors went to the south of the country and they disappear from the story. Grettir stayed behind with Thorfinn and kept to himself; most of the time he didn't say much. Thorfinn saw that he was given food but didn't take much notice of him. Grettir didn't spend much time with him and wouldn't go out with him during the day. Thorfinn was annoyed with this but yet didn't care to refuse to feed him. Thorfinn was hospitable and a great one for entertainment and he liked other people to be entertained. Grettir was always going visiting and used to go to other farms there on the island. There was a man called Audun who lived in a place called Vindheim. Grettir went there every day and became great friends with him; Grettir was always staying there all day long.

One evening very late when Grettir was about to go home he saw a great fire erupting up on the ness which was down below Audun's farm. Grettir asked what this unusual thing was. Audun said there was no need for him to know that.

'It would be said,' said Grettir, 'if anything like that was seen in our country, that it was flaming up from gold.'

The farmer replied, 'There is only one sort of person who can be in charge of that fire and he is the sort that it won't do you any good to get curious about.'

'I still want to know,' said Grettir.

'There on the ness stands a mound,' said Audun, 'and in it was laid Kar the Old, Thorfinn's father; first of all he and his son had only one farm on the island, but after Kar died he has haunted the place so much that he has emptied out all the farmers who had land here so that now Thorfinn has the whole island to himself; and no one is harmed by these hauntings who is under Thorfinn's protection.'

Grettir thanked him for telling him.

'I shall come tomorrow morning, and have some tools for digging ready for me.'

'I would rather,' said Audun, 'that you had nothing to do with this, because I know that Thorfinn will become your enemy.'

Grettir said he would risk that. Now the night passed. Grettir is there early; the digging tools were ready for him. The farmer goes with him to the mound. Grettir now opened the mound and went hard at it; he didn't stop until he got down to the roof-beams. Then it was coming towards evening. Then he pulled up the roof-beams. Audun tried hard to stop him going into the mound. Grettir told him to look after the rope.

'And I'm going to find out what there is down here.'

Then Grettir went into the mound; it was dark there and not at all sweet-smelling. Now he looked around to see what the place was like. He found some horse's bones and then he bumped into the back of a chair and found that there was a man sitting on the chair. There was a great deal of valuables in gold and silver heaped together and there was a chest set under the man's feet full of silver. Grettir took all this treasure and carried it to the rope, and when he was going to the entrance someone took hold of him firmly. Then he let go of the treasure and turned towards the man and they began to wrestle rather roughly. Everything near them was thrust out of the way; the mound-dweller attacked fiercely. Grettir gave way for a long time and it came to the point that he realised that it was no good holding back. Now neither spared the other; they dragged each other to where the horse-bones were; they struggled with each other among them for a long time and each of them at various times began to get the worst of it, but the end of it was that the mound-dweller fell on his back and this made a great crash. Then Audun abandoned the rope and thought that Grettir must be dead. Now Grettir drew his sword Iokulsnaut and struck the mound-dweller on the neck, cutting off his head; he placed it by his rump.[13] Then Grettir went to the rope with the treasure but Audun had gone right away, so he had to pull himself up the rope by his hands. He had tied the treasure in a noose and pulled it up afterwards. Grettir had become very stiff from his dealings with Kar; now he went back to Thorfinn's farm with the treasure. By that time everyone had begun their meal. Thorfinn looked sharply at Grettir when he came into the dining hall and asked what he had to do that was so pressing that he could not act with ordinary courtesy towards other people. Grettir said:

'"There are many little matters that turn up in the late evenings".'

Then he spread out on the table all the treasure that he had taken from the mound. There was one object of value there that Grettir had particularly got his eye on; this was a *cutlass*, such a good weapon that he said he had never seen a better. It was the last thing he set down. Thorfinn looked very pleased when he saw the treasure and the *cutlass*, for it was their heirloom and had never been out of the family.

[13] A ritual act to prevent the dead person returning to haunt.

'Where did you get this treasure?' said Thorfinn.
Grettir uttered a verse:

> I have clearly been disappointed
> in my expectation of bright rings in the mound,
> wave-light reducer [gold-spender, generous man];
> soon may men hear of this.
> Yet I see this, that not many a Hrotti-storm Ull [warrior]
> will seek there with great joy for Fafnir's bog [gold].[14]

Thorfinn replied, 'It's not just anything that puts you off; no one before has ever been eager to open the mound. But because I know the money that is buried in the ground or put in mounds is in the wrong place, I shall not blame you for this, considering that you have brought it all to me; but where did you get this fine *cutlass*?'
Grettir replied in a verse:

> I managed to get the *cutlass*
> that makes men's wounds grow
> in the mighty dark mound,
> wave-fire harmer [generous man]; the ghost fell;
> and the precious fire
> of the din of the harmer of helmets [*cutlass*],
> dangerous to men, would never pass far
> from my hand if I owned it.

Thorfinn replied, 'You have spoken well, but you will have to achieve something which has the makings of greatness in it before I will give you the *cutlass*, for my father never let me have it in his whole life.'
Grettir said, 'One cannot tell who will get the greatest benefit from it in the end.'
Thorfinn took charge of the treasure and kept the *cutlass* by his bed. So the winter passed until Christmas came without anything noteworthy happening.

[14] The verse implies that no treasure was to be found in the mound; but perhaps a negative is missing in the first line.

19

The summer before this Earl Eirik Hakonarson had set out abroad to England to meet King Knut the Great, his brother-in-law,[15] and had left his son Earl Hakon behind in charge of Norway and put him under the guidance of his brother, Earl Svein, to look after him and see to the government, for Hakon was still only a child. But before Earl Eirik left the country he summoned the *landed men* and influential farmers to see him; they discussed many things connected with the laws and affairs of state, for Earl Eirik was a conscientious ruler. It was considered a very bad thing in the country that highwaymen and *berserks* were in the habit of challenging noblemen to *duels* for the sake of money or women; the one who fell always had to fall uncompensated. Because of this many received dishonour and lost their property and some lost their lives altogether, and so Earl Eirik banned all *duels* in Norway; he also outlawed all robbers and *berserks* who caused breaches of the peace. Thorfinn Kar's son of Haramarsey was very much involved in these measures, for he was an intelligent man and a close friend of the earls. There are two brothers mentioned as having been the worst offenders; one was called Thorir Thomb and the other Ogmund the Bad. They were from Halogaland by origin and were taller and stronger than other men. They used to go into a *berserk* rage and spared no one when they were in a fury. They carried off men's wives [and daughters] and kept them with them for a week or a fortnight and then took them back home to where they belonged; they stole things wherever they went and performed other acts of hooliganism. Earl Eirik made them outlaws throughout Norway. Thorfinn was the one who most strongly recommended their conviction; they considered that they had plenty to pay him back for.

After this the earl left the country, as is told in his saga,[16] and Earl Svein held power and was in charge of the government of Norway. Thorfinn went back home and remained there almost until Christmas, as was said before. Towards Christmas Thorfinn made arrangements to go to a house which he had in a place called Slysfiord; this was on

[15] Earl Eirik had married Gyda, daughter of Knut's father Svein Forkbeard.

[16] Cf. *Fagrskinna* 132–3 and 136. *Eiríks saga* is also mentioned in *Fagrskinna* 110, but does not survive as a separate text.

the mainland. He had invited there many of his friends. Thorfinn's wife could not go with her husband because their young daughter lay ill, and they both stayed at home. Grettir was also there, and eight farm-hands. Now Thorfinn left for the Christmas feast with thirty freed men;[17] it was very entertaining and enjoyable there. Now Christmas Eve came; the weather was clear and calm. Grettir was out for the greater part of the day and saw ships sailing up and down along the coast, for everyone was visiting each other wherever a party had been arranged. The farmer's daughter was then recovered so that she could walk around with her mother's help. So the day passed. Then Grettir saw a ship rowing to the island; it wasn't very big and it was set with shields from stem to stern; the ship was painted above the water-line. They rowed strongly and made for Thorfinn's boat-shed, and when the ship ran aground the men on it jumped over the side. Grettir counted these men and saw that there were twelve of them. They didn't look very friendly to him. They lifted up the ship and carried it ashore. Then they ran to the boat-shed. Inside was Thorfinn's galley, the big one. It always took no fewer than thirty men to launch it, but the twelve of them shoved it straight away down onto the stony beach. Then they lifted up their ship and carried it into the boat-shed. Then Grettir realised that they were going to make themselves at home. He went to meet them and welcomed them and asked who they were and what was the name of their leader. The one he had addressed replied immediately and said his name was Thorir, nicknamed Thomb, and said that with him was his brother Ogmund; the rest were their mates.

'I expect,' said Thorir, 'that Thorfinn, your host, has heard of us; is he at home?'

Grettir replied, 'You are certainly lucky, because you have come at just the right time if you are the men I think you are; the master of the house is away with all the free men of the household and will not be home until after Christmas. His wife is at home, and his daughter. If I had any grudge to repay him, this is just the way I would choose,

[17] Slaves were taken to Iceland by the first settlers; they had mainly been captured on viking raids. They had mostly been freed and had become tenant farmers or farm labourers by the eleventh century, but freedmen and their descendants are mentioned in a number of sagas. *Frelsingi*, however, is sometimes used of labourers in general.

because there is everything you want here, both ale and other entertainment.'

Thorir was silent while Grettir made his speech. Then he spoke to Ogmund:

'Did not everything go just as I supposed it would?' he said. 'I wouldn't mind getting my own back on Thorfinn for getting us outlawed; and this man tells us just what we want. There's no need to drag any information from him.'

'"Everyone has a right to say what he likes",' said Grettir, 'and I shall entertain you as well as I can, so come to the house with me.'

They thanked him and said they would accept his invitation. When they came to the farm, Grettir took Thorir by the arm and let him into the *living-room*; Grettir was very talkative. The mistress of the house was in the *living-room* and was having the wall-hangings put up and getting it decorated. When she heard Grettir's voice she stopped in the middle of the room and asked who he was welcoming so heartily. He replied:

'It is the right thing to do, my lady, to welcome guests; Mr Thorir Thomb and his eleven friends are here and they are going to spend Christmas here. It's a very good thing, because we hadn't got much of a party before.'

She replied, 'I don't count them as good or respectable people, for they are the most terrible robbers and evil-doers; I would willingly have sacrificed almost everything I have for them not to have come here just now. And you are making a poor repayment to Thorfinn for saving you without a penny from shipwreck and maintaining you the whole winter like a free man.'

Grettir replied, 'You would be doing better to be giving the guests some fresh clothes after their journey instead of nagging at me; there will be plenty of time for that later.'

Then Thorir said, 'Don't be angry, my lady; you won't be any worse off, even though your husband isn't at home, because you'll get a man in place of him, and so will your daughter and all the women here.'

'That is spoken like a man,' said Grettir; 'now they'll have nothing to complain about.'

Now all the women ran out and they fell into great despair and weeping. Grettir said to the *berserks*:

'Hand over everything to me that you want out of your way, your weapons and dirty clothes, because we'll never get these people to do anything until they have got over their fear.'

Thorir said he didn't care what the women were moaning about, 'but there certainly is a great difference to be seen between you and the other people here; I should think we might well make you our comrade.'

'That's for you to decide,' said Grettir, 'but I don't treat everyone as equals.'

Then they set aside nearly all their weapons. After this Grettir said:

'I think you had better sit down and have something to drink, because you must be thirsty after your rowing.'

They said they were just ready for that, but said they didn't know where the cellar was. Grettir asked if they would let him see to it and arrange everything; the *berserks* said they would be very pleased to do so. Grettir went and got ale and gave them a drink; they were very tired and took deep draughts. He helped them unstintingly to the strongest ale there was and kept doing so for a long time. He also told them many amusing stories; all this brought a great deal of noise from them. The household had no desire to join them. Then Thorir said:

'I have never met a stranger so kind to us as this man; how would you like us comrades to repay you for what you have done for us?'

Grettir replied, 'I don't wish for any repayment at present, but if we are still such good friends when you leave as it seems we are now, then I will become your comrade; even though I cannot do such mighty deeds as any of you, yet I shall not hinder you from doing great things.'

They were very pleased at this and wanted to cement their comradeship straight away with oaths. Grettir said that was not advisable.

'For it is true, as the saying goes, that "drink is another man", and we must not rush into this any further than I have suggested already; neither of us has a very good temper.'

They said they did not intend to change their minds.

Now the evening was getting on so that it was beginning to get very dark. Then Grettir saw that they were getting pretty weary from the drink. Then he said:

'Don't you think it's about time to go to bed?'

Thorir agreed, 'and we will carry out our promise to the lady of the house.'

Grettir went out and spoke in a loud voice:

'Go to bed, ladies,' he said. 'Those are Mr Thorir's orders.'

They replied by cursing him; it was like the howling of wolves to hear them. At this moment the *berserks* came out. Grettir said:

'Let's go outside, and I'll show you Thorfinn's wardrobe.'[18]

They agreed to this; they came to a very big storehouse. It had an outside door with a strong lock on it. It was quite a stronghold. Next door was a big strongly built lavatory, and there was a partition between the two buildings; the buildings were raised off the ground and you had to go up a few steps to get to them. The *berserks* now began a bit of horseplay, and gave Grettir a push. He dodged away from them, and when they were least expecting it, he ran out of the building and took hold of the latch and shut the door and locked it. Thorir and his companions thought at first that the door had swung to on its own, and took no notice. They had a lamp with them, for Grettir had been showing them many things of value that belonged to Thorfinn; they looked at these for a while. Grettir hurried back to the farm and as soon as he came to the door he shouted out and asked where the mistress of the house was. She didn't answer because she was afraid to do so. He said:

'We've almost got a good bag here; are there any weapons here of any use?'

She replied, 'There are some weapons, but I don't know what good they will be to you.'

'We'll discuss that later,' he said; 'now everyone must do their best. We won't get a better opportunity.'

The mistress said, 'Now "God would indeed be with us" if we could do something to improve matters. The big barbed spear that belonged to Kar the Old is hanging over Thorfinn's bed; a helmet and a coat of mail is there as well, and that good *cutlass*, and these weapons won't fail if you have enough courage.'

Grettir snatched the helmet and spear and fastened the *cutlass* at his side and went out quickly. The mistress called to the farm-hands and told them to go and help him, such a fine fellow as he was. Four of them ran to get weapons, but the other four didn't dare go anywhere near.

[18] In medieval Icelandic farmhouses there were often store-rooms for clothes, weapons, tools etc., separate from the *living-room*s, and they were entered from outside.

Now to return to the *berserks*, they were thinking that Grettir was a long time coming back; they were beginning to suspect that there might be some treachery. They ran to the door and found that it was locked; then they tried the wooden partition so that it creaked in every board. At length they managed to break down the partition and so got out into the passageway and from there out to the steps; then the *berserk* fury came upon them and they howled like dogs. At that moment Grettir reached them; he thrust the spear with both hands at the middle of Thorir's body just as he was going to come down the steps, so that it went straight through him. The head of the spear was both long and broad. Ogmund the Bad was following close behind Thorir and pushed him forward against the thrust so that it pierced right up to the barbs; then the spear came out between Thorir's shoulders and so on into Ogmund's chest. They both fell down dead from the spear. Then each of the others jumped down from where they stood on the steps. Grettir attacked them one at a time, sometimes striking with the *cutlass*, sometimes thrusting with the spear, and they defended themselves with pieces of wood that were lying on the ground and anything else they could get hold of; it was very dangerous to fight them because of their great strength, even though they had no weapons. Grettir killed two of the Halogalanders there in the yard. Then four of the farm-hands came out; they hadn't been able to agree which weapons each of them should take. They attacked, then, when the *berserks* began to run way, but when they turned back to fight them, the farm-hands retreated up to the buildings. Six of the *vikings* fell there, and Grettir was the slayer of them all. Then the other six fled; they got down to the boat-shed and went into it; then they defended themselves with oars. Then Grettir got some heavy blows from them, so that he was close to being severely injured. Then the farm-hands went back inside the farm and told great stories of their heroism. The mistress told them to go and find out what had become of Grettir, but none of them could be got to go. Grettir killed two in the boat-shed, but four got out past him. Then each pair went off in different directions; he chased the ones that were nearer. Now the night began to get dark. They ran into a certain barn on the farm which was mentioned before called Vindheim. There they fought for a long time, but in the end Grettir killed them both; he was then terribly tired and stiff, and it was well on into the night. The weather became very cold and there was drifting snow. He didn't care then to go looking for the two *vikings* that remained; now he went back to the farm. The mistress of the house had a lamp lit by the windows on the top floor so that he could use it to guide him the right way; and so it was that he was able to find his way home because he saw the light.

When he reached the door the mistress went to meet him and welcomed him.

'You have,' she said, 'done a great deed and delivered me and my household from such a dishonour as we would never have got atonement for if you hadn't saved us.'

Grettir said, 'I think I am pretty much the same person as I was this evening when you spoke to me so abusively.'

The mistress replied thus: 'We didn't know that you were such a hero as we have now found you to be; you may take anything you like that is on the farm, which it is right to give, and honourable for you to accept. But I expect that Thorfinn will reward you even better when he comes home.'

Grettir replied, 'I don't need much reward at the moment, but I will accept your offer until your husband comes home; and I expect that you will be able to sleep in peace as far as the *berserks* are concerned.'

Grettir didn't drink much that evening and lay fully armed during the night. In the morning when it began to get light the men of the island were summoned together; then a search was started for the *berserks* who had got away the evening before. They were found towards the end of the day under a stone, and they had died of the cold and their wounds. Then they were carried to some rocks below the high-water line and buried there. After that they went home and the islanders considered that they had entered the reign of peace.

Grettir uttered this verse when he got back to the mistress of the house:

> We have made graves by the sea
> for twelve war-fire trees [warriors];
> alone I was able to bring them all
> without hesitation sheer death.
> Any deeds that one can do,
> splendid well-born gold-willow [woman],
> will be counted worthy
> if ones like this are thought mean.

The mistress said, 'You certainly have few equals among men now living.'

She made him sit in the place of honour and treated him with the greatest consideration; so the time passed until Thorfinn was to come home.

20

After Christmas Thorfinn got ready to return home and sent the many he had invited away with good gifts; then he went with his companions until he approached his boat-shed. They saw a ship lying on the sand and soon recognised it to be his big galley; Thorfinn had still heard nothing about the *vikings*. He told them to hurry ashore:

'For I suspect,' he said, 'that this is not the doing of friends.'

Thorfinn was the first of his party to go ashore and he went straight to the boat-shed; he saw a ship standing there and recognised that it was the *berserks*' ship. Then he spoke to his men:

'I have a suspicion,' he said, 'that something must have happened here such that I would give the island and everything on it for it not to have happened.'

They asked why this was so. Then he said:

'The *vikings* who are the worst I know of in the whole of Norway have come here, they are Thorir Thomb and Ogmund the Bad; they will not have done us much of a favour, and I haven't much faith in the Icelander.'

He discussed this for some time with his companions. Grettir was in the house, and it was because of him that people were not quicker going down to the beach; he said he didn't care if the master had a few anxious moments about what had happened. But the mistress asked his leave to go. He said she could go where she wanted, but said he was not going anywhere. She went straight away to meet Thorfinn and welcomed him. He was glad to see her and said:

'God be praised that I see you safe, and my daughter as well; but what has been happening to you since I left home?'

She said, 'It has turned out all right, but we were on the brink of such a great dishonour that we would never have got atonement for it if your winter lodger had not helped us.'

Then Thorfinn said, 'Now we shall sit down and you must tell me what has happened.'

Then she told him in detail everything that had taken place there, and was full of praise for Grettir's boldness and courage. Meanwhile Thorfinn was silent, and when she had finished her story, he replied thus:

'The saying is true that "one should never judge a man too soon"; but where is Grettir now?'

His wife said, 'He is at home in the *living-room*.'

Then they went back to the farm. Thorfinn went up to Grettir and embraced him and thanked him very courteously for the chivalry with which he had acted towards him.

'And I will say to you,' said Thorfinn, 'what few men say to their friend, that I hope that sometime you will need men's help, and then you will find out whether I can be of any use to you; but I can never reward you for your kindness if you are never in need of anything. But there is a place for you to stay here with me whenever you need to and you will be treated by the household as my most honoured guest.'

Grettir thanked him very much, 'and I would have accepted your offer even if it had been made before.'

Now Grettir stayed there during the winter and became great friends with Thorfinn; he also became renowned throughout Norway for this deed, especially in the places where they had committed the greatest misdeeds, the *berserks*.

In the spring Thorfinn asked Grettir what he wanted to do. He said he was going to go north to Vågan while the fair was being held there. Thorfinn said he was welcome to what money he wished. Grettir said that at the moment he had no need of funds except for some pocket-money. Thorfinn said he could have that with pleasure, and went with him down to the ship. Then he gave Grettir the good *cutlass*; Grettir wore it as long as he lived and it was a great treasure. Thorfinn told him to come to him whenever he needed help.

Now Grettir went north to Vågan, and there was a very great number of people there; many there who had never seen him before welcomed him because of the famous deed he had done in killing the *vikings*; many men of rank invited him to go and stay with them, but he wanted to return to his friend Thorfinn. He took a passage in a merchant ship which belonged to a man called Thorkel; he lived at Salten in Hålogaland, and was a man of rank.

When Grettir came back to Thorkel's house, he gave him a hearty welcome and asked Grettir to stay the winter with him, and was very pressing in his invitation. Grettir accepted and stayed with Thorkel for the winter and was given the best treatment.

21

There was a man called Biorn who was staying with Thorkel; he was impetuous in disposition and of a good family, being somewhat related to Thorkel. He was not popular with most men because he carried tales about the people staying with Thorkel; by doing this he caused many people to leave. He didn't get on very well with Grettir; Biorn thought he was not half as important as himself, but Grettir would not give way to him in anything, and they fell to loggerheads. Biorn was a very self-assertive man and was full of his own importance; many young men supported him in this and they often used to hang around together outside in the evenings.

It happened in early winter that a fierce brown bear left its den and became so savage that it spared neither men nor animals; people thought it must have woken up because of the noise that Biorn had been making with his pals. The beast became so troublesome that it was tearing men's flocks to pieces; Thorkel suffered the worst from this, because he was the wealthiest man in the district.

One day Thorkel got his men together to go with him to find out where the bear's den was. They found it in the cliffs by the sea; there was a small cliff there and a cave formed by an overhanging rock on a cliff-face, and a narrow path to approach it. There was a sheer drop underneath the cave and at the bottom there was a heap of rocks by the sea. It was certain death for anyone who fell over. The bear used to lie in the den during the day, but always left it when night fell; no fences could protect the sheep from it, dogs were no use against it. This was considered a really great problem. Biorn, Thorkel's kinsman, said that the hardest bit was done now they had found the den.

'Now we shall see,' he said, 'how we namesakes get on together.'[19]

[19] Biorn's name is also the word for bear in Old Norse.

Grettir went on as if he hadn't heard what Biorn had said about this.

It happened every evening, when everyone was going to bed, that Biorn slipped out. One night Biorn went to the den; he found that the beast was there and it was growling horribly. Biorn lay down by the narrow path and had his shield with him and was going to wait until the beast set out as usual. Bruin got wind of the man and delayed coming out. Biorn got rather sleepy lying there and cannot keep awake; just at that moment the beast leaves its den and is now able to see where the man was lying. It hooked its paw underneath and pulled the shield off him and threw it down over the cliff. Biorn jumped violently at this, and when he awoke, took to his heels and ran back to the house. He only just escaped being grabbed by the beast. His friends knew about this, because they had been keeping watch on Biorn's movements; they found the shield in the morning and made a huge joke of it.

[At Christmas] Thorkel himself went to the den and seven others with him; Biorn was there, and Grettir, and some other of Thorkel's companions. Grettir had on a fur cloak and he put it down while they went for the animal. It was difficult to attack there because they couldn't do anything except thrust with spears, and it pushed them out of the way with its mouth. Biorn kept on urging them on to the attack, but yet never went near enough to be in any danger himself; and when no one was noticing, Biorn snatched up Grettir's cloak and threw it into the den at the bear. They were unable to achieve anything and towards the end of the day they turned home. But when Grettir was about to go back, he missed his cloak; then he noticed that the bear had pulled the cloak under itself. Then he said:

'Who [of you fellows] has been making a fool of me and thrown my cloak into the den?'

Biorn replied, 'Only someone who will not be afraid to admit it will have done it.'

Grettir replied, 'I never make a big thing of anything like that.'

Then they set off home; and when they had been going for a while, Grettir's garter broke. Thorkel told them to wait for him; Grettir said there was no need. Then Biorn said:

'You needn't think Grettir is going to leave his cloak behind; obviously he wants to win fame for himself and is going to kill single-handedly the animal which eight of us have had to give up trying with.

Then he would be living up to his reputation, but today he has not distinguished himself.'

'I'm not sure,' said Thorkel, 'how well you've been doing yourself, but you two are certainly not heroes in the same class, and you'd better not say too much about him.'

Biorn said that neither of them was going to tell him what to say. Now they were out of sight of each other. Then Grettir turned back to the narrow path; now there was no question of arguing about who was doing the attacking. Then he drew the sword Iokulsnaut; he had a loop fastened to the hilt of the *cutlass* and he slipped it round his wrist. He did this because he thought he would be better able to do what he wanted if his hands were free. He went straight along the path, and when the beast saw the man, it jumped up with great ferocity and made at Grettir and struck at him with the paw on the opposite side to the precipice. Grettir parried with the sword and it struck the paw just above the claws and cut it off there. Then the animal tried to strike with its sound paw, and shifted itself onto the stump, but it was shorter than it expected, and then the animal fell into Grettir's arms. Then he grasped the beast by the head between its ears and thus held it away from himself so that it couldn't get close enough to bite him. Grettir has said that he found it the greatest trial of his strength he had performed to hold the beast down. But because the animal struggled violently and there wasn't much room, they both rolled down over the cliff. Now the beast was the heavier and so was underneath when they hit the rocks; Grettir was on top and the beast was severely wounded on the side which faced downwards. Then Grettir grasped his *cutlass* and stabbed the bear to the heart and that was the death of it. After that he went back to the house and took his cloak, and it was all torn to shreds. He took with him the part of the paw that he had cut off.

Thorkel was sitting drinking when Grettir came into the *living-room*; they all laughed at the tatters of the cloak that Grettir was wearing. Now he placed that bit of the paw he had cut off on the table.

Thorkel said, 'Where is my cousin Biorn now? I have never seen you strike such a blow, and I think you ought to offer satisfaction for the dishonour you have done him.'

Biorn said he would have to wait for that, 'and I couldn't care less whether he is pleased or not.'

Grettir uttered the following verse:

Often the battle-Niord [warrior],
who went and visited the hibernator this autumn,
came frightened home at dusk though neither was in danger.
No one saw me sit late at night by the bear's den;
yet I came out from the rocky cave of the wool-otters [bears].

'It is true,' said Biorn, 'that not only have you acted very boldly, but also you speak of us each in very different terms; I perceive that you are aiming these taunts at me.'

Thorkel spoke, 'I beg you, Grettir,' he said, 'not to take vengeance on Biorn, but I will pay a full *wergild* on his behalf in compensation if you will be reconciled.'

Biorn said he ought to have better things to do with his money than pay compensation for this.

'I think "the oak should keep what is scraped from another", as far as Grettir and I are concerned.'

Grettir said he was quite satisfied with this.

'Then for my sake, Grettir,' said Thorkel, 'please let Biorn be while you are in my house.'

'Very well,' said Grettir.

Biorn said he would go about without fear of Grettir wherever they came up against each other. Grettir grinned at this, but refused to accept the money in payment for Biorn, and they stayed there during the winter.

22

In the spring Grettir went north to Vågan with merchants; he and Thorkel parted on friendly terms. Biorn went west to England and captained the ship belonging to Thorkel which was going there. Biorn stayed there during the summer and bought for Thorkel the goods he had commissioned him to get; he sailed back east towards the end of autumn. Grettir stayed in Vågan until all the ships sailed away; then he sailed south with some merchants until they came to the port which is called Garten. This is at the entrance to Trondheimsfiord, and there they put up the ship's awnings.[20] When they had finished, a ship sailed

[20] On sea journeys along the coast, the crew sometimes pitched tents ashore, but often set up an awning over the ship to sleep under. See Shetelig and Falk 349.

along the coast from the south; they soon recognised it as a ship that had been to England. The men on it came to land a little further out along the beach and went ashore. Grettir and his companions went over to them; when they met, Grettir saw that Biorn was among them, and said:

'I am glad we have met here; we can now attend to our former differences. Now I want to find out which of us is the stronger.'

Biorn said that was a thing of the past as far as he was concerned, 'but if there has been anything between us, then I am willing to make it up in such a way that you will think yourself well done by.'

Then Grettir uttered a verse:

> I was able to defeat the greedy-tooth [bear];
> there was talk about that once;
> the harsh-minded one tore hard
> the mighty long cloak from the man.
> The audacious ring-Baldr [Biorn] caused this,
> but now he shall pay for it;
> I do not think I am often too boastful
> in competitive speeches.

Biorn said that more significant grievances than this had been made up with money. Grettir said that not many people had behaved maliciously towards him, and he had never yet taken money in compensation for such a thing, and he was not going to now.

'We shall not both leave this place unscathed, if I have my way. I declare you to be a coward if you dare not fight.'

Now Biorn realised that it was no good trying to talk himself out of it, so he took up his weapons and went up on land. Then they set to and fought, and it wasn't long before Biorn was wounded, and soon after he fell dead to the ground, and Biorn's companions saw this. They went aboard their ship and made along the coast to the north to go to see Thorkel, and they told him what had happened. He said that it had not happened sooner than one would have expected. Soon after this Thorkel went south to Trøndelag and met Earl Svein there. After the killing of Biorn, Grettir went to Møre and went to see his friend Thorfinn and told him what had happened. Thorfinn welcomed him.

'And I am glad,' he said, 'that you are in need of a friend; you shall stay with me until this matter is cleared up.'

Grettir thanked him for his offer and said that he would now accept it.

Earl Svein was at Stenkjer in Trøndelag when he heard of Biorn's killing. At that time Biorn's brother Hiarrandi was there with him; he was one of the earl's men. He was very angry when he heard of Biorn's killing and he asked for the earl's support in prosecuting the offender. The earl promised him this; then he sent someone to Thorfinn and summoned both him and Grettir to come before him. He set out immediately, and Grettir with him, in accordance with the earl's summons, and they went inland to Trøndelag to meet him. Then the earl held a meeting to deal with the case and told Hiarrandi to be present. Hiarrandi said he was not going to weigh out his brother for money:[21]

'I shall either go the same way as he, or else avenge him,' he said.

Now when the case was examined, it seemed to the earl that Biorn had given Grettir great provocation, and Thorfinn offered to pay as much compensation as the earl should deem sufficient for the honour of the heirs, and stressed what a great deliverance Grettir had brought men in the north of the country when he killed the *berserks*, as was related above.

The earl replied, 'It is true what you say, Thorfinn; that was a very good riddance for the country, and it is very fitting for us to accept compensation at your intercession. And besides, Grettir is well known for his strength and courage.'

Hiarrandi would not agree to any reconciliation, and the meeting was adjourned. Thorfinn got his cousin Arnbiorn to accompany Grettir every day, for he knew that Hiarrandi was out for his life.

23

It happened one day when Grettir and Arnbiorn were strolling out along the street for pleasure, and they were walking past a certain gateway, a man leapt out from the gateway brandishing an axe and struck at Grettir with both hands. He was not expecting this and was slow to draw back. Arnbiorn happened to see the man; he grabbed at Grettir and thrust him forward so hard that he fell on his knee. The axe struck his shoulder-blade and passed under his arm; it was a great wound. Grettir sprang round quickly in response and drew his *cutlass*;

[21] I.e. he would not accept monetary compensation.

he realised that it was Hiarrandi. The axe was stuck in the street, and he was not able to pull it up quickly; meanwhile Grettir struck at Hiarrandi and hit him in the arm up near the shoulder so that it cut it off. Then Hiarrandi's companions ran up, five of them together. A battle began between them. The outcome was swift: Grettir and Arnbiorn killed the five[22] who had been with Hiarrandi, but one got away, and he went straight to the earl and told him what had happened. The earl was mighty angry when he heard this, and summoned an *assembly* for the following day. Thorfinn came to the *assembly*. The earl brought charges against Grettir for the killings, and he pleaded guilty and said he had been forced to do it in self-defence.

'I think I also have the evidence on me,' said Grettir. 'I would have been killed if Arnbiorn had not saved me.'

The earl said it was a pity that he hadn't been killed. 'It will lead to the death of many a man if you live.'

By this time Grettir's comrade and friend Bersi Poet-Torfa's son had arrived at the earl's. He and Thorfinn approached the earl and begged for pardon for Grettir and offered that the earl might make his own judgement on the case as long as Grettir was assured of personal safety and allowed to stay in the country. The earl was reluctant to accept any settlement, but nevertheless allowed himself to be persuaded by their entreaties. A truce was agreed on Grettir's behalf until the spring, but the earl would not agree to a settlement until Gunnar, brother of Biorn and Hiarrandi, could be present. Gunnar was a householder in Tunsberg. In the spring the earl summoned Grettir and Thorfinn east to Tunsberg, for he planned to stay there while the sea traffic there was at its height. So they went there to the east. The earl was already there in the town when they got to the east. There Grettir met his brother Thorstein Dromund. He welcomed him warmly and invited him to stay with him. Thorstein was a householder there in the town. Grettir told him about his affairs and Thorstein was sympathetic, and told him to watch out for Gunnar. So time passed until the spring.

[22] There is a discrepancy in the numbers.

24

Gunnar was in the town and was waiting for a chance to get at Grettir, whenever there was an opportunity. It happened one day that Grettir was sitting in a certain shop drinking, because he did not want to come across Gunnar. And when he was least expecting it, someone rushed at the door so hard that it broke apart. Four fully-armed men leapt in; it was Gunnar and his companions. They attacked Grettir. He grabbed his weapons, which had been hanging up above him. He then drew back up into the corner and defended himself from there. He had his shield in front of him and was using his *cutlass*. Their attack didn't go too well. He landed a blow on one of Gunnar's companions; he did not need a second. Grettir then beat them back across the room. They then retreated out along the shop; then a second of Gunnar's men fell. Then Gunnar and his companions[23] tried to get away; the latter got to the doorway and tripped on the threshold and fell all his length and was slow to get up. Gunnar had his shield in front of himself and gave way before Grettir, but he attacked fiercely and leapt up onto the cross-bench by the doorway. Then Gunnar's arms were sticking in through the doorway, together with his shield. Grettir then struck down between Gunnar and his shield and cut off both hands at the wrists. He fell backwards out through the doorway. Grettir struck him his death-blow. And at that moment the one who had been with him got to his feet and went straight to see the earl and told him what had happened. Earl Svein was mighty angry at this tale and immediately summoned an *assembly* in the town, and when Thorfinn and Thorstein Dromund heard this they got together their connections and friends and came in a great party to the *assembly*. The earl was very touchy and it was difficult to get him to listen to anything. Thorfinn was the first to approach the earl and said:

'The reason I have come here is to offer you honourable atonement for these killings that Grettir has committed. You alone shall decide the terms as long as the man has his life.'

The earl replied in great anger, 'You never tire of asking for pardon on Grettir's behalf, but it seems to me that you have not got a very good case in this instance. He has now killed three brothers, one after

[23] Another discrepancy in the numbers.

another; they were such fine men that none of them was willing to take payment for another. It is no good, Thorfinn, your begging for Grettir, for I am not going to let such injustice take place in this country as to accept compensation for wrongful deeds like this.'

Then Bersi Poet-Torfa's son stepped forward and asked the earl to accept atonement.

'I am willing,' he said, 'to contribute my wealth to it, because Grettir is a man of noble family and a good friend of mine. You must realise, sire, that it is better to spare one man's life and have in return the goodwill of many men, while being yourself able to determine the amount of compensation, than to fight against a settlement that is honourable to you and not be certain of whether you will get your man or not.'

The earl replied, 'You are acting well in this, Bersi, and are showing as always that you are a good fellow; but still I am reluctant to break the laws of the land by sparing those who have deserved death.'

Then Thorstein Dromund stepped forward and saluted the earl and made an offer on Grettir's behalf, and presented his case with great eloquence. The earl asked what led him to intercede on behalf of this man. Thorstein said that they were brothers. The earl said he had not realised that.

'But you are showing an honourable disposition even though you wish to help him. But because we have determined not to accept monetary compensation for this affair, we shall assess each side at the same price. We are going to have Grettir's life whatever it costs, as soon as we can get it.'

The earl then leapt up and would not consider a settlement with Thorstein's party and they went back to Thorstein's premises and took up their positions there. And when the earl saw that, he got all his men to arm themselves and they then went there in battle order, and before the troop arrived, the others had positioned themselves for defence in front of the entrance to the premises. Foremost stood Thorfinn and Thorstein and Grettir, then Bersi; each of these had a large troop of men. The earl ordered them to hand Grettir over and not get themselves into a fix. They offered all the same offers as before; the earl refused to listen. Thorfinn and Thorstein said it would cost the earl a great deal more to have Grettir's life.

'For one fate shall befall us all, and people will say that you are paying a great deal for the life of one man if we are all felled to the ground.'

The earl said none of them should be spared; they were now on the very point of starting to fight. Then many people of good will approached the earl and begged him not to head towards such a great disaster, saying that there would be an enormous cost before they were killed. The earl realised that this was wholesome advice; he allowed himself to be somewhat cooled down. Then moves were made towards a settlement; Thorfinn and Thorstein were eager for this, as long as Grettir's life was spared. The earl spoke:

'I want you to know this,' he said, 'although I am making a great compromise here over these killings, that I consider this to be no settlement; but I do not care to fight against my own men, though I can see that you are not rating me very high in this affair.'

Then said Thorfinn, 'This is a greater honour for you, sire, for you alone are to determine the amount of compensation.'

Then the earl said that Grettir was to go in peace as far as he was concerned out to Iceland as soon as there were ships going there, if that would satisfy them. They said they would accept that. They discharged money to the earl so that he was content with it, and parted without warmth. Grettir went with Thorfinn. He and his brother Thorstein parted in friendship. Thorfinn became renowned for the support he had given Grettir in withstanding the great odds he had had to face. None of the men who had stood by Grettir regained the favour of the earl from that time forth, except only Bersi. Thus said Grettir:

Thorfinn, companion of Thund's people [warriors],
was destined to be a help to us
when the woman shut and locked
in the refuge of the dead[24] came to demand my life.

And the great ship of the Red Sea,
rock-god's slayer Regin's house[25]
it was who more than any other man
kept me from Byleist's niece [Hel, i.e. death].

[24] Hel (see Index); her coming to demand Grettir's life was when death seemed imminent.

[25] The first two lines of this stanza give the name Thorstein Dromund. Rock-god's (giant's) slayer is Thor; Regin is a dwarf, whose abode is stone (*stein*). The great ship of the Red Sea is Dromund (see Index).

And also this:

> The prince's men found it not an easy task
> to do us harm when Bear [= Bersi] wished to burn
> the fortress of stratagems [breast, heart]
> with shield's fire [sword].

Grettir went back north with Thorfinn and stayed with him until he could get him onto a ship with merchants who were bound for Iceland, and gave him many fine presents in the way of clothing and a painted saddle complete with bridle. They parted on the most friendly terms. Thorfinn told him to come and see him if he ever returned to Norway.

25

Asmund Hærulang was living at Biarg while Grettir was abroad, and he was considered then a worthy farmer in Midfiord. Thorkel Krafla died during the time that Grettir was not in Iceland. Thorvald Asgeirsson was then living at As in Vatnsdal and became a great leader. He was father of Dalla, whom Isleif married, who later was bishop in Skalaholt. Asmund got the greatest help from Thorvald in supporting lawsuits and many other matters. A man called Thorgils was brought up at Asmund's. He was known as Thorgils Maksson. He was a close relation of Asmund's. Thorgils had great physical strength and amassed great wealth under Asmund's guidance; he bought on Thorgils's behalf the land at Lækiamot, and he lived there. Thorgils was a good housekeeper and went to Strandir each year. He got whales there and other catches. Thorgils was a very courageous man. He used to go right to the easterly Almenningar. At that time the career of the *foster-brothers* Thorgeir Havarsson and Thormod Kolbrun's poet was at its height. They had a boat and went on raids all over the place and were not considered to be all that fair men.

It happened one summer that Thorgils Maksson found a whale on Almenningar. He immediately set about flensing it with his companions. And when the *foster-brothers* heard about this, they went over there and to begin with it looked as though their discussions might turn out well. Thorgils offered that they should have a half share of the part of the whale that had not yet been cut up, but they wanted to have what was uncut to themselves, or else to divide equally both cut and uncut. Thorgils absolutely refused to give up any of what was cut. Then they started threatening, next both sides took up weapons and after that they fought. Thorgeir and Thorgils attacked each other for a long time without anyone interfering to upset the balance between them, and they both went at it furiously. Their exchange was both hard and long, but the upshot of it was that Thorgils fell dead to the ground before Thorgeir. But Thormod and the other men of Thorgils's party fought a separate battle. Thormod was victorious in their exchange; three of Thorgils's companions fell at his hands. After the killing of Thorgils his companions went back down to Midfiord and took Thorgils's body with them. His loss was considered a severe one. The *foster-brothers* took possession of the whole of the whale there. This encounter was referred to by Thormod in the memorial poem that he composed about Thorgeir.[26] Asmund Hærulang heard about the killing of his kinsman Thorgils. He was the principal[27] in the suit for the killing of Thorgils. He went to the spot and named witnesses to the wounds and took the case to the Althing, for that was then considered to be the legal requirement when the business had taken place in another quarter.[28] And so time passed.

26

There is a man named Thorstein. He was son of Thorkel Kuggi, son of Thord Gellir, son of Olaf Feilan, son of Thorstein Red, son of Aud the Deep-minded. Thorstein Kuggason's mother was Thurid, Asgeir Ædikoll's (madcap's) daughter. Asgeir was Asmund Hærulang's uncle.

[26] See *Thorgeirsdrapa* in Index.

[27] Prosecution of a homicide was the duty of the closest relative in medieval Icelandic law. There were no state prosecutions.

[28] This does not accord with what is said either in *The Book of the Icelanders*, where in ch. 5 it says that the ancient law was that a case must be prosecuted in the *assembly* closest to where the event giving rise to it took place, or in *Grágás*, where it appears that the question was which assemblies the principals in the case belonged to, not where the event took place. If the principals were from different quarters, then the case was taken to the Althing. Compare *The Saga of Gisli*, ch. 19.

Thorstein Kuggason had responsibility for the suit concerning the killing of Thorgils Maksson as well as Asmund Hærulang. The latter now sent word to Thorstein that he was to come and see him. Thorstein was a great fighter and a very great bully. He went straight away to see his kinsman Asmund and they discussed the suit for the killing. Thorstein was very heated, declared that no compensation should be accepted for it, said that they had plenty of family backing to ensure that either outlawry or blood-vengeance should pay for the killing. Asmund said he would stand by him however he wanted to proceed. They rode north to their kinsman Thorvald and asked for his support, and he readily agreed. They prepared the case against Thorgeir and Thormod. Thorstein rode back to his farm. He was then living in Liarskogar in the district of Hvamm. Skeggi was living at Hvamm. He enlisted into the case with Thorstein. Skeggi was son of Thorarin Fylsenni (foal-brow), son of Thord Gellir. Skeggi's mother was Fridgerd, daughter of Thord of Hofdi. They came with great numbers to the Althing and presented their cases with great zeal. Asmund and Thorvald rode there from the north with sixty men and stayed in Liarskogar many nights.

27

Thorgils was then living at Reykiaholar. He was son of Ari, son of Mar, son of Atli the Red, son of Ulf the Boss-eyed who settled Reykianess. Thorgils Arason's mother was Thorgerd, daughter of Alf of the Dales. Alf's second daughter was Thorelf, mother of Thorgeir Havarsson. Thorgeir was able to look for great support to this family through his connections, for Thorgils was the most prominent leader in the Western Fiords *Quarter*. He was a man of such a princely nature that he gave any free man food for as long as he wished to accept it; consequently there were always a lot of people staying at Reykiaholar. Thorgils's farming supported a very high style of living. He was a benevolent man and of great wisdom. Thorgeir used to stay with Thorgils during the winters but went to the Strands in the summers. After the killing of Thorgils Maksson, Thorgeir went to Reykiaholar and told Thorgils what had happened. Thorgils told him he was welcome to stay there with him:

'But I guess,' he said, 'they will give you a hard time in their suit, and I am not keen to make the problems worse. I shall now send someone to Thorstein and offer compensation for the killing of Thorgils, but if he will not accept a settlement, I shall not defend the case very vigorously.'

Thorgeir said he would leave it to him. In the autumn Thorgils sent a man to Thorstein Kuggason to seek for a settlement, but he was firmly opposed to accepting compensation in the suit for the killing of Thorgils, but as for the other killings he said he would act in accordance with the proposals of sensible men. And when Thorgils heard this he called Thorgeir to speak with him and asked what support he thought would be most advantageous for him. Thorgeir said he would most rather go abroad, [if he had a chance, and] if he was outlawed. Thorgils said he would see what he could do. There was a ship beached in Northriver in Borgarfiord. On this ship Thorgils secretly bought a passage for the *foster-brothers*. So the winter came to an end.

Thorgils heard that Thorstein's party was assembling a great following for the Althing and was waiting in Liarskogar. He delayed his own departure because he wanted Thorstein and his party to have ridden away south by the time he came from the west, and so it turned out. Thorgils rode south and the *foster-brothers* with him. On this trip Thorgeir killed Boggul-Torfi of Marskelda; it was also then he killed Skuf and Biarni of Hundadal. Thus says Thormod in Thorgeirsdrapa:[29]

> The hero had the good fortune
> to pay back Mak's son for his zeal;
> then there was a storm of swords;
> the raven was able to tear raw flesh.
> The sea-horse rider [seafarer, i.e. Thorgeir] was also afterwards
> at the killing of Skuf and Biarni;
> the keen one eagerly
> put his hand to battle.

Thorgils settled for the killing of Skuf and Biarni on the spot there in the valley and it delayed him there longer than he had previously intended. Thorgeir went to the ship and Thorgils to the *assembly* and

[29] On these events see *Fóstbræðra saga*, ch. 8, where this verse appears.

only arrived when the case was already before the court. Then Asmund Hærulang called upon the defence to put the case concerning the suit for the killing of Thorgils Maksson, [but Thorstein Kuggason stood by the court with all his troop fully armed]. Thorgils approached the court and offered monetary compensation for the killing as long as Thorgeir should then be free of all charges. He tried to bring as a defence in the suit that the right to all catches was supposed to be free to everyone as common property in Almenningar.[30] The *lawman* was then asked whether this was a valid defence. Skapti was *lawman* at this time and he sided with Asmund for the sake of his relationship with him. He said that it would be legally valid if they were men of equal standing, but said that farmers should be given preferential rights over men of no fixed abode. Asmund said that Thorgils had offered the *foster-brothers* an equal share of the part of the whale that was uncut when they arrived on the scene, and that was then the end of their defence. Thorstein and his kinsmen then pressed their case vigorously and refused to accept anything other than Thorgeir's outlawry. Thorgils realised that there were only two courses to take, to go to it with force, though it was uncertain what they would gain by it, or to let them do as they pleased; and because of the fact that Thorgeir had been got onto a ship Thorgils abandonded the defence; Thorgeir was outlawed but monetary compensation was accepted for Thormod and he was to retain his civil rights. Asmund and Thorstein were considered to have increased their standing greatly from this suit. People then rode home from the *assembly*. Some people reckoned that Thorgils had not made much effort with the case, but he took little notice of this and let everyone say what they liked about it. But when Thorgeir learned of his outlawry he said this:

'I would be well pleased for those who have made me outlaw to be repaid in full before we are done, if I had my way.'

There was a man called Gaut and he was known as Sleita's son. He was a kinsman of Thorgils Maksson. Gaut had a place on the ship Thorgeir was to sail on. He was very hostile towards Thorgeir and gave him surly looks, and when the merchants saw that, it seemed to them not a good thing for them to travel on the same ship. Thorgeir

[30] Almenningar means 'public land'. Generally in Iceland the foreshore and anything washed up on it was the property of the farmer who owned the land behind.

said he didn't care how much Gaut frowned at him, but still it was decided that Gaut should give up his place on the ship and go off up north. There was no difficulty between him and Thorgeir on this occasion, but yet there arose from it trouble between them as later events showed.

28

Grettir Asmundarson returned from abroad that summer to Skagafiord. He had become such a renowned person for his strength and bravery that none other of the young people seemed comparable. He rode straight back to Biarg and then Asmund welcomed him decently. Atli now had charge of the running of the farm. The brothers got on well together.

Grettir's self-conceit now grew so great that he thought nothing was beyond him. By now many of the men who had been boys when Grettir had been at the games on Midfiardarvatn with them, before he went abroad, were now full-grown men. One of these was Audun who was now living at Audunarstadir in Vididal. He was son of Asgeir, son of Audun, son of Asgeir Ædikoll. Audun was a good farmer and a capable man. He was the strongest of all the men there in the north. He was considered the most peaceable man in the district. It now occurred to Grettir that he remembered having been worsted by Audun at the ball game, as was told earlier, and he wanted to find out which of them had advanced further in physical strength since. So Grettir set out to Audunarstadir. This was early in the haymaking season. Grettir put on all his finest gear and rode on a painted saddle, very finely worked, which Thorfinn had given him. He had a good horse and weapons all of the best. Grettir arrived at Audunarstadir early in the day and knocked at the door. There were few people at home. Grettir asked whether Audun was at home. He was told that he had gone to a *shieling* to fetch food. Grettir slipped the bridle off his horse. The homefield was unmown and the horse went to where the grass was thickest. Grettir went to the house[31] and seated himself on the edge of the *platform* and

[31] *Skáli* was normally a large undivided building used as the main living area in the farm, where the family and household would eat, work and sleep. Cf. *living-room* in Glossary.

then fell asleep. A little later Audun came home. He saw that there was a horse in the homefield with a painted saddle. Audun was carrying food on two horses and was carrying *skyr* on one horse, and it was in skin bags tied up at the top. These were called *skyr*-pouches. Audun unloaded the horses and carried in some *skyr* in his arms. He could not see where he was going. Grettir had stretched his leg out from the edge of the *platform* and Audun fell forward and the *skyr*-pouch ended up under him and its neck-band came off. Audun leapt up and asked what sort of devil was there. Grettir said his name. Audun said:

'That was a silly thing to do; and what do you want here?'

'I want to have a fight with you,' said Grettir.

'I must see to my food first,' said Audun.

'That's fine,' said Grettir, 'if there's no one else you can get to do it.'

Audun then bent down and grabbed up the *skyr*-pouch and flung it in Grettir's arms and told him first to accept a present from him. Grettir got *skyr* all over him. He felt that to be a greater humiliation than if Audun had given him a great wound. Then they set on to each other and wrestled with considerable violence. Grettir attacked furiously, but Audun gave way; he found now that Grettir had outgrown him. Everything in their path was knocked away and they pushed each other all over the room. Neither of them held back, but Grettir got the best of it and in the end Audun went down; he had torn off all Grettir's weapons. They struggled hard and there was a lot of crashing around them, and then there came a great din below the farm and Grettir heard someone ride to the buildings and dismount and enter smartly; he saw a handsome man enter in a red tunic and he had a helmet on his head. He entered the *living-room* because he heard the great to-do from their fighting. He asked what was up in the building. Grettir said his name.

'And who is it asking?'

'My name is Bardi,' said the newcomer.

'Are you Bardi Gudmundarson from Asbiarnarness?'

'The very same,' said Bardi. 'And what are you up to?' he said.

Grettir replied, 'Audun and I are having a bit of sport.'

'I don't know about sport,' said Bardi, 'and it is not an equal match; you are a bully and unnecessarily contentious, while he is peaceable and good-natured. So let him get up immediately.'

Grettir replied, '"There are many who try to reach over the door for the latch"; I would have thought you would have been better to be avenging your brother Hall than interfering in what Audun and I are doing.'

'People are always saying that to me,' said Bardi, 'but I am not sure that vengeance is practicable. But still I want you to leave Audun alone, for he is a good man.'

Grettir did so at Bardi's insistence, though he didn't like it. Bardi asked what was the trouble between them. Grettir uttered a verse:

> I am not sure whether Ialfad [Odin/Audun[32]]
> will not make your throat swell too
> for your contentiousness and zeal.
> It is a torment.
> That was how the companion of the gold-Gaut
> [Bardi, whose friend is Audun]
> stopped the young mountain-band's [Grettir's] shouting[33]
> long ago when I was at home.

Bardi said it was certainly understandable if he really had something to avenge himself for.

'I shall now arbitrate between you' said Bardi, 'I want you to separate with things as they are, and let this be the end of the matter.'

And they let this stand, because they were kinsmen, and Grettir was rather displeased with Bardi and his brothers.[34] They all rode off together. And when they had got on their way, then Grettir said:

'I have heard that you are planning to go south to Borgarfiord this summer. I now wish to offer to you, Bardi, to go south with you, and I think I shall then be doing by you better than your deserts.'

Bardi was pleased at this and agreed to it straight away and bade him accept his thanks in return. Then they parted. Then Bardi turned back and spoke:

[32] A pun on the similarity between the two names; Ialfad is a name for Odin. In fact Audun is too, though there is no etymological connection.

[33] mountain band = snake; Grettir also means snake.

[34] Bardi's brothers, none of whom have been mentioned as present here, were Hall (mentioned earlier in this chapter; now dead), Stein and Steingrim; see *Heiðarvíga saga* and *Laxdæla saga*. 'They all' in the next sentence appears to mean the two last, together with Bardi and Grettir.

'There is one condition,' he said, 'that is that you do not go unless my foster-father Thorarin permits it, for he is in charge of the expedition.'

'I should have thought you might well have been able to make your own decisions. I do not,' said Grettir, 'let others decide about my travels, and I shall not be pleased if you reject my company.'

Now each went their own way, and Bardi said he would let Grettir know 'if Thorarin is willing for you to go.' Otherwise he was to stay where he was.

Grettir rode home to Biarg, and Bardi to his farm.

29

In the summer there was arranged a well-attended horse-meeting on Langafit down below Reykir. Many people went to it. Atli at Biarg had a fine horse, grey-brown with a dark streak down its back, from the same strain as Kengala. Father and son valued the horse highly. The brothers Kormak and Thorgils at Mel had a brown horse, a trusty fighter. They and Atli at Biarg were to set them on against each other. There were many other good horses there. Kormak's kinsman Odd Pauper-poet was to lead on his kinsmen's horse that day. Odd was becoming a strong man and behaved boisterously, difficult to deal with and violent. Grettir asked his brother Atli who was to lead on his horse.

'I'm not quite sure,' he said.

'Do you want me to be with it?' said Grettir.

'Keep control of yourself then, brother,' said Atli, 'because it is proud men we have to deal with here.'

'They must answer for their own arrogance,' said Grettir, 'if they don't keep it within bounds.'

Now the horses are led forward, and the mares were standing out on the river-bank and were tethered together. There was a deep pool out over the bank. The stallions attacked each other very well, and provided the finest entertainment. Odd stood by his horse energetically, but Grettir was inclined to give way and held his horse's tail with one hand and in the other had a stick, which he used to drive his horse on. Odd was standing rather forward of his horse, and one could not be sure whether he was not prodding Atli's horse back from its attack.

Grettir gave no sign that he had noticed this. The horses moved over towards the river. Then Odd jabbed his stick at Grettir and it hit his shoulder-blade, because Grettir had had his shoulder turned towards him. It was a heavy blow causing a weal to rise up, but Grettir's skin was hardly broken. At that moment the horses reared high up. Grettir darted under his horse's haunches and drove his stick so hard at Odd's side that three of his ribs were broken, and Odd was flung out into the pool as well as his horse and all the mares that were tethered. Someone swam out to him and he was pulled out of the river. A great shouting was raised at this. Kormak and his men leapt for their weapons, as did the men of Biarg on their side. And when the men of Hrutafiord and the men of Vatnsness saw this, they went between them and so they were separated and went home, each side uttering evil threats against the other; and yet they stayed put for a while. Atli had little to say about this, but Grettir was rather unrelenting and said they would meet on another occasion if he had his way.

30

There was a man called Thorbiorn who lived at Thoroddsstadir in Hrutafiord. He was son of Arnor Hynef (downy-nose), son of Thorodd, who had taken land on that side of Hrutafiord as far as opposite to Bakki. Thorbiorn was one of the strongest of men; he was known as Oxen-might (strong as an ox). His brother was called Thorodd; he was known as Poem-bit. Their mother was Gerd, daughter of Bodvar of Bodvarsholar. Thorbiorn was a great man for fighting and kept a large band of men with him. He was renowned for finding it harder to get workers than other men did and paid almost no one wages. He was not regarded as an easy man to get on with. He had a kinsman called Thorbiorn and he was known as Ferdalang (far traveller). He was a trader and the two Thorbiorns had entered into partnership together. He was always at Thoroddsstadir and he was not thought to provide much to compensate for the other Thorbiorn. He was given to fault-finding and mockery of various people.

There was a man called Thorir, son of Thorkel at Bordeyr. Thorir lived to begin with at Melar in Hrutafiord—his daughter was Helga whom Sleitu-Helgi married—but after the battle at Fagrabrekka Thorir moved south to Haukadal and lived at Skard, and sold the land at Melar to Thorhall Gamlason the Winelander.[35] His son was Gamli, who married Grettir's sister Rannveig, daughter of Asmund Hærulang. The pair were living at this time at Melar and they got on well. Thorir at Skard had two sons. One was called Gunnar, the other Thorgeir. They were fine young men, and had by now taken over their father's farm, but were always with Thorbiorn Oxen-might. They became domineering.

That summer that was being told of before, Kormak and Thorgils and their kinsman Narfi rode south to Nordrardal on business. Odd Pauper-poet was on the trip with them. He had now recovered from the stiffness that he had got at the horse-meeting. And while they were to the south of the heath, Grettir set out from Biarg and with him two of Atli's farm-hands. They rode over to Burfell and then over the ridge to Hrutafiord and came to Melar in the evening. They stayed there three nights. Rannveig and Gamli welcomed Grettir warmly and invited him to stay on with them, but he wanted to ride home. Then Grettir found out that Kormak's party had come back from the south and had lodged at Tunga for the night. Grettir set out early from Melar. Gamli offered him men to go with him. Gamli's brother was called Grim. He was the boldest of men. He rode with Grettir as well as one other person. They were five in all; they rode until they got to Hrutafiord ridge, west of Burfell. A great stone stands there which is called Grettir's Lift. He strove for a long time during the day to lift the stone and thus stayed until Kormak's party came up. Grettir turned towards them and both parties dismounted. Grettir said it would now be more like free men to cut as hard as they could rather than to fight with sticks like tramps. Kormak told them to respond valiantly and to do their best. After that they jumped to it and fought. Grettir was the foremost of his men and told them to see that no one went round behind him; they attacked for a while and both sides were wounded. Thorbiorn Oxen-might had ridden that day over the ridge to Burfell, and as they were riding back he saw the encounter. With him at that time were Thorbiorn Ferdalang and Gunnar and Thorgeir, sons of Thorir, and Thorodd Poem-bit. And when they got there, Thorbiorn called on his men to intervene. The others were in such furies that they could do nothing. Grettir

[35] See *Hrómundar þáttr halta* and *The Book of Settlements*, ch. 168.

was driving all before him. The two sons of Thorir found themselves facing him and they both fell down together as he pushed them away. They got absolutely furious at that, and Gunnar struck Atli's workman his death-blow. And when Thorbiorn saw that, he ordered them to separate; he said he would combine his forces with those who were willing to abide by his command. Now two of Kormak's workmen had fallen. Then Grettir realised that it would hardly do if Thorbiorn sided against him and so he let the battle be abandoned. Everyone was wounded who had been in the encounter. Grettir did not like their being separated. After that both parties rode home. They did not reach a settlement of this affair. Thorbiorn Ferdalang made great mock of this; as a result relations began to get worse between the people of Biarg and Thorbiorn Oxen-might, so that it resulted in outright hostility, as later events show. No compensation was offered to Atli for his workman; he went on as if he had not realised. Grettir stayed on at Biarg until *Double-month*. It is not said that he and Kormak met again as far as is told.

31

Bardi Gudmundarson and his brothers rode home to Asbiarnarness when they and Grettir parted. They were sons of Gudmund Solmundarson. Solmund's mother was Thorlaug, daughter of Sæmund the Hebridean, foster-brother of Ingimund the Old. Bardi was a great gentleman. He now rode straight away to see Thorarin the Wise, his foster-father. He welcomed Bardi and asked what support he had managed to enlist, for they had earlier been making plans for Bardi's expedition. Bardi replied that he had got a man to accompany him whose support he thought better than that of two other men. Thorarin was silent at this, and said:

'It must be Grettir Asmundarson.'

'"A wise man's guess is a prophecy",' said Bardi. 'It is the very same person, my foster-father.'

Thorarin replied, 'It is true that Grettir can far outdo other men who are now about in our land, and it would take a great deal to overcome him with weapons if he is in full form. But I am doubtful about how long his luck will last and you will need not to have all disaster-prone men[36] on your expedition, and it will be bad enough even if he does not go along; he shall not go at all if I have my way.'

'I was not expecting, my foster-father,' he said, 'that you would grudge me the most valiant man, however it turns out. Not everything can be guarded against when people are under such pressure as I find myself.'

'You will be all right,' said Thorarin, 'if I look after things.'

So it had to be done as Thorarin wished, word was not sent to Grettir, and Bardi went south to Borgarfiord and the Battle of the Heath took place. Grettir was at Biarg when he found out that Bardi had ridden south. He was angry at this, that no word had been sent him, and said that was not going to be the end of the matter. So he found out when they were expected to be back from the south, and he then rode down to Thoreyiargnup and prepared to lie in wait for Bardi's party as they rode from the south. He went from the farm onto the hillside and waited there. That same day Bardi's party rode from the south off Two-days moor from the Battle of the Heath; they were six of them and all badly wounded. And when they got in front of the farm, Bardi said:

'There is a man up there on the hillside, big, with weapons; who do you think it is?'

They said they did not know who it was. Bardi spoke:

'I think,' he said, 'that it is Grettir Asmundarson, and if so, he will be wanting to meet us. I expect he was displeased that he hadn't gone with us, and I think we shall be an rather a poor position if he starts any trouble. I shall now send down to Thoreyiargnup for men and not be at the mercy of his bullying.'

They said that was very sensible, and that is what they did. Then Bardi and his men rode on their way. Grettir saw them going and went round to intercept them, and when they met, they greeted each other. Grettir asked for news, and Bardi said unabashedly exactly what had happened. Grettir asked who the men were that were with him. Bardi said it was his brothers and his brother-in-law Eyiolf.

'You have now purged yourself of blame,' said Grettir, 'and so the next thing is for us to try which of us here is the stronger.'

[36] *ógæfumenn*: 'unlucky men', those whose enterprises always turn out to be disastrous. Grettir was the archetypal *ógæfumaðr*; his lack of *gæfa* is one of the main themes of the saga; see Introduction.

Bardi said, '"I have had jobs closer to home" than fighting with you for no reason, and I think I have quitted myself of that.'

'I think you have turned coward, Bardi,' said Grettir, 'if you do not dare fight with me.'

'Call it what you will,' said Bardi, 'but I would rather you directed your bullying elsewhere than at me. Moreover it is not improbable that you will, for now your domineering is going beyond bounds.'

Grettir found his prophecies annoying, and began to wonder whether he should attack one of them, and he thought it would be unwise when there were six of them and only one of him. And at that moment men came up from Thoreyiargnup to help Bardi and his men. Grettir then let them get away and went to his horse, while Bardi and his companions continued on their way, and there were no farewells between them at parting. Bardi and Grettir had no further dealings as far as is told.

Grettir has said that he felt confident in fighting most men, even if there were three of them at once, and he would not run away from four without a try, but would only fight against more to save his life, as it says in this verse:

> Experiencer of Mist's moot [battle],
> I am confident against three
> whatever hostile deeds have to be done
> in Hild's storm [battle].
> I am unwilling to face more harm-doers
> than four in the noise-rich greed of Gungnir
> if I am able to decide.

After his parting from Bardi, Grettir went back to Biarg. Then Grettir found it a great pity that he could nowhere put his strength to the test, and he asked around whether there was anything that he could have a go at.

32

There was a man called Thorhall, who lived at Thorhallsstadir in Forsæludal. Forsæludal is up from Vatnsdal. Thorhall was son of Grim, son of Thorhall, son of Fridmund who settled Forsæludal. Thorhall was married to a woman called Gudrun. Their son was called Grim, their daughter Thurid, who was now nearly grown up. Thorhall was a pretty wealthy man, mainly in livestock, so that no one had as many animals on the hoof as he. He was not one of the leading men, but still was a respectable farmer.

His farm was subject to a lot of haunting and he found it almost impossible to get shepherds so as to feel he could manage. He sought the advice of many wise men as to what he should do about it, but no one was able to offer any advice that did any good. Thorhall rode to the *assembly* each summer; he had some fine horses. It happened one summer at the Althing that Thorhall went to the *booth* of *Lawman* Skapti Thoroddsson. Skapti was the wisest of men and able to give good advice if he was asked. There was this difference between him and his father: Thorodd had the power of prophecy and was said to be a devious man by some people, but Skapti offered every one advice which he believed would be helpful if it was not departed from; consequently he was said to be an improvement on his father. Thorhall entered Skapti's *booth*. He welcomed Thorhall, for he knew that he was a man of property and asked what news he had to tell. Thorhall said: 'I would like to get some helpful advice from you.'

'I have no great ability as regards that,' said Skapti; 'but what's your problem?'

Thorhall said: 'It's like this, that I cannot hold on to my shepherds. They get easily upset, and some don't finish their time. And now there is no one that will take it on if they know what is up.'

Skapti replies: 'It must be that there is some evil creature there if people are so much more reluctant to look after your cattle than other people's. Now since you have come to me for a solution, I will give you a shepherd whose name is Glam, who is from Sweden, from Sylgsdalir, and came out last summer; he is big and strong and not much to most people's liking.'

Thorhall said he was not bothered about that as long as he would look after the sheep properly. Skapti said there was no hope for anyone else, if he could not look after them with his strength and daring. Thorhall then went out. This was at the conclusion of the *assembly*. Thorhall found he had two light fawn-coloured horses missing and went himself to look for them. From this people assumed that he was not a man of consequence. He went up beneath Sledaas and southwards beside the mountain called Armannsfell. Then he saw where some one was coming down from Godaskog carrying brushwood on a horse. They soon reached each other. Thorhall asked him his name and he said he was called Glam. This man was heavily built and strange in appearance, with eyes dark and wide open, wolf-grey in the colour of his hair. Thorhall was rather taken aback when he saw this man, and yet he asked him, realising that this must be the one he had been directed to:

'What work are you best at doing?' said Thorhall.

Glam said he was fine at looking after sheep in winter.

'Will you look after my sheep?' said Thorhall. 'Skapti has handed you over to me.'

'My employment will turn out best for you if I make my own decisions, because I am awkward if things are not to my liking.'

'That will be no bother to me,' says Thorhall, 'and I would like you to come to me.'

'I don't mind doing that,' says Glam. 'But are there any problems with it?'

'It is believed to be haunted,' said Thorhall.

'I'm not afraid of ghosts,' said Glam, 'and I will find it the less boring.'

'You will need to be like that,' said Thorhall, 'and it will be better there not to be too much of a wimp.'

After this they fix their terms and Glam was to come at the *Winter Nights*. Then they parted and Thorhall found his horses where he had just been searching for them. Thorhall rode back and thanked Skapti for the favour he had done him.

Summer passed, and Thorhall heard nothing of the shepherd and no one knew anything of him, but at the arranged time he came to Thorhallsstadir. The farmer welcomed him, but none of the others took to him, and least of all the farmer's wife. He took over the shepherding, and found this no hard task; he had a loud and deep voice and the flock all ran together when he shouted. There was a church at Thorhallsstadir; Glam refused to go to it. He did not care for singing and was not religious, awkward and uncivil; everyone found him repulsive.

Thus it went on until Christmas-eve arrived. Then Glam got up early and called for his food. The farmer's wife replies:

'It is not the custom for Christian people to eat on this day, for tomorrow it is the first day of Christmas, and so it is obligatory to fast to begin with today.'

He replied: 'You go in for a lot of superstitions that I see no point in. I do not know that people are any better off now any more than then when people didn't bother with such things. I thought ways were better when people were said to be heathens, and I want my food and no messing about.'

The farmer's wife said: 'I know for sure that it will go ill for you today if you go ahead with this wicked act.'

Glam told her to get the food straight away, said that otherwise things would be the worse for her. She dared nothing other than do what he wished. And when he had finished he went out, and was in rather a nasty mood. The weather had become so that it was dark if one looked around and flurries of snow came out at one and there was a blustery wind, and it got worse as the day passed. People could hear the shepherd in the early part of the day, but less as the day went on. Then it began to snow and there was a blizzard in the evening. People went to the service, and so time passed until nightfall. Glam did not come home. There was now discussion about whether there should not be a search for him, but because the storm was still raging and it was pitch dark no search took place. He did not come home during the night of Christmas-eve. So people waited on until after the service. As soon as it was fully day people went on the search and found the sheep all over the place in snowdrifts, battered by the weather, or strayed up onto the mountains. Then they came upon a big area of trampled snow high up in the valley. It looked to them as though there had been some rather violent struggle, for stones had been pulled up in various places, and the earth as well. They examined the spot carefully and saw where Glam was lying a little way off from them. He was dead and *blue* as Hel and swollen up like an ox. They were nauseated by him and the thought of him made them shudder. Nevertheless they tried to move him to the church and could only get him as far as the edge of a gully a little way down from where they were and they went home without further ado and told the farmer what had happened. He asked what seemed to have been the cause of Glam's death. They said they had followed some tracks that were as big as if the base of a cask had been slammed down from where the trampling was and up to the bottom of the cliffs that were there at the top of the valley, and alongside them were great splashes of blood. People concluded that the evil creature that had previously been there must have killed Glam, and that he must have caused it a great wound which had finished it off, for there has never been any trace of this evil creature since.

On the second day of Christmas there was a second attempt made to get Glam to the church. Draught animals were hitched to him and they were unable to shift him at all where the land was level and there was no slope to go down. They left him without more ado. On the third day the priest went with them and they searched all day and Glam could not be found. The priest would not go there again, and the shepherd was found when the priest was not in the party. They then gave up trying to get him to the church and buried him under a heap of stones where he lay. Soon after people discovered that Glam was not resting in peace. This was a source of great affliction to people, so that many fell into a faint if they saw him, and some lost their wits. Soon after Christmas people thought they could see him at home there on the farm. People were enormously afraid. Many fled. Next Glam began to ride on the buildings[37] at night so that they were in danger of being wrecked. He went on with this almost night and day. People scarcely dared to go up into the valley even if they had good reason. This was thought in the district to be a source of great trouble.

33

In the spring Thorhall engaged a household and set up a farm on his land. The visitations began to get fewer while the sun was at its highest. So time passed until midsummer. That summer a ship came out and arrived at Hunavatn. On it was a man called Thorgaut. He was of foreign origin, big and strong. He had the strength of two men. He was without employment and on his own. He wanted to get some work because he had no money. Thorhall rode to the ship and went to Thorgaut, asked if he was willing to work for him. Thorgaut said he might well be and said he was not fussy about what it was.

'You must assume,' said Thorhall, 'that it is not a place for wimps

[37] I.e. to sit on the ridge beating his heels on the roof either side.

because of the visitations that have been going on there for a while, and I don't want to hide anything from you.'

Thorgaut replies: 'I don't consider it to be all over with me if I see little phantoms. No one else will be able to cope if I become afraid, and I shall not change my job because of that.'

Now they easily agree on their terms, and Thorgaut is to look after the sheep for the winter. Now the summer passed. Thorgaut took over the flock at the start of winter. He got on well with everyone. Glam was continually paying his visits and riding the buildings. Thorgaut found this very entertaining and said the villain would need to approach nearer 'if I am going to be afraid.'

Thorhall told him not to get involved. 'It will be best if you don't fall foul of each other.'

Thorgaut said, 'Truly the heart has been shaken out of you, and I am not going to collapse after half a day because of this nonsense.'

So now it went on through the winter right up to Christmas. On Christmas-eve the shepherd set out towards the flock. Then the farmer's wife said:

'I hope it is not going to happen all over again.'

He replied: 'Don't have any fear of that, my lady,' he said. 'There will be something to tell of if I don't return.'

Then he went back to his sheep. The weather was rather cold and there was driving snow. Thorgaut usually returned home when it was half dark, but this time he did not return home at that time. The people attending church arrived as usual. It already seemed to people to be turning out not unlike the last time. The farmer wanted to have a search made for the shepherd, but those at the service excused themselves and said they were not going to risk themselves out into the hands of trolls at night, and the farmer did not dare to go, and no search was made. On Christmas-day when people had eaten, men went and searched for the shepherd. They went first to Glam's cairn, because people thought he must have had something to do with the disappearance of the shepherd. And when they got close to the cairn, they saw that something had really happened, and they found there the shepherd and his neck was broken and every bone in his body smashed. Then they moved him to the church, and there was never any harm done to anyone because of Thorgaut afterwards. But Glam began to increase in power afresh. He now began to throw his weight about so much that everyone fled from Thorhallstadir except just the farmer and his wife. The same herdsman had been there for a long time. Thorhall did not want to lose him because of his kindness and his care with the animals. He was getting on in years and he was very reluctant to leave. He also realised that everything the farmer owned would go to wrack and ruin if no one was there to look after it. And on one occasion after the middle of the winter it happened one morning that the farmer's wife went to the cowshed to milk the cows at the usual time. It was by then fully day, for no one dared to go out before that except the herdsman. He used to go out as soon as it got light. She heard a great crack in the cowshed and a horrible bellowing. She ran inside the house shouting and said she did not know what on earth was going on in the cowshed. The farmer went out and came to the cows and they were all goring each other. He didn't care for that very much and went on up to the barn. He saw where the herdsman was lying with his head in one stall and his feet in another. He was lying on his back. The farmer went up to him and felt him and soon realises that he is dead and his back broken. It had been broken over the stone partition of the stall.

Now the farmer decided it was impossible to stay and left the farm with everything he could take with him. But all the animals that remained there Glam killed, and after that he went through the whole valley and laid waste all the farms up above Tunga. Thorhall then stayed with friends for the rest of the winter. No one was able to take horse or dog up into the valley, for it would be immediately killed. But when spring came and the sun was at its highest, the visitations lessened somewhat. Thorhall now wanted to return to his land. He didn't find it easy to get workmen, but still he set up home at Thorhallsstadir. Everything went the same as before. As soon as autumn came, the hauntings began to increase. The attacks were then mainly aimed at the farmer's daughter, and in the end she died of it. Many things were tried, but nothing worked. It looked to people as though the whole of Vatnsdal would be laid waste if no remedy was found.

34

Now the story is to be taken up, that Grettir was at home at Biarg in the autumn after his parting from Viga-Bardi at Thoreyiargnup. And when it came close to the *Winter Nights* Grettir rode out from home northwards over the ridges to Vididal and stayed at Audunarstadir. He and Audun were fully reconciled and Grettir gave him a fine axe and they confirmed their friendship together. Audun lived a long time at Audunarstadir and was blessed with descendants. His son was Egil who married Ulfheid, daughter of Eyiolf Gudmundarson, and their son was Eyiolf who was killed at the Althing. He was father of Orm, Bishop Thorlak's chaplain.

Grettir rode north to Vatnsdal and went on a visit to acquaintances in Tunga. There lived there at that time Iokul Bardarson, Grettir's mother's brother. Iokul was a big man and strong and a very overbearing man. He was a seafaring man and very difficult to deal with, but yet an able man. He welcomed Grettir and he stayed there three nights. At that time there was so much talk of Glam's hauntings that there was no topic of conversation more frequent. Grettir enquired in detail about the happenings that had taken place. Iokul said nothing more had been told about it than was justified.

'But have you a desire, kinsman, to go there?'

Grettir said he did. Iokul told him not to do so.

'For it is tempting providence, and your kinsmen have a great deal at stake in you,' he said. 'There is no other young person who comes anywhere near up to you, but "only evil can come of evil" in the case of Glam, and it is much better to be involved with human beings than with such monsters.'

Grettir said he had a mind to go to Thorhallsstadir and see what had been going on there. Iokul said:

'I see now that it is no good trying to dissuade you, but it is true what they say, that "success and ability don't always go together".'

'"Disaster is waiting outside the door for the next person, when it has entered in to one", and watch out for what will happen to you yourself before it's all over,' said Grettir.

Iokul replies, 'It may be that we can both foresee something of the future, but that neither of us can do anything about it.'

After that they parted, and neither was pleased with the other's prophecies.

35

Grettir rode to Thorhallsstadir and the farmer welcomed him. He asked where Grettir was bound for, but he said he wanted to stay the night there if the farmer was happy with that. Thorhall said he would be very grateful for his being there.

'But few think there is much profit in staying here at the moment. You must have heard tell of what is going on here, but I very much want you to [have no trouble on my account. But even if you] get away unharmed, I know for certain that you will lose your horse, for no one who comes keeps his mount here unscathed.'

Grettir said there were plenty of horses, whatever became of this one. Thorhall was pleased that Grettir wanted to stay there, and welcomed him with open arms. Grettir's horse was locked up securely. They went to bed and the night passed without a visit from Glam. Then said Thorhall:

'Things have taken a turn for the better with your arrival, for every night Glam has been accustomed to go up and ride the buildings or break down the doors, as you can see from the evidence.'

Grettir said, 'It is bound to turn out in one of two ways, either he won't hold off for long, or else the change in his habits will be for more than one night. I shall stay another night and see how it goes.'

Then they went to Grettir's horse, and it hadn't been interfered with. It all seemed to the farmer of a piece. Now Grettir stays there another night, and there was no visit from the villain. Then the farmer thought things were really looking up. Then he went to see Grettir's horse. The building had been broken into when the farmer got to it, and the horse dragged out to the entrance and every bone in its body was broken. Thorhall told Grettir what had happened and told him to escape.

'For death is certain if you await Glam.'

Grettir replies, 'I cannot take less in return for my horse than a sight of the villain.'

The farmer said there was no advantage in seeing him.

'For he has nothing in common with humanity. But every moment you are willing to stay here seems good to me.'

So the day passed by, and when it was time for bed, Grettir would not undress and lay down on the *platform* opposite the farmer's *bed-closet*. He put a fur poncho over himself and he wrapped one edge down under his feet and the other under his head and looked out through the head-hole. There was a very firm support at the edge of the *platform* and he braced his feet against it. All the door-frame had been broken away from the outer doors, and now there was a hurdle fastened across it and fixed rather roughly. The end partition of the hall had all been broken away, the one that had been in front of the doors, both above the beam and beneath. All the bedding had been thrown about. It was not very inviting there. There was a light burning in the hall during the night. And when about a third of the night had passed, Grettir heard outside a great banging. Then something climbed up onto the building and rode the hall and beat with its heels so that every timber creaked. This went on a long time. Then it came down from the building and went to the door and when the door opened, Grettir saw the villain stretch in its head and it seemed to him enormously big and amazingly large-featured. Glam moved slowly and straightened up when he got inside the door. He towered high up into the roof, turned towards the hall and laid his arms up on the cross-beam and leaned in over the hall. The farmer did not let anything be heard from himself because he thought it was plenty when he heard what was going on outside. Grettir lay quiet and did not move. Glam saw that some sort of heap lay on the *platform* and he made his way in down the hall and took hold of the poncho rather hard. Grettir pushed against the *platform* support and it did not move. Glam jerked again much harder and the poncho held firm. A third time he pulled it with both hands so hard that he pulled Grettir up from the *platform*. They now ripped the poncho in two between them. Glam looked at the bit he was holding on to and wondered greatly who could be pulling so hard against him. And at that moment Grettir leapt under his arms and took him round the middle and pressed against his back as hard as he could and intended that Glam should bend over backwards, but the villain pushed at Grettir's arms so hard that he was forced to give way by the superior strength. Then Grettir went backwards from one *platform* to the other. The supports all came away and everything was broken that lay in their path. Glam wanted to get outside, but Grettir dug in his heels wherever he could and still Glam managed to drag him out to the entrance. Then they had an almighty struggle, for the villain wanted to get him outside the farm, but bad as it was to have dealings with Glam inside, Grettir realised that it would be worse to wrestle with him outside, and so he resisted going outside with all his strength. Glam put on an extra burst of strength and jerked him towards himself when they got to the porch. And when Grettir sees that he cannot hold back with his feet, he does two things at once, he leaps as hard as he can into the villain's embrace and kicks back with both feet at a stone part-buried in the ground that stood on the threshold. The villain was not expecting this. He had been struggling to pull Grettir towards himself, and so Glam toppled over backwards and was flung in reverse out against the doorway so that his shoulders caught the lintel and the roof gave way, both the beams and the frozen thatch. Thus he fell face upwards and backwards outside the building with Grettir on top of him.

There was bright moonlight outside and gaps in the heavy cloud. Sometimes it clouded over and sometimes it cleared away. At the moment Glam fell, the cloud cleared from the moon and Glam glared up at it and Grettir himself has said that this was the only sight he ever saw that took him aback. Then he felt so weakened by everything, his weariness and seeing Glam squint at him fiercely, that he was unable to draw his *cutlass* and lay just about between life and death.[38] And such was the greater power of evil in Glam than in most other revenants that he then spoke as follows:

'You have displayed great zeal, Grettir,' he said, 'in seeking me out, and it will not seem surprising if you don't gain a great deal of good fortune from your encounter with me. But I can tell you this, that you have now acquired half the strength and development that was intended for you if you had not met me. I cannot now deprive you of the strength that you have already acquired, but I can ensure that you never become any stronger than you are now, and yet even now you are strong enough, as many will find out to their cost. You have become renowned up to now for your deeds, but from now on you will become guilty of crimes and deeds of violence, and nearly everything you do will lead to your misfortune and failure. You will be made outlaw and be compelled always to live in the open on your own. I also lay this upon you that these eyes of mine will be always before your sight, and you will find it hard to be alone and this will bring you to your death.'

And when the villain had said this, then the weakness that had afflicted Grettir passed from him. He then drew his *cutlass* and cut off Glam's

[38] Literally between this world and Hel, the abode of death. Cf. Hel in Index.

head and put it by his rump.[39] The farmer then came out and he had got dressed while Glam had been making his speech, but he dared not come anywhere near until Glam had fallen. Thorhall praised God for it and thanked Grettir warmly for having defeated this unclean spirit. Then they set to and burned Glam to cold cinders. After that they [put his ashes into a bag] and buried them as far as possible from pastures and routes taken by people. After that they went back to the house and it was almost day. Grettir lay down because he was very stiff. Thorhall sent people to the neighbouring farms for witnesses, showed and told what had happened. Everyone who heard was greatly impressed by this deed. It was universally acknowledged that there was no one comparable in the whole country as regards strength and valour and all kinds of ability with Grettir Asmundarson.

Thorhall sent Grettir on his way in fine style and gave him a splendid horse and proper clothes, because those were all ripped to pieces that he had been wearing before. They parted on friendly terms. Grettir rode from there to As in Vatnsdal and Thorvald welcomed him and asked in detail about his encounter with Glam and Grettir told him of their dealings together and said his strength had never been put harder to the test, such a long encounter as they had had together. Thorvald told him to be careful how he went.

'And then you will be all right, but otherwise you will be in for trouble.'

Grettir said there had been no improvement in his temper and said he was now much worse controlled than before, and found it harder to bear being crossed. He noticed this great difference in himself, that he had become a person so afraid of the dark that he dared go nowhere on his own after it got dark; there appeared to him then all sorts of apparitions, and it has since been used as a saying that "Glam has lent someone his eyes" or "they have been given gloomsight"[40] when things seem very different from what they are. Grettir rode home to Biarg when he had finished his business and he stayed at home for the winter.

[39] See ch. 18, note 13.

[40] The name Glam is etymologically related to gloom and gloaming, though these words are not derived from the name.

36

Thorbiorn Oxen-might held a great autumn feast and many people went to it. This was while Grettir was going up north to Vatnsdal in the autumn. Thorbiorn Ferdalang was there at the feast. There was much talk there. The people of Hrutafiord asked about the encounter between him and Grettir on the ridge in the summer. Thorbiorn Oxen-might gave quite a sympathetic account of Grettir, said Kormak would have come off worse if no one had come up to separate them. Then said Thorbiorn Ferdalang:

'There are two things to be said,' he said, 'that I did not notice this Grettir doing anything exceptional, and also I think he panicked when we came up, and he was very keen to part, and I did not see him trying for vengeance when Atli's workman was killed, and so I judge there is never any determination in him when he has not got plenty of men behind him.'

Thorbiorn went in for a great amount of scoffing about this. Many agreed that this was uncalled-for derision, and that Grettir would not want to let matters rest there if he heard of these words. Nothing further of note took place at the feast. They all went home. There was a great deal of hostility between them during the winter, though neither attacked the other. Nothing noteworthy happened during the winter.

37

Early the following spring a ship came out from Norway. This was before the *assembly*. They had much news to tell, first of all that there had been a change of ruler in Norway, there had now come to power King Olaf Haraldsson; but Earl Svein had fled the country in the spring after the Battle of the Nesses. There were many remarkable things said of King Olaf, including that he was most eager to receive men who had some particular abilities, and he took them into his service. Many young men were very attracted by this and were keen to go abroad. And when Grettir heard all this, he developed a mind to sail. He was hoping for some advancement for himself from the king like other people. There was a ship beached at Gasir in Eyiafiord. Grettir got himself a passage and prepared for going abroad. He again did not have much to take with him. Asmund was now getting very infirm from old age and did not get up much. He and Asdis had a young son called Illugi, a very promising young man. Atli now took over all the running of the farm and the management of the property. This was thought to be a great improvement, as he was kindly and prudent. Grettir went to the ship. On the same ship Thorbiorn Ferdalang had taken a passage before they realised that Grettir would be sailing on it. Many tried to dissuade Thorbiorn from travelling on the same ship as Grettir, but Thorbiorn said he would go nevertheless. He got ready for going abroad and was rather late in his preparations. He did not get north to Gaseyr until the ship was fully prepared. Before Thorbiorn left the west of Iceland Asmund Hærulang had contracted a sickness and was bedridden. Thorbiorn Ferdalang came late in the day to the sands. Everyone was then ready for their meal and they were washing their hands outside by their *booth*. When Thorbiorn rode past between the *booths* they greeted him and asked him for news. He said he had none to tell.

'Except that I suppose the great Asmund at Biarg is now dead.'

Many agreed that it was a fine [farmer] had departed the world in him.

'But how did it come about?' they said.

He replied: 'It didn't take much to finish the great man off, for he stifled in the smoke from the fire like a dog; but it isn't a great loss, for he had become senile.'

They replied, 'That is a strange way to speak of such a man, and Grettir would not be very pleased if he heard it.'

'I can put up with that,' said Thorbiorn, 'and Grettir will have to wield his *cutlass* higher than last summer on Hrutafiord ridge, if I am going to be afraid of him.'

Grettir heard quite plainly what Thorbiorn said, and took no notice while Thorbiorn went on with his speech. But when he stopped, Grettir spoke:

'I prophesy for you, Ferdalang,' he said, 'that you will not die by the smoke from your fire, and yet maybe you won't die of old age either. And it is an odd thing to do to speak disrespectfully of innocent people.'

Thorbiorn said, 'I will not take any of it back, and you did not seem to me to have behaved so toughly when we got you out of it when the men of Mel were knocking you about like an ox-head.'

Grettir then uttered a verse:

A tongue too long in talk
has a bow-slinger [warrior] often;
so some suffer heavy vengeance for it.
Many a wound-snake-wall-wielder [shield-wielder, i.e. warrior]
has committed less offence
and got death by it, Ferdalang.

Thorbiorn said: 'I think myself no closer to death than before, in spite of your chatter.'

Grettir replied: 'My prophecies have not taken long to mature up to now, and they will continue so. Beware if you will; there will not be a better time.'

Then Grettir struck at Thorbiorn, and he shielded himself with his arm, intending to ward off the blow, but the blow struck his arm above the wrist and then the *cutlass* sprang against his neck so that his head flew off. The merchants said he had a heavy hand, and such made good king's men, and they did not think it a great loss though Thorbiorn was dead, for he had been both quarrelsome and derisive. Soon after they set out to sea and arrived late in the summer in Norway, to the south off Hordland. They then learned that King Olaf was in residence in the north in Trøndelag. Grettir got a passage north there with some merchants, for he wanted to go and see the king.

38

There was a man called Thorir who lived at Gard in Adaldal. He was son of Skeggi, son of Bodolf. Skeggi had taken possession of Kelduhverfi up as far as Kelduness. He was married to Helga, daughter of Thorgeir of Fiskilæk. His son Thorir was very much one of the leading men and a trader. He had two sons. One was called Thorgeir, the other Skeggi. They were both promising young men and pretty well grown up at this time. Thorir had been in Norway the summer that King Olaf came from the *West* from England and had then got onto very good terms with the king and also with Bishop Sigurd, and an indication of this is that Thorir had had a great cargo-ship built in a forest and asked the bishop to consecrate it, and he did so. After that Thorir went out to Iceland and had the cargo-ship knocked to pieces when he got tired of voyages, but the prow-pieces of the ship he had fixed up over his house-doors and they remained there long afterwards and were such good indicators of the weather that a whistling sound came from one of them with a south wind, and from the other with a north wind. And when Thorir heard that King Olaf had gained sole power over all Norway, he thought it was time to claim friendship with him. So Thorir sent his sons to Norway to see the king and intended that they should enter his service. They arrived in the south of the country late in autumn and got themselves an oared boat and went north along the coast, planning to go and see the king. They got to a harbour to the south of Stad and lay there a few nights. They looked after themselves well with food and drink and kept inside, since the weather was not good.

Now we must return to how Grettir and his party were travelling north along the coast and met a lot of harsh weather, because it was the beginning of winter. And as they were making their way north to Stad they met really bad weather with snow and frost and reached land with difficulty one evening, all of them exhausted, and they made a grassy beach and managed to save their goods and provisions. They had a miserable time of it, the merchants, because they had been able to bring nothing to light a fire with, and they thought their safety and lives more or less depended on one. They lay there in the evening in a bad way. Later in the evening they saw a large fire start up on the other side of the channel that they had arrived at. And when Grettir's shipmates saw the fire, they talked about it, saying that anyone would be lucky who managed to get hold of it, and were doubtful about whether they should launch out their ship, but they all thought it would not be safe to do so. Then they had a great discussion about whether anyone would be capable of reaching the fire. Grettir was little impressed and said there had been men whom this would not have worried. The merchants said that it was no help to them what had been, if there was no one to look to now.

'But do you have faith in yourself, Grettir?' they said, 'for you are said to be the most able of the Icelanders, and you can see clearly what our position is.'

Grettir replied, 'It does not look to me such a great feat to get the fire, but I am not sure whether you will repay better than the one who does it asks.'

They said, 'Why do you think us such base men that we would not reward that well?'

'I can have a go, if you think it is so essential, but I do not feel confident that I shall do very well out of it.'

They said that was not how it would be and blessed him for his offer. Then Grettir prepared himself for swimming and threw off his clothes. The only thing he wore was a hooded cloak and homespun breeches. He tied the cloak up round himself and threw a bast rope round his waist and took with him a tub. Then he leapt overboard.

He swam now straight across the channel and went ashore. He sees a building standing there and heard men's voices from it and much merriment. Grettir approached the house. Now we must tell who it was that was there, that it was the sons of Thorir who had come here, as was mentioned above. They had been staying there many nights waiting for a break in the weather so that they could get north past Stad. They were sitting drinking and were in a party of twelve. They lay in the main harbour, and there had been built there a refuge for the use of those travelling along the coast, and there had been brought into the building a lot of straw. There was a large fire on the floor. Grettir now made his way into the house, not knowing who was there. His cloak was all icy when he got ashore and he was absolutely huge to look at as if he were a troll. Those who were there were much taken aback at this and thought it must be a monster. They hit him with everything they could lay their hands on and there was now a great uproar among them, but Grettir beat them off with his arms. Some of them struck at him with firebrands. The fire then spread over the whole building. At that he got out with the fire and so returned to his companions. They were full of praise for his venture and bravery and said there could be no match for him. So the night passed, and they thought they were immediately saved when they got the fire.

The next morning the weather was good. They woke up early, the merchants, and got ready to leave, and talked about going to see those who had had the fire to see who they were. They cast off the ship and crossed the channel. Then they did not find the building, but saw the ashes, a great heap, and in them they found many human bones. They now realised that the refuge must have burned up completely, together with the people who had been in it. They asked whether Grettir had caused this catastrophe, and declared this the greatest of crimes. Grettir said it had now come about as he had suspected, that they would give him a poor reward for getting the fire, and said it was a waste of time to help those who were not men of honour. This was a source of great disservice to Grettir in that the merchants said, wherever they went, that Grettir had burned these men to death in the building. It was then soon discovered that in the building had lost their lives the sons of Thorir of Gard, who were named above, and their companions. Now they drove Grettir away off the ship and refused to have him with them. He was now so despised that almost nobody would do anything for him. He thought that things were now looking pretty bad and wanted somehow or other to get to see the king and made his way north to Trøndelag. The king was there and had heard all this before Grettir came. He had been greatly vilified before the king. Grettir was several days in the town before he managed to get to see the king.

39

It was one day while the king was sitting in council, that Grettir went before the king and greeted him politely. The king looked at him and said:

'Are you Grettir the Strong?'

He replied, 'I have been so called, and I have come here hoping for some remedy from you for the slanderous accusation that has been made about me, and which I consider myself not guilty of.'

King Olaf said, 'You are powerful enough, but I don't know what success you will have in ridding yourself of this accusation. But it looks more likely that you would not have intentionally burned the men in the building.'

Grettir said he would very much like to disprove this accusation if the king thought there was any way of doing it. The king told him to tell the truth about what had taken place between them. Grettir then told everything as was described above, and added that they were all alive when he got outside with the fire.

'I will now offer to submit to any procedure to prove my innocence that you consider lawful.'

King Olaf then said: 'We will grant that you bear iron for this affair, if you are lucky enough to be able to.'

Grettir was well pleased by this. He now began to fast in preparation for bearing the iron, and time passed until the day came when the ordeal was to take place. Then the king went to church and the bishop and a multitude of people, for there were many who were curious to see Grettir, so much had been told about him. Then Grettir was conducted to the church. And when he came to the church there were many who were there who looked at him and said that he was unlike most people as regards strength and size. Grettir now went in down along the floor. Then a scarcely grown lad leapt out rather in a flash and said to Grettir:

'It is a strange custom now here in this land where people are supposed to be Christians, that criminals and plunderers and thieves should be allowed to go in peace and undertake ordeals. And what is there for a criminal to do but extend his life as long as he can? Here we have an evil man who has been proved to be guilty of crimes and has burned innocent men inside a house, and yet he is given the benefit of an ordeal, and this is a great scandal.'

He went up to Grettir, stuck out his fingers at him and made faces at him and called him a mermaid's son and many other evil names. Grettir lost his temper at this and could not control himself. He swung up his fist and struck the lad under the ear so that he immediately fell unconscious, and some say that he was already dead. But no one could say where the lad came from or what became of him, but people think it most likely that it was an unclean spirit sent to cause trouble to Grettir. There was now a great uproar in the church, and the king was now told that the one that was supposed to be bearing the iron was in a scrap. King Olaf now came out along the church and saw what was going on and spoke:

'You are not a man much blessed with success, Grettir,' said the king, 'when the ordeal has now to be abandoned when everything was ready for it, and it seems it is not easy to do anything with your disposition to failure.'

Grettir replied, 'I had hoped that I would gain more honour from visiting you, my lord, than now seems likely, in view of my descent,' and he gave details of how they were related, as was told above.[41]

[41] See ch. 1. They had a great-great-grandfather in common, Ofeig Burlufot.

'I am now very keen,' said Grettir, 'that you should take me into your service. You have got many with you who will not seem better fighting men than I.'

'I can see,' said the king, 'that there are few men such as you in respect of strength and valour, but you are much too prone to failure for you to be able to stay with us on that account. Now you may go in peace as far as I am concerned, wherever you will, for the duration of the winter, but in the summer you must go out to Iceland, for it is there your bones are fated to lie.'

Grettir replies, 'I would like first to clear myself of the charge of the burning, if I might, because I did not do that intentionally.'

'That is very likely,' said the king, 'but because the ordeal has now been rendered invalid as a result of your lack of forbearance, you will be unable to rid yourself of this charge any further than you have already, and "evil always comes from thoughtlessness". And if ever anyone was under a curse, then it is not least likely to be you.'

After this Grettir stayed in the town for a while and got no further with King Olaf than has now been told. Then he went to the south of the country and planned to go east to Tunsberg to see his brother Thorstein Dromund. And there is nothing told of his travels until he came east to Iadar.

40

At Christmas Grettir came to a farmer called Einar. He was a rich man and married and had a daughter of marriageable age whose name was Gyrid. She was a handsome woman and was considered a very good match. Einar invited Grettir to stay with him over Christmas, and he accepted. It was widespread in Norway at that time that highwaymen and criminals rushed down from the forests and challenged men to hand over their women or carried off people's animals by force where there were not many people around to prevent them. It happened in this case that it was one day during the Christmas season that a large number of criminals came to Einar's together. The one who was their leader was called Snækoll. He was a great *berserk*. He challenged farmer Einar either to give up to him his daughter or to fight for her if he felt enough of a man to do so; but the farmer was past his prime and no fighting man. It seemed to him that he had a great problem on his hands and he asked Grettir in private what he could suggest.

'For you are said to be a man of renown.'

Grettir told him to agree only to what seemed to him to be not dishonourable. The *berserk* sat on horseback and had a helmet on his head and hadn't fastened the face-guards. He had a shield with an iron rim in front of himself and he behaved in a very menacing fashion. He said to the farmer:

'Choose straight away one way or the other; but what does that great lump of a fellow suggest who is standing there by you, isn't it the case that he wants to have some sport with me?'

Grettir said, 'There's nothing to choose between the farmer and me, for neither of us is the quarrelling type.'

Snækoll said, 'You will both of you be a bit afraid of fighting me if I get angry.'

'"When that happens we shall see how it will be",' said Grettir.

The *berserk* now perceived that they were using delaying tactics; he began to roar loudly and bit on the edge of his shield and put the shield up in his mouth and stretched his mouth over the corner of the shield and went on wildly. Grettir threw himself across the field, and when he came level with the *berserk*'s horse he kicked with his foot down under the point of the shield so hard that the shield went up in the man's mouth so that it tore apart his jaws and his lower jaw fell down on his chest. He then did two things at once, he grasped the helmet with his left hand and pulled the *viking* off the horse, and with his right hand he drew the *cutlass* he had on and cut his throat, severing the head. And when Snækoll's companions saw this they fled in all directions. Grettir did not bother to chase them, for he saw there was no pluck in them.

The farmer thanked him heartily for this deed, and many others did too. This achievement was considered to have been the result of being quick off the mark and tough. Grettir was entertained well there over Christmas. The farmer sent him on his way generously. Grettir then went east to Tunsberg and found his brother Thorstein. He welcomed Grettir joyfully and asked about his travels and his defeat of the *berserk*. Grettir uttered a verse:

Struck on Snækoll's snack-port [mouth]
war-urger's battle-bowl [shield]
that got a kick from ankle's thorn-tree [foot];
so iron-clad wall of arrows' passage [shield]
split tooth-yard's dwelling [jaw]
and jaw was severed onto chest.

Thorstein said, 'Much would go nicely for you, kinsman, if you weren't always tripping up.'

Grettir replies, '"The word still gets round of what is done".'

41

Now Grettir stayed with Thorstein for the rest of the winter and on into the spring. It happened one morning when the brothers, Thorstein and Grettir, were lying up in their bedroom, that Grettir had laid his arms out over the bedclothes. Thorstein awoke and saw this. Grettir awoke a little later. Then said Thorstein:

'I have seen your arms, kinsman,' he said, 'and I am not surprised at the heaviness of some of your strokes, for I have seen no one's arms that compare with yours.'

'You can be sure,' said Grettir, 'that I would not have been able to achieve what I have done if I wasn't fairly tough.'

'I would have preferred it,' says Thorstein, 'if they had been more slender and a bit more fortunate.'

Grettir says, 'It is true what they say, that "no one shapes himself". Let me now see your arms.'

Thorstein did so. He was the longest of men and skinny. Grettir smiled when he saw them and said, 'I don't need to look any longer at this; your ribs are like a bunch of hooks, and I don't think I have ever seen such a pair of tongs as you have got for arms, and I think you can scarcely have the strength of a woman.'

'That may well be,' said Thorstein, 'but you can be sure of this, that these slender arms of mine will avenge you, or else you will never be avenged.'

'Who can tell how that will turn out in the end?' says Grettir. 'But it seems very unlikely to me.'

No more is told of their conversation. The spring now passed. Grettir got a place on a ship and went out to Iceland in the summer. The brothers parted on friendly terms and never saw each other again.

42

Now the story must be taken up where we left off previously, that Thorbiorn Oxen-might learned of the killing of Thorbiorn Ferdalang which was narrated above. He was very angry at this and said he would like blows to be owed in turn in each other's court.

Asmund Hærulang lay sick for a long time in the summer, and when he felt the end was coming, he called together his kinsmen to see him and said that he wished Atli to take over the management of his property when he was gone.

'But I fear,' said Asmund, 'that you will find it difficult to live a quiet life in the face of oppression. But I would like all those who are connected to me to support him as well as they can. But there is little advice I can give Grettir, because I think his life is doomed to be all ups and downs, and though he is a strong man, I am afraid that he will have more problems to deal with than helping out his kinsmen. And though Illugi is young, yet he will develop into a fine man if he keeps out of trouble.'

And when Asmund had arranged things with his sons as he wanted, he succumbed to his sickness. He died a little later and was buried at Biarg, for Asmund had had a church built there, and the people round about thought it a great loss. Atli now became an influential farmer and kept a large household. He kept it well supplied. Towards the end of summer he went out onto Snæfellsness to get some dried fish. He took a large number of horses and rode out to Melar in Hrutafiord to his brother-in-law Gamli. Then Gamli's brother Grim Thorhallsson and one other man joined Atli on his journey. They rode west through Haukadalsskard and straight out onto the Ness, there bought a lot of dried fish and loaded it onto seven horses. They set out towards home when they had finished getting ready.

43

Thorbiorn Oxen-might heard that Atli and Grim had gone away from home. Staying with him were Gunnar and Thorgeir, sons of Thorir of Skard. Thorbiorn envied Atli for his popularity and so he incited the brothers, the sons of Thorir, to waylay Atli on their return from the Ness. They then rode home to Skard and waited there until Atli and his companions were going up through with their train. And when they came out by the farm at Skard they were seen to pass. The brothers then jumped to it quickly with their workmen and rode after them. And when Atli's party saw them coming, he told them to unload the horses.

'And they will be wanting to offer me compensation for the workman of mine that Gunnar killed last summer. Let's not start anything before they do, but defend ourselves if they start anything against us.'

Now the others come up and immediately dismount. Atli welcomed them and asked what news, 'or are you going to compensate me at all, Gunnar, for my farm-hand?'

Gunnar answers, 'You men of Biarg deserve something other than that I should pay good money for that, and anyway greater compensation ought to be paid for the killing of Thorbiorn, whom Grettir slew.'

'I am not responsible for that,' said Atli, 'and anyway you are not the principal in that suit.'

Gunnar said it was all the same, 'and let's now go for them, and make the most of Grettir not being about.'

They leapt at Atli and there were eight of them in all, and six in Atli's group. Atli stepped out in front of his men and drew the sword that had belonged to Iokul, which Grettir had given him. Then Thorgeir said:

'"Those who have a high opinion of themselves have much in common". Grettir carried his *cutlass* high last summer on Hrutafiord ridge.'

Atli replies, 'He must also be more used to great deeds than I.'

Then they fought. Gunnar went furiously for Atli and was in a frenzy. And when they had been fighting for a while, Atli said:

'There is no point in our killing each other's workmen, and the best thing is that we ourselves engage with each other, for I have never fought with weapons before now.'

Gunnar would not agree. Atli told his workmen to guard the baggage, 'and I will find out what they are going to do about it.'

He then went forward so hard that Gunnar and his companions gave ground. Atli then killed two of the brothers' followers. After that he turned against Gunnar and struck at him so that it cut through across the shield just under the handle and it hit the leg below the knee, and he immediately struck another blow inflicting a fatal wound. Now there is to tell of Grim Thorhallsson that he attacked Thorgeir and they engaged for a long time, for they were both of them valiant men. Thorgeir saw the fall of his brother Gunnar. Then he wanted to get away. Grim ran after him and chased him until Thorgeir stumbled and fell on his face. Then Grim struck him between the shoulders with an axe so that it went right in. They gave quarter to the three of their followers who remained. After that they dressed their wounds and loaded up the horses and so went home and gave notice of these killings. Atli stayed at home with a large number of men in the autumn. Thorbiorn Oxen-might was very displeased and yet could do nothing, for Atli was very popular. Grim stayed with him during the winter and also his brother-in-law Gamli. Glum Ospaksson, his other brother-in-law, was also there. He was then living at Eyr in Bitra. They kept a large garrison at Biarg, and there was much merry-making during the winter.

44

Thorbiorn Oxen-might took on the suit for the slaying of the sons of Thorir. He prepared the case against Grim and Atli, but they prepared a defence on the grounds that the waylaying and unprovoked attack rendered the brothers outside the law's protection.[42] The cases were brought to the Hunavatn *Assembly* and both sides attended with a large following. Atli found it easy to get support, for he had a great store of kinsmen. Then friends of both parties became involved and discussed a settlement and everyone said that Atli was a well-behaved person, not given to starting trouble but not one to give way when pressed. Thorbiorn realised that there was no way of ensuring a more honourable outcome than by accepting the settlement. Atli stipulated that he would accept banishment neither from the district nor from the country. Men

[42] Those who made an unprovoked attack could be deemed outlaws after their deaths so that no compensation or vengeance would be due.

were then chosen to arbitrate, Thorvald Asgeirsson on behalf of Atli, but on Thorbiorn's side was Solvi the Splendid. He was son of Asbrand Thorbrandsson, son of Harald Ring, who had taken possession of Vatnsness right down to Ambattara on the west, and on the east right in to the river Thver and on the other side of it across to Biargaos and all that side of Biorg down to the sea. Solvi was a very showy person and a wise man, and it was for this reason that Thorbiorn preferred him to arbitrate on his behalf. And after this they announced the terms, that the sons of Thorir were to be compensated for by half-payment, but half was to be cancelled because of the waylaying and unprovoked attack and conspiracy to kill Atli. The killing of Atli's workman who was killed on Hrutafiord ridge should be equivalent to that of the two who fell with the sons of Thorir. Grim Thorhallsson was to lose the right of abode in the district, but Atli was to pay all the compensation himself. These terms were very acceptable to Atli, but less so Thorbiorn, and yet they parted nominally reconciled, though Thorbiorn could not help saying that the business between them would not be over if he had his way. Atli rode home from the *assembly* and thanked Thorvald heartily for his support. Grim Thorhallsson then moved south to Borgarfiord and lived after that at Gilsbakki and was an influential farmer.

45

There was a man with Thorbiorn Oxen-might who was called Ali. He was a workman and rather bad-tempered and not a great worker. Thorbiorn told him to work harder or he said he would beat him. Ali said he had no great eagerness to do so and was very argumentative in response. [Thorbiorn told him he mustn't dare to do anything else. The other did not lessen his answering back until] Thorbiorn could no longer put up with him and got him down on the ground under himself and thrashed him. After that Ali ran off from his job and went north over the ridge to Midfiord. He did not stop until he got to Biarg. Atli was at home and asked him where he was making for. He said he was looking for a position.

'Are you not one of Thorbiorn's workmen?' said Atli.

'We did not get on very well together, ' said Ali. 'I wasn't there long, and I didn't like it while I was there. We parted with him causing a nasty tune in my throat and I'm never again going to go and work there whatever else becomes of me. And it is true that there is a great difference as to which of you treats his household better. I would very much like to work with you now if there is any chance.'

Atli replies, 'I have plenty of workmen without trespassing on Thorbiorn for the men he has taken on, and it seems to me you lack stamina, so go back to him.'

Ali said, 'I shall not go there unless I am forced.'

Now Ali stayed for a while. One morning he went to work with Atli's workmen and worked as if he had several pairs of hands. Ali went on like this into the summer. Atli took no notice of him, though he let him be fed because he was pleased with his work. Thorbiorn now learns that Ali is at Biarg. He then rode to Biarg with two men and called Atli to speak with him. Atli went out and greeted them. Thorbiorn said:

'You are trying to start things up again with me, Atli, in being awkward and causing me annoyance. Why is it you have taken away my workman? This is an unjustifiable thing to do.'

Atli replies, 'It is not clear to me that he is your workman, but I don't want to hold on to him if you have proof that he belongs to your household. But I have no intention of dragging him out of the house.'

'You can have your way for the moment,' said Thorbiorn, 'but I am demanding the man back and I lay a ban on his working. But I shall come back another time, and it is not certain that we shall part then better friends than we are now.'

Atli replies, 'I shall wait here at home and accept whatever turns up.'

Then Thorbiorn rode home. And when the workmen came back in the evening, Atli reported his conversation with Thorbiorn and told Ali to get on his way and said he did not wish to keep him there. Ali replies:

'The old saying is true: "Those who are too highly praised are the worst for letting me down." And I didn't expect you would drive me away when I have worked fit to burst this summer and had hoped that you would stand up for me, but you go on like this in spite of appearing so kindly. Now I shall be beaten up here before your eyes if you refuse me any support or help.'

Atli gave way when he heard what he said, and he did not feel like driving him away. Now time passed until they started the haymaking.

It happened one day a little before midsummer that Thorstein Oxen-might rode to Biarg. He was geared out with a helmet on his head and girded with a sword and a spear in his hand. It was a feather-bladed spear and the blade was very broad. It was a wet day outside. Atli had sent his workmen out to mow, but some of his men were in the north near Horn getting supplies. Atli was at home with few other people. Thorbiorn arrived there during the day at about midday. He was on his own and rode to the outer doors. The door was closed and there was no one outside. Thorbiorn knocked at the door and then went round the back of the building so that he could not be seen from the doorway. The people inside heard the knocking and a woman went out. Thorbiorn caught a glimpse of the woman and did not let himself be seen, because he had another task in mind. She went to the *living-room*. Atli asked what was up. She said she hadn't seen any arrival outside. And while they were discussing this, Thorbiorn struck a great blow on the door. Then said Atli:

'It is me he wants to see, and he must have business with me, however important it is.'

He then went out into the doorway. He could see no one outside. It was very wet out and so he did not go outside and he rested one hand on each doorpost and so looked around. At that moment Thorbiorn rushed round in front of the door and thrust his spear at the middle of Atli's body with both hands so that it stuck through him. Atli's reply, when he received the thrust, was:

'"They are very fashionable now, these broad spears",' he says.

Then he fell forwards on the threshold. Then the women who had been in the *living-room* came out. They saw that Atli was dead. By then Thorbiorn was already on his horse and he gave notice of the killing at his hands and then rode home. Asdis, the lady of the house, sent for men to come and Atli's body was laid out and he was buried by the side of his father. His death was much lamented, for he had been both wise and popular. No compensation was paid for the killing of Atli, and moreover no one demanded any atonement, for Grettir was responsible for the prosecution whenever he came back out. These affairs remained as they were for the summer. Thorbiorn did not gain much goodwill from this deed and yet he remained on his farm without doing anything.

46

The same summer we have just been talking about, a ship came out to Gasir before the *assembly*. Then news was given of Grettir's travels. Among other things they told about the house-burning. Thorir of Gard was furiously angry at this story, and he felt he had to seek vengeance against Grettir. Thorir rode with a very large number of men and raised the case of the burning at the *assembly*, but people felt that they couldn't do anything about it while there was no one to answer to it. Thorir said he would accept nothing else but that Grettir should be made outlaw over the entire country for such a crime. Then *lawspeaker* Skapti replies:

'Indeed this is an ill deed, if it is as it is said. But "a story told by one person is always only half told", for most people prefer to give the worst side of the story if there are two sides to it. Now I shall not give the decision that Grettir should be outlawed for this as matters stand.'

Thorir was a powerful man in his district and a very important person, and popular among many people of power. He pushed so hard for this that nothing could be done to prevent Grettir being found guilty. Thorir then made Grettir outlaw over the whole country and was afterwards the harshest of all his opponents, as events frequently showed. He then repeatedly put a price on his head as was done to other full outlaws and with that rode home. Many said that this was done more out of zeal than in accordance with the laws, but yet that was how matters stood. Nothing now happened of note until after midsummer.

47

In late summer Grettir Asmundarson came out to Hvita in Borgarfiord. People from all over the district went to the ship. All this news reached Grettir at the same time, first that his father was dead, second that his brother was slain, third that he was made outlaw over the whole country. Then Grettir uttered this verse:

> All came at once to wise verse teller:
> my outlawry; the man must be long quiet about
> his father's death and also his brother's.

Yet there shall many a Hedin's maid's meeting tree [warrior]
be sadder today for such griefs,
O sword-breaker [warrior].

They say that Grettir's mood was unchanged at this news and he was as cheerful as before. Now Grettir remained at the ship for a time, for he could find no means of transport that suited him.

There was a man called Svein who lived at Bakki up from Thingness. He was a good farmer and a merry man and often recited poetry of an entertaining kind. He had a mare, dark in colour, the fastest of horses. Svein called it Sodulkolla. Grettir left Vellir one night, not wanting the merchants to know of it. He got himself a black hooded cloak and covered his clothes with it and so disguised himself. He went up past Thingness and so up to Bakki. It had then got light. He saw a dark horse near the hayfield and went up to it and put a bridle on it, mounted it and rode up along Hvita and below Bæ and so to Flokadalsa and so up onto the bridle-ways above Kalfaness. The workmen at Bakki were getting up at that time and told the farmer that this man had mounted the horse. He got up and smiled at this and spoke as follows:

Shield-storm demander [warrior, i.e. Grettir] rode on from here;
thief let his hand grasp Sodulkolla, the helm-pine [Grettir].
This Thund-cloud-Frey [Grettir] will be full valid
for other dirty deeds than this;
it has been a bit of an outrage against me.

Then he took his horse and rode in pursuit. Grettir rode until he came up in front of the farm at Kropp. There he met a man who said his name was Halli and said he was on his way down to the ship at Vellir. Grettir uttered a verse:

Tell in the wide settlements,
quick-tempered bow-pine,
that you have met right up near Kropp, Sodulkolla;
there was sat on mare—run for your life, Halli—
a fellow, who for long has played the gambling game,
in a black cape.

And now they part, and Halli went down along the bridle-paths and right down to Kalfaness when Svein met him. They greeted each other straight away. Then said Svein:

> Did you see where rode, the cheeky,
> sly lazybones, horse from nearby farms?
> This is a great trial to us.
> The local men must declare
> the punishment for the thief for that.
> However that may be,
> his body shall bear bruises if I catch him.

'You will be able to do that,' said Halli, 'for I met the man who said he was riding Sodulkolla, and told me to report this down among the farms and in the district. He was a man of huge size and had on a black cloak.'

'He must have some opinion of himself,' said the farmer, 'and I shall find out who he is,' and after that he rode in pursuit of him.

Grettir arrived in Deildartunga. There was a woman outside there. Grettir went to speak to her and uttered a verse:

> Well-born gold-dame [woman],
> take sea-fire keeper [man, i.e. the farmer] a game-poem:
> dale-eel [Grettir] has snatched away steed;
> and word-bold Ygg's drink-server [poet, i.e. Grettir]
> would ride the mare so madly
> that I may stay the night at Gilsbakki.

The woman memorised the verse. After this he rode on his way. Svein got there soon afterwards and she had not yet gone inside, and when he arrived, he spoke this:

> What sword-wind's pusher [warrior, i.e. Grettir] rode just now
> hence in battling weather
> hard on a black horse?
> Shifty-eyed, he will truly flee
> quite far away today;
> the bold fellow has lost his valour.

She then spoke as she had been instructed. He thought about the verse and said:

'It is not unlikely that this man is more than a match for me. Nevertheless I shall catch up with him.'

He rode now through the farms. Each could see where the other was going all the time. The weather was both windy and wet. Grettir arrived at Gilsbakki during the day and when Grim Thorhallsson found out, he welcomed him very warmly and invited him to stay with him. He accepted the invitation. He set Sodulkolla free and told Grim how he had come by her. Then Svein arrived and dismounted and saw there his horse. He spoke this:

Who has ridden our mare?
What will the payment turn out to be?
Who has seen a greater thief?
What game is the hooded one playing?[43]

Grettir had by then taken off his wet clothes and heard the bit of verse;

I rode the mare to Grim's.
He is a great man compared to this cotter.
I will not pay much for it.
Let us be friends.

'With this we shall be quits,' said the farmer, 'and the horse-ride is fully repaid.'

Afterwards they both recited their verses, and Grettir said he couldn't blame him, since he was looking after what was his own. The farmer stayed there the night, as well as Grettir, and they had great fun with all this. They called them the Sodulkolla verses. In the morning the farmer rode home and he and Grettir parted on good terms. Grim told Grettir all the news from the north, from Midfiord, of what had happened while he had been abroad, including that no compensation had been paid for Atli, but that Thorbiorn Oxen-might's domineering was so excessive that it was doubtful whether Madam Asdis would be able to continue at Biarg if it went on. Grettir now stayed few nights with Grim, for he did not want any news of him to precede him north over the heaths. Grim told him to call on him if he needed any help.

[43] Cf *Háttatal*, verse 40, Snorri Sturluson's *Edda* p. 190.

'But I want to avoid the legal penalty of becoming guilty of harbouring you.'

Grettir said he was acting well.

'But it is more likely that I shall have greater need later on.'

Grettir now rode north over Two-days moor and so to Biarg and got there at night. Everyone was asleep except his mother. He went to the rear of the buildings and to the entrance that was there, for he knew of a way in there and so into the main room and to his mother's bed, and he felt his way there. She asked who it was. Grettir told her. She then sat up and kissed him and sighed heavily and said:

'Welcome, my son,' she said. 'But I cannot place much reliance on my offspring: the one is killed who was my greatest support, and you have been made an outlaw and irredeemable, and the third is so young that he cannot do anything.'

'It is an old saying,' says Grettir, 'that "you get over one trouble by suffering another that is greater". But there are other ways of consoling oneself than just with compensation payments, and it is more than likely that Atli will be avenged. But as far as I am concerned, people will find they are variously pleased with their lot when we have dealings together.'

She said this was not unlikely. Grettir stayed there awhile with few people knowing about it and he made enquiries about what the people of the district were up to. No one had heard that Grettir had arrived in Midfiord. He found out that Thorbiorn Oxen-might was at home and that there were not many people with him. This was after the home-field haymaking.

48

One fine day Grettir rode west over the ridges to Thoroddsstadir. He got there about midday and knocked on the door. Some women went out and greeted him. They did not recognise him. He asked for Thorbiorn. They said he had gone to the meadows to bind hay and with him his sixteen-year-old son called Arnor. Thorbiorn was a very hard-working man and was hardly ever idle. And when Grettir had learned this he bade them farewell and rode away on down the road to Reykir. There is a stretch of marshy ground down from the ridge there and on it there was a large hayfield and Thorbiorn had had a lot of hay mown there, and it was now completely dry. He was going to take it home in bales with the boy's help, and a woman was gleaning. Grettir now rode up onto the patch that was mown, but the father and son were higher up and had made one bale and were working on another. Thorbiorn had stood his shield and sword against the bale, but the boy had a small axe by him. Thorbiorn saw the man and said to the boy:

'There is a man there riding towards us, and let us stop baling the hay and see what he wants.'

And they did so. Grettir dismounted. He had a helmet on his head and was girded with his *cutlass* and a great spear in his hand with no barbs on it, and the socket was inlaid with silver. He sat down and knocked out the shaft-pin, for he did not want Thorbiorn to be able to send it back. Then Thorbiorn said:

'That is a big man, and I am unable to recognise anyone out in the open if this is not Grettir Asmundarson, and he must have plenty of complaints against us. And let us face him bravely and give no sign of wavering. We must use a stratagem, and I shall approach him from the front and see how we get on together, for I am confident I can deal with anyone if I can meet him on his own. But you go behind him and strike with both hands between his shoulders with your axe. You have no need to worry about him harming you, since his back will be turned towards you.'

Thorbiorn had no helmet, nor his son either. Grettir walked over the marshy ground, and as soon as he came within shooting distance of them, he shot his spear at Thorbiorn. But it was looser on the shaft than he thought and it swerved in flight and flew off the shaft and down into the ground. Thorbiorn took his shield and put it in front of himself, and drew his sword and turned to face Grettir when he saw who it was. Grettir then drew his *cutlass* and swung round with it a little so that he noticed where the boy was standing behind him, and he kept therefore on the move. And when he saw that the boy was come within striking distance of himself, he raised the *cutlass* high in the air; he struck the back of the blade on Arnor's head so hard that the skull broke, and that was his death. Then Thorbiorn leapt at Grettir and struck at him, but he intercepted with his buckler on his left arm and warded it off, and he struck down with his *cutlass* and split Thorbiorn's shield and the *cutlass* struck his head so hard that it stuck in his brains, and from this he fell down dead. Grettir inflicted no further wounds on them. Then he tried to find his spear and could not. He went then to his horse and rode out to Reykir and gave notice of the killings. The woman who was on the patch of meadow watched the killings. She then ran home terrified and said that Thorbiorn was killed and his son too. This came as a great surprise to those at the farm, for no one knew about Grettir's movements. People were sent for from the next farms. There soon came a lot of people there; they moved the bodies to the church. Thorodd Poem-bit took up the suit for the killings and he immediately got a band of men around him.

Grettir rode home to Biarg and saw his mother and told her what had happened. She was pleased at this and said he had now demonstrated his affinity to the men of Vatnsdal.

'But yet this will be the beginning and foundation of your convictions. I know for certain that you will not be able to have a long stay here because of Thorbiorn's family, and yet they must now realise that there is much that annoys you. Grettir then uttered a verse:

> Hafli's opponent [Thorbiorn][44] was attacked with weapons
> in Wetherfiord [Hrutafiord] in Thrott's storm [battle].
> Might of ox and bull [Oxen-might] was in a fury.
> Now Atli's unatoned breath-robbing
> has just been fittingly repaid to him.
> He sank already dead to the peaceful plain.

Madam Asdis said this was true, 'but I do not know what you plan to do now.'

Grettir said he would now go to see his friends and kinsmen in the country to the west.

'And there shall no trouble come to you on my account,' he said.

He then got ready for his journey, and mother and son parted affectionately. He went first to Melar in Hrutafiord and told his brother-in-law Gamli all about how the killing of Thorbiorn had come about. Gamli told him to get himself out of Hrutafiord quickly, 'for as long as they keep their troop of men, Thorbiorn's family. But we shall support you in the suit for Atli's killing, as far as we can.'

After that Grettir rode west across Laxardal Heath and did not stop

[44] Hafli is a giant, whose opponent is Thor; both parts of the name Thorbiorn are names for Thor.

until he got to Thorstein Kuggason in Liarskogar and he stayed there for a long time in the autumn.

49

Thorodd Poem-bit went about making enquiries about who could have killed Thorbiorn and his son. And when they got to Reykir they were told that Grettir had been there and given notice of the killings at his hands. Thorodd now realised how it had been. He went then to Biarg and there was a large number of men there and he asked whether Grettir was there. The mistress said that he had ridden away and she wouldn't be concealing him 'if he were here. You ought to be well content to leave the situation as it is. There has not been too much vengeance taken for Atli's killing, though this is put against it. You did not enquire whether I was upset by that; and it is now right for things to stay as they are.'

They then rode home, and felt there was nothing to be done. The spear that Grettir had lost was not found until within living memory. The spear was found during the latter days of *Lawman* Sturla Thordarson, and it was in the marshy ground where Thorbiorn fell, and it is now known as Spear-marsh. And this is considered as evidence that Thorbiorn was killed there, though in some places it says that he was killed at Midfitiar.

The family heard that Grettir was at Liarskogar. They then got men together and set out for Liarskogar. And when Gamli found out at Melar, he sent information to Thorstein and Grettir about the movements of the men of Hrutafiord. And when Thorstein found this out, he sent Grettir in to Tunga to Snorri *Godi*, for there was a breather being taken in their disputes at that time, and advised Grettir to ask Snorri for help. But if he wasn't there, he told Grettir to go west to Reykiaholar to Thorgils Arason.

'And he will take you in for the winter. Stay in the Western Fiords until these suits are settled.'

Grettir said he would abide by his advice. He then rode in to Tunga and went to talk to Snorri *Godi* and asked him to take him in. Snorri answers:

'I am getting to be an old man, and I don't feel like keeping outlaws if I am under no obligation. But what was the reason that the old fellow turned you away?'

Grettir said Thorstein had often been good to him, 'but there is now need of more than just him if it is to do any good.'

Snorri said, 'I shall put in a good word for you, if it would be of any help to you, but you must find yourself somewhere to stay elsewhere than with me.'

They parted with these words. Grettir now turned west towards Reykianess. The men of Hrutafiord arrived with their band of men at Samsstadir. There they learned that Grettir was gone from Liarskogar and they turned back.

50

Grettir came to Reykiaholar just before the beginning of winter and asked Thorgils for winter quarters. Thorgils said that he was welcome to food like other free men.

'But the fare here is nothing very special.'

Grettir said he was not fussy about that.

'There is another problem here,' said Thorgils. 'There are some men planning to stay here who are thought to be rather unruly, and these are the *foster-brothers* Thorgeir and Thormod. I don't know how well you will get on together, but they are always to stay here when they want. Now you can stay here if you wish, but I am not having any of you causing trouble with anyone else.'

Grettir said that he would not be the first to start on anyone, especially if that was how the farmer wanted it.

Soon afterwards the *foster-brothers* arrived. There was no warmth between Thorgeir and Grettir, but Thormod was more relaxed. Farmer Thorgils said the same thing to the *foster-brothers* as he had said to Grettir, and they held him in such high esteem that neither offered the others a cross word, even though there was no sympathy between them. So passed the first part of the winter.

It is said that farmer Thorgils owned the islands that are called Olaf's Islands. They lie out in the fiord a *league* and a half out from Reykianess.[45] There Thorgils kept a fine ox and it had not been fetched

[45] The distance is about 12 km.

back in the autumn. Thorgils kept saying that he wanted to get it before Christmas. One day the *foster-brothers* got ready to fetch the ox, if they could get a third man to help them. Grettir offered to go with them, and they agreed. The three of them then set out on a ten-oared boat. The weather was cold and there was a north wind. The boat was standing on Hvalshausholm. They sailed out and the wind was increasing somewhat; they got to the islands and caught the ox. Then Grettir asked whether they would rather load on the ox or hold the boat, for there was a fair amount of surf round the island. They told him to hold the boat. He stood by the middle of the boat on the side facing away from the shore; the sea came up under his shoulder blades and he held it so that it did not move at all. Thorgeir lifted the ox from the back and Thormod from the front and so lifted it out onto the boat, then sat down to row, and Thormod rowed in the bow, Thorgeir forward amidships and Grettir in the stern, and they made in down the bay. And when they got in past Hafraklett the weather stormed against them. Then said Thorgeir:

'The stern is losing power now.'

Grettir replies, 'The stern will not lag behind if the rowing is done properly forward.'

Thorgeir then went so hard at the oars that both rowlocks came away. Then he said:

'You take over, Grettir, while I fix the rowlocks.'

Grettir then pulled hard on the oars while Thorgeir fixed the rowlocks. But by the time Thorgeir began to row again the oars were so worn away that Grettir had shaken them to pieces against the gunwale. Thormod said it would be better to row less hard and not do any damage. Grettir snatched up two transoms that were lying in the boat and drove two great holes in the side of the boat and rowed so hard that every timber creaked. But because it was a good vessel and the crew rather of the tougher sort, they reached Hvalshausholm.

Grettir asks whether they would rather take the ox home or haul up the ship. They chose rather to haul up the ship, and they hauled it up with all the sea water that was in it, and the bits of ice, and it was very frozen up. But Grettir led the ox, and it was very stiff in its joints and very fat. It became very exhausted. And when it got down by Tittlingsstadir, the ox could go no further. The *foster-brothers* went into the house, for neither side wanted to help the other at their task. Thorgils asked about Grettir, and they said where they had left him. He then sent men to meet him and when they got down below Hellisholar they saw a man coming towards them with a beast on his back and it was Grettir carrying the ox. They were all amazed how much he could manage. Thorgeir felt quite envious of Grettir's strength.

One day shortly after Christmas Grettir went to bathe on his own. Thorgeir knew of this and said to Thormod:

'Let's go and see how Grettir responds if I go for him when he comes out of the bath.'

'I'm not very keen on that,' said Thormod, 'and it won't do you any good.'

'I shall go nevertheless,' said Thorgeir. He now went off down the slope carrying his axe high in the air. Grettir was coming up from the bath, and when they met Thorgeir spoke:

'Is it true, Grettir,' he said, 'that you have declared that you would never run from a lone person?'

'I'm not so sure of that,' said Grettir, 'but I've never run far from you,' declared Grettir.

Thorgeir then swung up his axe. At that moment Grettir threw himself at Thorgeir's body and brought him down with a very great crash. Thorgeir then said to Thormod:

'Are you going to stand by while this devil on top of me kills me?'

Thormod then took hold of Grettir's legs and tried to pull him off Thorgeir and found he was unable. He was girded with his *cutlass* and was going to draw it. Then farmer Thorgils came up and told them to behave and not meddle with Grettir. They did so and turned it into a joke. They didn't get involved with each other again, as far as is told. It was thought that Thorgils had been very fortunate to be able to control such overbearing men.

And when spring came they all left. Grettir went inland to Thorskafiord. He was asked how he had liked his entertainment and his winter stay at Reykiaholar. He answers:

'My stay there was such, that I was always very pleased with my food, when I got to eat it.'

After that he went west across the heaths.

51

Thorgils Arason rode to the *assembly* with a large following. There came there all the important people in the land. He soon met with *Lawman* Skapti and they had a talk together. Then said Skapti:

'Is it true, Thorgils, that you have kept through the winter the three men who are considered the most unprincipled men, moreover all of them outlaws, and controlled them in such a way that none of them harmed any other?'

Thorgils said that this was true. Skapti said:

'That shows great statesmanship. But what is your estimation of their characters, or of what sort of champion each of them is?'

Thorgils said, 'I think they are all very valiant in heart, but there are two of them that I think do know what fear is. But there is a difference, for Thormod is a man with the fear of God and is a very religious person, but Grettir is so afraid of the dark that he dares go nowhere when it begins to get dark if he is left to himself. But my kinsman Thorgeir I think does not know what fear is.'

'Their characters must be just as you say,' says Skapti. With that they ended their conversation.

At this Althing Thorodd Poem-bit brought forward a suit for the slaying of Thorbiorn Oxen-might, for he had not presented one at Hunavatn *Assembly* because of Atli's family. He thought that here his case would be less likely to be thrown out. Atli's family went to Skapti about the case and he said he could see a legal argument so that full compensation would be awarded them. Then the cases were brought to arbitration and most people were of the opinion that the killings should be set against each other, those of Atli and Thorbiorn. And when Skapti learned this, he went to the arbitrators and asked how they worked that out. They declared that they were farmers of the same status who were killed. Skapti asked:

'Which came first, Grettir being made outlaw or Atli being killed?'

And when it was worked out, then there turned out to have been a week in it, between Grettir being outlawed at the Althing and the other event which happened just after the *assembly*. Skapti said:

'I had an idea that you might make a mistake in the preparation of the case, that you made him a principal who was already outlawed and was not eligible either to defend his own case or to bring a prosecution. Now I declare that Grettir has nothing to do with the suit for the killing, and the one who is legally next liable is to take over the suit.'

Then said Thorodd Poem-bit, 'Who then is to answer for the killing of my brother Thorbiorn?'

'You must see to that for yourselves,' says Skapti, 'but Grettir's family are not going to squander money for him or his deeds if he is not being redeemed from outlawry.'

And when Thorvald Asgeirsson found out that Grettir was declared ineligible for the suit, they made enquiry about who were next in line. The closest relations turned out to be Gamli at Melar's son Skeggi, and Glum of Eyr from Bitra's son Ospak. They were both men of great zeal, and ambitious. Thorodd now had to pay compensation for the killing of Atli; it came to two *hundreds* of silver. Then Snorri *Godi* put in:

'Are you willing, you men of Hrutafiord,' he said, 'to forego this payment if Grettir is made free? For I think he will be a cause of much smarting in outlawry.'

Grettir's family responded well to this and said they were not bothered about the money, if he got peace and freedom. Thorodd said he could see that his situation was difficult, and said that for his part he was willing to accept this. Snorri told them to make sure first whether Thorir of Gard would add his approval that Grettir should be redeemed. But when he found out about this he flew into a rage and said Grettir should never get out of or be released from outlawry.

'And the further shall he be from redemption,' he said, 'that more money shall be placed on his head than on any other outlaws.'

And since he was so opposed to it, nothing came of the redemption. Gamli and his associates took possession of the money and put it by. But Thorodd Poem-bit got no compensation for his brother Thorbiorn. He and Thorir then both put a price on Grettir's head, three *marks* of silver each of them. This was thought a new departure, for there had never been more than three *marks* put up before. Snorri said it was unwise to play about to keep a man an outlaw who could cause so much trouble, and said many would suffer for it. Men parted at this point and rode home from the *assembly*.

52

When Grettir got over Thorskafiord Heath to Langadal, he let his hands sweep up the possessions of the small farmers and took what he required from everyone. He took weapons from some and clothes from others. Their reactions were various, but they all said they had been forced to hand them over when he had gone. At that time Viga-Styr's brother Vermund the Slender was living in Vatnsfiord. He was married to Thorbiorg, daughter of Olaf Peacock Hoskuldsson. She was known as Thorbiorg the Stout. Vermund was ridden to the *assembly* at the time Grettir was in Langadal. He went down over the ridge to Laugabol. A man lived there called Helgi. He was the most prominent of the farmers there. From there Grettir took a fine horse which belonged to the farmer. From there he went in to Gervidal. A man lived there called Thorkel. He was well provided with resources but mean-minded. Grettir took from there whatever he wanted and Thorkel dared not object or withhold anything. From there Grettir went on to Eyr and so out along that side of the fiord and took from everyone both food and clothing and treated many people roughly and most found it hard to put up with. Grettir now got very bold and stopped taking precautions. He went on until he got to Vatnsfiardardal and went to a *shieling* there. He stayed there many nights and lay in the woods there and slept and had no sense of danger. And when the shepherds found out they went to a farm and said that a fiend was come into the district that they found difficult to deal with. The farmers then gathered together and had thirty men. They hid in the wood so that Grettir did not know about it, and they made the shepherds keep watch for when there should be an opportunity against Grettir, though they did not know precisely where the man was. Now it happened one day when Grettir was lying sleeping that the farmers came upon him. And when they saw him they had a discussion about how they should capture him so that there would be fewest casualties, and they arranged that ten of them should make a dash at him, and some of them should fix fetters on his legs. They now did this and flung themselves down on him, but Grettir reacted so violently that they were flung off him and he got onto his knees. At that point they managed to throw fetters on him and on his legs. Then Grettir kicked so hard at the ears of two of them that they lay senseless. Now one after the other leapt on him but he cleared them away hard and long, and yet in the end they managed to pin him down and tied him up.

After that they held a discussion about what should be done with him. They asked Helgi of Laugabol to take charge of him and look after him until Vermund returned from the *assembly*.

He answers that 'I've got more important things to be done than have my workmen sit watching him, for I've got difficult land and I'm not having him in my way.'

Then they asked Thorkel of Gervidal to take charge of him. They said he was not short of anything. Thorkel objected and said there was no chance of this, 'since I am alone in the house with my old lady, and a good way off from other people; and you are not putting that burden on me,' he said.

'You, Thoralf of Eyr,' they said, 'take charge of Grettir and treat him well for the duration of the *assembly*; otherwise pass him on to the next farm and be responsible that he doesn't get free. Hand him over bound in the same way as when you take charge of him now.'

He answers, 'I will not take charge of Grettir, for I have neither the means nor the money to keep him. He has also not been taken on my land. It seems to me more of a trouble than an honour to take charge of him or to do much with him, and he is never coming into my house.'

After this they tried with each of the farmers, and they all refused. And it is based on this discussion of theirs that some merry people have composed the piece of lore called the Passing Round of Grettir[46] and included in it merry words for people's entertainment. And when they had discussed this for a long time, then they came to an agreement together on this that they would not let their good fortune turn to ill, and they set to and raised a gallows straight away there in the wood and were going to hang Grettir, and they made a great noise about it. Then they saw three people riding up along the valley. One of them was in coloured clothes. They guessed that this must be Madam Thorbiorg from Vatnsfiord, and so it was. She was making for the *shieling*. She was a very remarkable person and very intelligent. She

[46] Fragments of a poem of this name survive, but it is not likely to be as old as the saga, and may not be about Grettir Asmundarson. See Ólafur Halldórsson, 'Grettisfœrsla', *Opuscula* I (1960), Bibliotheca Arnamagnæana XX, 49–77; repr. *Grettisfærsla*, Reykjavík: Stofnun Árna Magnússonar (1990), 19–50.

ruled the district and decided everything whenever Vermund was away from home. She came across to where the gathering was and she was helped off her horse. The farmers welcomed her. Then she said:

'What sort of an assembly is this you are holding, and who is this thick-necked man sitting here tied up?'

Grettir gave his name and greeted her. She answers:

'What made you do this, Grettir,' she said, 'that you should want to cause breaches of the peace among my *assembly-men*?'[47]

'"I cannot avoid everything"; I had to be somewhere.'

'This is a great misfortune,' she says, 'that these miserable people should capture you without your being able put up a better show. And what do you plan to do with him now?'

The farmers told her that they were going to hang him on gallows for his misdeeds. She replied:

'It may be that Grettir deserves that, but it is too much for you Isfirdingers to take on, to take Grettir's life, for he is a renowned man and comes of a great family, even if he is not a successful person. But what will you do to earn your life, Grettir, if I give you life?'

He answers, 'What do you suggest?'

'You shall swear an oath,' she said, 'to do no misdeeds here around Isafiord; you shall take no vengeance on those who have been involved in this expedition to capture you.'

Grettir said it should be as she wished. Then he was freed. And he has said that that was the time he had to work hardest of all to restrain his temper in not striking them when they crowed over what they had done to him. Thorbiorg told him to go home with her and gave him a horse to ride. He then went back to Vatnsfiord and stayed there until Vermund came home, and the lady treated him well. She became renowned for what she had done widely in the area. Vermund put on black looks when he came home and found out why Grettir was there. Thorbiorg told him everything that had happened with the Isfirdingers.

'What had he done to earn from you,' said Vermund, 'that you should give him life?'

'There were many factors that contributed to this,' said Thorbiorg,

[47] Thorbiorg got her *godord* from her previous husband, but at this time it was probably actually held by her present husband Vermund; she is acting as his deputy in his absence.

'first,' she says, 'that you will be reckoned a greater leader than before, in having a wife who dared do such a thing. Then his kinswoman Hrefna[48] would have expected me not to let him be killed. Thirdly, he is a man of the greatest achievements in many respects.'

'You are a wise woman,' said Vermund, 'in most things, and I am grateful to you.'

Then he said to Grettir, 'You put on a poor showing, a champion like you, when wretched people were able to capture you, and that is always the fate of unruly men.'

Grettir then uttered this verse:

> My success was really at a low ebb
> in the midst of sea-thatch fiord [Isafiord]
> that old pigs should hold me
> by the ends of my legs.[49]

'What were they going to do with you?' said Vermund, 'when they had caught you?'

Grettir said:

> Many said I deserved the reward that
> Sigar gave his daughter's wooer
> until men found the rowan tree
> gloriously grown with the leaf of honour.[50]

Vermund said, 'Would they have hanged you if they had been left to themselves?'

Grettir said:

> I would myself have stuck my head
> into the baited noose pretty soon

[48] Hrefna was grand-daughter of Grettir's great-grandfather Onund Woodenleg, and Thorbiorg's sister-in-law. See *Laxdæla saga*, ch. 50, according to which she had died long before this, soon after 1003.

[49] Literally head-bones.

[50] Sigar had his daughter's wooer Hagbard hanged (cf. Saxo Grammaticus, Book 7). The rowan tree was the salvation of Thor (*björg Þórs*) according to Snorri Sturluson's *Edda*, p. 82, and is here a pun for Thorbiorg.

if Thorbiorg, allwise one,
had not saved this poet.

Vermund said, 'Did she invite you to stay with her?'
Grettir replies:

The both hands' help of Sif's man
bade me go with her.
She who granted me quarter
gave Thund's darling's thong
a fine horse.[51]

'You will live a great life and a hard one,' says Vermund, 'and you have been given a lesson about being on the watch for your enemies. But I have no desire to keep you and be rewarded with the resentment of many powerful people. It is still best for you to look to your family, but there will be few prepared to take you in if they have any alternative. You are also not easily drawn into co-operation with other men.'

Grettir stayed in Vatnsfiord for a while and from there went on to the Western Fiords and sought the help of many men of rank, and there was always some reason why no one could take him in.

53

Towards the end of autumn Grettir turned back southwards and didn't stop until he got to Liarskogar, to his kinsman Thorstein Kuggason, and he was welcomed there. Thorstein invited him to stay with him for the winter, and he accepted this. Thorstein was a great man for work and building and kept his men busy. Grettir was not a man much given to working and so they did not get on very well together. Thorstein had had a church built on his farm. He had a bridge built on the road leading from his farm. It was built with great ingenuity. On the outside of the bridge under the beams that supported the bridge there was

[51] Line 1 contains another pun for the name Thorbiorg. In line 4, Thund is a name for Odin, his darling (wife) was Iord, Earth, whose thong is a snake; Grettir is a name for a snake, so this is a pun for Grettir.

a device with rings and sounding bells, so that they could be heard right over at Skarfsstadir, half a sea-*league* away;[52] if anyone went over the bridge, then the rings were shaken. Thorstein devoted a lot of work to this creation, for he was very good at ironwork. Grettir was full of energy in hammering the iron, but did not always feel like it, but still he behaved well during the winter, so that nothing significant happened. But when the men of Hrutafiord found out that Grettir was staying with Thorstein, they got a band together at the beginning of spring. But Thorstein found out; he told Grettir that he was to find himself some other refuge than staying there.

'For I can see that you don't want to work, and men who won't work are no use to me.'

'Where do you suggest I go then?' said Grettir.

Thorstein told him to go south across the country and see his family.

'But come to me if they are of no help to you.'

Grettir now did so, went south to Borgarfiord to see Grim Thorhallsson and stayed there on until after the *assembly*. Grim sent him to *Lawman* Skapti at Hialli. Grettir travelled south across the Lower heaths and did not stop until he reached Tunga, to Thorhall son of Asgrim Ellida-Grimsson, and he kept out of the inhabited areas. Thorhall acknowledged Grettir for the sake of his forefathers, though Grettir was very well known by name all over the country for his abilities. Thorhall was a sensible man and treated Grettir well, but he did not want him staying there indefinitely.

54

Grettir went from Tunga up to Haukadal and from there north onto Kiol and remained up there for much of the summer, and now there was no guarantee that he wouldn't rob people of their things, those on their way north or from the north over Kiol, for he found it difficult to get supplies. It happened one day that Grettir was spending most of his time north on Dufunefsskeid and saw a man riding southwards along Kiol. He sat high on his mount and had a fine horse with a bridle with large studs and large knobs on the top. He had another horse in train with baggage on it. This man had a deep-brimmed hat on his

[52] The distance is actually about 8 km.

head and his face could not be seen very well. Grettir rather liked the look of the horse and his things and went to meet him and greeted him and asked him his name, and he said he was called Lopt.

'I know what you are called,' he said, 'you will be Grettir Asmundarson the Strong. And where are you going?'

'I haven't decided about that,' said Grettir, 'but what I want to know is whether you are willing to hand over some of the stuff you have got with you.'

Lopt answers, 'Why should I give you what is mine? And what will you give for it?

Grettir answers, 'Have you not heard that I never give any payment, and that most people nevertheless find that I get what I want?'

Lopt said, 'Offer these terms to those whom you think suitable, but I am not going to lose what is mine in that way. And let each of us go his way,' and rode on past Grettir and drove on his horse.

Grettir said, 'We shall not part so quickly,' and took hold of the reins of Lopt's horse in front of his hands and held them with both hands. Lopt said:

'Get on your way, you will get nothing from me if I can manage to keep hold of it.'

'We shall see about that,' says Grettir.

Lopt reached down by the cheek-pieces and grasped the reins between the rings and Grettir's hands, pulling so hard that Grettir's hands slid down along the reins until he had drawn the whole of the bridle from his grasp. Grettir looked into his palms and saw that this man had more than a little power in his fists and glanced after him and said:

'Where are you planning to go now?'

Lopt replies and said:

> I shall go into storm-resounding pot [Hallmund's cave]
> below the tumbling great-freezes [glaciers].
> There shall ground-salmon [serpent, i.e. Grettir] meet
> little stone [*hall*] and fist-land [hand, Icelandic *mund*: Hallmund].

Grettir said, 'It will not be very straightforward to find where you live if you don't describe it more clearly.'

He then spoke and said:

It is not easy for me
to hide it from you
if you wish
to come there.
It's from the dwellings
of Borgfirders
where men call it
Ball-glacier.

Then they parted. Grettir now realised that he could not match this man's strength. Then Grettir uttered a verse:

Illugi the swift and moderately keen in weapon-shower [battle]
Atli
were placed far off from me,
I would rather be seldom thus placed,
when fearless Lopt the poor drew once
thongs from my hand;
the wise lady will have to wipe her eyelids
if I am afraid.

After this Grettir went south off Kiol and rode to Hialli and went to see Skapti and asked him for help. Skapti answers:

'I am told that you have been behaving rather badly and robbing men of their goods, and that is unseemly for you, a man of such noble descent. It would be a good deal easier to discuss it if you were not robbing. But since I am supposed to be *lawman* in the land, it will not do for me to take in outlaws and so break the law. I wish you would find somewhere where you don't need to fall upon people's property.'

Grettir said he would very much like to, but said however that he found it pretty well impossible to be on his own because of his fear of the dark. Skapti said it was no good being only able to put up with things when they were as he most wished.

'And trust no one so well that there is a repetition of what happened to you in the Western Fiords. Many a man has been brought to his death by being too trusting.'

Grettir thanked him for his sound advice and went back to Borgarfiord in the autumn and went to see his friend Grim Thorhallsson, and told him what Skapti had suggested. Grim told him to go north to Fiskivotn on Arnarvatn Heath, and that is what he did.

55

Grettir went up onto Arnarvatn Heath and made himself a shelter there of which the remains can still be seen, and fitted himself out there, for he was now determined to do anything rather than steal; he got himself nets and a boat and caught fish for his food. He found it very miserable on the mountain, for he was very afraid of the dark. And when other outlaws found out that Grettir had ended up there, then many of them had a mind to find him, for they thought he would be a great protection for them. There was a man from the north of the country called Grim. He was outlawed. The men of Hrutafiord[53] made a bargain with this man that he should kill Grettir and they promised him freedom and gifts of money if he succeeded. He went to see Grettir and asked to be taken in. Grettir answers:

'It does not seem to me that you would be any better off if you were with me. You outlaws are also unreliable, but I very much dislike being on my own if there is an alternative. I also want only to have a person with me who is ready to do any work that is required.'

Grim said that was exactly his intention and was very insistent about staying. Grettir then let himself be persuaded and took him in. He stayed there now on into the winter and lay in wait for Grettir and found it no easy task to attack him. Grettir was suspicious of him and had his weapons by him night and day, and he never dared to go for him while he was awake.

One morning when Grim got back from fishing he went into the shelter and stamped his feet, wanting to see whether Grettir was asleep, but he made no reaction and lay still. The *cutlass* was hanging up above Grettir. Grim now thinks that there will never be a better opportunity. He now makes a great clatter, so that Grettir should make some comment, and there was none. He now felt certain that Grettir must be asleep and stole quietly to the bed and reached for the *cutlass* and took it down and drew it. At that moment Grettir leapt out onto the floor

[53] Men of the North (i.e. of Iceland) according to the principal manuscript.

and grasped the *cutlass* just as the other was lifting it, and with his other hand Grim's shoulders and threw him down with such a great fall that he lay almost unconscious.

'So that's how you've turned out, though you claimed to be so reliable.'

He then got the truth out of him and afterwards killed him. And now Grettir realised what taking in outlaws led to. And so the winter passed. Grettir found nothing a greater distress than his fear of the dark.

56

Thorir of Gard now heard where Grettir had got to and wanted to arrange some plan by which he could be killed. There was a man called Thorir Red-beard. He was a very burly man and always getting involved in fights, and for that reason he had been made outlaw over the whole land. Thorir of Gard sent word to him and when they met he asked Red-beard to go on an errand for him and kill Grettir the Strong. Red-beard declared that was not an easy task, said that Grettir was a clever man and always on his guard. Thorir told him to have a go.

'And it is a valiant deed for such a brave person as you are, but I shall get you released from outlawry and give you plenty of money as well.'

Red-beard accepted this proposal. Thorir told him how he should set about getting Grettir. After this Red-beard went to the east of the country, for he thought then there could be less suspicion about his movements. He came onto Arnarvatn Heath when Grettir had been there one winter. And when Grettir and Red-beard met, he asked Grettir to take him on. He answers:

'I have no intention of letting more people play tricks on me as often as the one that came here last autumn and went on so plausibly, but when he had been here a little while he tried to find an opportunity to kill me. So I am not going to risk that again, taking in outlaws.'

Thorir answers, 'I cannot blame you at all for not trusting outlaws, but you may have heard about me going around fighting and oppressing people, but never of me being so dastardly as to betray my liege lord. So "existence is hard for a bad man", in that many think he is just like any other. And I would not have come here if I had had any better prospects, but I don't think we need be at anyone's mercy if we stand by each other. Now you could take a risk with me for a while, to see how you like me. Then send me away if you find any baseness in me.'

Grettir answers, 'I may as well take another risk with you, but you can be sure of this, if I have any suspicion of treachery in you, it will be your death.'

Thorir told him to do that. After this Grettir took him on and found that he must have the strength of two men, whatever he set to work on. He was ready for any task Grettir wanted to send him to do. Grettir did not need to turn his hand to anything, and never had he found his life so pleasant since he had started his outlawry; and yet he was so much on his guard that Thorir never found an opportunity against him. Thorir Red-beard stayed with Grettir two winters on the heath. He now began to get tired of being on the heath. He now considered what plan he could adopt without Grettir noticing. One night in the spring there was a great storm of wind while they were asleep. Grettir awoke and asked where their boat was. Thorir leapt up and ran to the boat and broke it all to pieces and threw the bits in different directions and it was as though the wind had scattered them. After this he went into the shelter and announced in a loud voice:

'Things have not turned out well, my friend,' he said, 'in that our boat is all broken to pieces and the nets are lying far out in the lake.'

'Fetch them in then,' said Grettir, 'for I think it is your fault that the boat is broken.'

Thorir answers, 'The trouble is as regards abilities, that the thing I am least good at is swimming, though at almost anything else I think I am a match for any ordinary man. You must acknowledge that I have not made you do any work since I came to you. I would not ask you to do this if I was capable of doing it.'

Grettir got up and took his weapons and went down to the lake. There the lie of the land was such that a ness went out into the lake, and there was an invisible creek the other side of the ness. The lake was deep right up to the shore [and had washed it away from under the bank so it was hollow as well]. Grettir said:

'Go out for the nets and let me see how able a man you are.'

'I told you before,' said Thorir, 'that I cannot swim, and I don't know where your valour and daring have gone.'

'I will get the nets,' said Grettir, 'but don't betray me when I am trusting you.'

Thorir answers, 'Don't think such baseness and dastardliness of me.'

Grettir said, 'You yourself will reveal your true nature to yourself, as to what sort of a person you are.'

Then he threw down his clothes and weapons and swam out for the nets. He swept them together and made for the shore and threw them up onto the bank. And when he was about to come ashore, Thorir grasped the *cutlass* and straightway drew it. He then leapt at Grettir as he was climbing up onto the bank and struck at him. Grettir threw himself backwards down into the water and sank like a stone. Thorir looked out across the lake and planned to fight him off from the shore if he came up. Grettir dived now as close as he could to the bank so that Thorir could not see him until he got to the creek behind him, and there came ashore. Thorir could not see this, the first thing he knew, Grettir lifted him up above his head and brought him down so hard that the *cutlass* flew out of his hand, and Grettir was able to pick it up and wasted no words on him and straightway cut off his head, and so ended his life. After this Grettir would never take in outlaws, and yet he could hardly bear being alone.

57

At the Althing Thorir of Gard heard about the killing of Thorir Red-beard. He now realised that it was not going to be easy to deal with this. He then made up his mind to ride from the *assembly* west over the Lower heaths taking about eighty men and planned to take Grettir's life. And when Grim Thorhallsson found out, he sent Grettir word and told him to be on his guard. Grettir always took note of people travelling about. It happened one day that he saw a large party of riders making for where he lived. He leapt then into a cleft between rocks and decided not to run away, for he hadn't seen the whole troop. Just then Thorir came up with the whole troop and told them now to separate Grettir's head from his body and said the villain would only be able to put up a poor showing. Grettir replies:

'"There's many a slip 'twixt the cup and the lip." You have also gone to great pains, and there are some who will have something to show for it before the game is over.'

Thorir urged the men hard to the attack. The cleft was narrow so that he found it easy to defend himself from one direction, but he was surprised that there was no attack from his rear to cause him any trouble. Thorir then lost a number of men, and some were wounded, and they got nowhere. Then spoke Thorir:

'I have heard,' he said, 'that Grettir was outstanding for strength and valour, but I didn't know that he had such supernatural power as I now see, because twice as many are falling that he has his back turned to. I now see that we have trolls to deal with and not men.'

He told them to withdraw, and they did so. Grettir was surprised that they should do so, but he was enormously tired. Thorir went away with his men and they rode north to the farmland. Their expedition was considered to have been most ignominious. Thorir had lost eighteen men, with many wounded.

Grettir now turned up into the cleft and came upon a man of huge size there. He was sitting up by the rock and was seriously wounded. Grettir asked him his name and he said he was called Hallmund.

'But I can tell you this to identify myself, that you thought I took fast hold of the reins on Kiol in the summer when we met. I think I have now paid you back.'

'I certainly think,' said Grettir, 'that you have been very decent to me, whether or not I am able to pay you back for that.'

Hallmund said, 'What I want now is that you should come and visit my home, for it must seem tedious to you up here on the heath.'

Grettir said he would be very happy. Now they both went together south under Ball-glacier. There Hallmund had a great cave and a stoutly-built impressive-looking daughter. They treated Grettir well and she healed them both. Grettir stayed there a great part of the summer. He made a poem about Hallmund, and this is part of it:

> Hallmund steps high with foot askew[54]
> in the mountain hall.

This verse is part of it:

> Battle-eager weapon-storm adder [sword]
> had to creep forth on wound-paths[55]

[54] Perhaps a metaphor for getting the worst of it.
[55] Compare *Háttatal*, verse 6, Snorri Sturluson's *Edda*, p. 170.

in Wetherfiord [Hrutafiord].
Trusty warriors will have a chance
to drink in memory of men of Kelduhverfi.
Keen Hallmund from the cave was the cause
why I got away.

It has been said that Grettir slew six men in the encounter, and Hallmund twelve. Towards the end of summer Grettir became keen to go back to inhabited parts to see his friends and relations. Hallmund told him to call on him when he went to the south of the country, and Grettir promised. He then went west to Borgarfiord and from there to Breidafiardardalir and asked Thorstein Kuggason's advice as to where he should try now. But Thorstein thought his opponents were now multiplying and said few would take him in.

'But you can go south to Myrar and see how things are there.'

Grettir now went south to Myrar in the autumn.

58

At that time Biorn Hitdælakappi was living at Holm. He was son of Arngeir, son of Bersi Godless, son of Balki who settled Hrutafiord, as was said above.[56] Biorn was a great leader and tough and frequently kept outlaws. Grettir came to Holm and Biorn welcomed him, for there had been friendship between their forebears. Grettir asked if he was willing to give him any help. Biorn said that he had committed so many offences over the whole country that people would avoid doing anything for him by which they would incur penalties.[57]

'But I shall do what I can for you if you leave those men in peace who are under my protection, however you treat other people here in the district.'

Grettir agreed to this. Biorn said:

'I have noticed that in the mountain that juts out the other side of Hitara there will be a good place to defend and at the same time a place to hide if it is carefully arranged. There is there a hole through the mountain and it can be seen from down on the road, for the main

[56] Ch. 5.
[57] Sheltering an outlaw was an offence under Icelandic law. Cf. chs 47, 54.

route passes down beneath it, but there is such a steep scree above that not many will get up if one able man is on the defence up in the refuge. Now it seems to me that the best plan and thing worth talking about is to stay there, for from there it is easy to go and get supplies down on Myrar and out to the sea.'

Grettir said he would abide by what he thought best if he was willing to suggest anything. Grettir then went to Fagraskogafiall and fixed it up there. He hung grey cloth over the hole in the mountain and from down on the paths it looked as though you could see right through. He went for provisions down into the inhabited area. The people of Myrar thought that with Grettir they had a visitor who really brought trouble. Thord Kolbeinsson was living on Hitarness then. He was a good poet. At that time there was great enmity between Biorn and Thord and Biorn would not have been more than half-way displeased if Grettir caused some harm to Thord's people or property. Grettir spent a lot of time with Biorn and they competed in many kinds of feats and it is indicated in the Saga of Biorn that they were considered equal in sports. But it is most people's opinion that Grettir has been the strongest in the country since Orm Storolfsson and Thoralf Skolmsson ceased their feats of strength.[58] Grettir and Biorn swam in one go right along Hitara down from the lake and out to the sea. They placed stepping-stones in the river there which have never since been shifted, neither by floods nor the freezing of the river nor the movement of glaciers. Grettir stayed on Fagraskogafiall for a whole winter without any attacks being made on him, even though many lost their property because of him and could do nothing about it, for he had a good fortification and was always good friends with those who lived nearest him.

59

There was a man called Gisli. He was son of Thorstein whom Snorri *Godi* had had killed.[59] Gisli was a big man and strong and wore splendid weapons and clothes and threw his weight about a lot and was somewhat boastful. He used to go on trading voyages and came out to

[58] See *Orms þáttr Stórólfssonar*.

[59] See *Eyrbyggja saga*, ch. 56 and *Heiðarvíga saga*, ch. 12.

Hvita in the summer when Grettir had been one winter on the mountain. Thord Kolbeinsson rode to the ship. Gisli welcomed him and offered him such of his wares as he wanted. Thord accepted the offer and they began to talk together. Gisli said:

'Is it true, as I am told, that you do not know how to get rid of an outlaw who is causing you a lot of trouble?'

Thord said, 'We haven't tried, but many find him difficult to get at, as many have discovered to their cost.'

'I am not surprised you find it difficult to deal with Biorn, when you can't get rid of this fellow. The trouble is that I shall be too far off next winter to be able to find a solution to this.'

'You will find that "the best thing to have from him is report".'

'You don't need to tell me about Grettir,' said Gisli, 'I've experienced harder climbs when I was in the field with King Knut the Great and in the British Isles, and I was thought to be pulling my weight. And if I got within range of him, I would have faith in myself and my weapons.'

Thord answers, said he would not be unrewarded if he got rid of Grettir, 'and there is a greater price on his head than on any other outlaw's, and before it was six *marks* of silver, but this summer Thorir of Gard added another three *marks*, and people think the one who gets it will have earned it.'

'"Anything will be done for money",' said Gisli, 'and that applies not least to us merchants. But now we must keep quiet with this talk. It may be that he will be more on his guard,' said he, 'when he knows that I am involved with you and the others in this. I plan to stay the winter out on Olduhrygg, but is any refuge of his on the way? He will not be on his guard against this; I shall not take a great crowd against him.'

Thord was pleased with this plan. He rode home afterwards and kept quiet about it. In this it happened, as they say, that "a wood is often full of ears". Some men had been present at his conversation with Gisli who were friends of Biorn of Hitardal and told him all about it. And when he and Grettir met, Biorn gave him an account of it and said now they would see how he could deal with it.

'It would not be unentertaining,' said Biorn, 'if you were to knock him about a bit without killing him if you can avoid it.'

Grettir grinned and was non-committal.

About the time of sheep rounding up in the autumn Grettir went down into Flysiuhverfi and got himself sheep. He got hold of four wethers. Some farmers noticed where he was going and went after him. Just at the moment he got to the beginning of the slope they caught up with him and tried to drive them from him, but they used no weapons against him. There were six of them in all and they spread out to get in his way. He got cross because of the sheep and took hold of two of the men and threw them down the slope so that they lay unconscious. And when the others saw this they were less keen to approach. Grettir took the sheep and hooked them together by their horns and flung them over his shoulders two and two, then went up to his hide-out. The farmers now turned back and felt they had not done well out of it and were now even less pleased with the way things were than before.

Gisli stayed with the ship during the autumn until it had been set up on blocks. A lot of things held him up, and as a result he was late setting out and he rode not long before the start of winter. He then went northwards and stayed the night under Hraun to the south of Hitara. In the morning before riding from there Gisli spoke to his companions:

'Now we shall ride in coloured clothes today and let the outlaw see that we are not like other tramps who pass here every day.'

There were three of them in all and they did so. And when they got out over the river, then he spoke to them again:

'I have been told about the outlaw here up in these heights and that it is not easy to pass here. But wouldn't he be rather pleased to meet us and see our things?'

They said that was what he usually did. Grettir had got up early in his hide-out. The weather was cold and freezing and there had been a fall of snow, and yet only a small one. He saw three men riding from the south across Hitara and the sun shone on their fine clothes and enamelled shields. It now occurred to Grettir who they must be and he thought he must get himself some stuff from them. He was curious to meet people who bragged so much, so he took his weapons and ran down the scree. And when Gisli heard the stones rattling, he said:

'There is a man coming down there from the hillside and rather a big one, and he wants to see us. Let's meet him bravely, because there is going to be a good catch here.'

His companions said this man would not run into their hands if he was not confident in himself.

'And it is well that "he who asks should get what he's asking for".'

After this they dismounted. Grettir came up just then and took hold of a clothes-bag which Gisli had behind him attached to his saddle and said:

'I shall have this; I often stoop to trifles.'

Gisli answers, 'That you shall not. Do you not know who it is you are dealing with?'

Grettir answers, 'I am not entirely clear about that; anyway it won't make much difference to me in this case since I am asking for such a trifle.'

'It may seem a trifle to you,' he says, 'but I would rather lose thirty *hundreds*. But you are taking your domineering a bit far, and let's go for him, boys, and see what he can do.'

They did so. Grettir gave ground before them and went back to a stone that stands there by the way and is called Grettir's Lift, and defended himself from there. Gisli urged his companions on hard. Grettir now saw that he was not such a hero as he made out, for he always kept behind his men. Grettir now got tired of this beating about the bush and swept round his *cutlass* and struck one of Gisli's companions his death-blow and leapt out from the stone and attacked so hard that Gisli fell back before him right out along the mountain. Then Gisli's other companion fell. Then Grettir said:

'There is no evidence of you having performed well in so many places, and you have not stood well by your friends.'

Gisli answers, ' "That fire is hottest that one is being burned by oneself", and it's terrible to deal with a devil like you.'

They then exchanged few blows before Gisli threw down his weapons and took to his heels out along the mountain. Grettir gave him time to throw down whatever he wished, and every time Gisli saw an opportunity he threw off some article of clothing. Grettir never chased him faster than to leave a space between them. Gisli ran right out across the mountain and so across Kaldardal and so above Aslaugarhlid and over Kolbeinsstadir and so out onto Borgarhraun. By then Gisli was in just his underclothes and became enormously tired. Grettir followed him and they were always just in range of each other. He then tore up a great piece of brushwood. But Gisli didn't stop until he came out to Haffiardara. It was very high and difficult to cross. Gisli was going to go straight out into the river. Grettir then raced after him and took hold of him, and then you could see the difference in strength between them. Grettir forced him down under him and said:

'Are you the Gisli who wanted to meet Grettir Asmundarson?'

Gisli answers, 'I have now met him, but I don't know how we shall part. Now keep what you have taken and let me go free.'

Grettir said, 'You obviously don't understand what I am saying to you, and I shall have to give you something to remember it by,' then pulled his shirt up over his head and let him have it with the branch across his back and both sides. Gisli tried all the time to twist away. Grettir basted him all over and then let him go. Gisli thought that he would rather have no lessons from Grettir than have such another beating. And he didn't do anything further to earn such a hiding. And as soon as Gisli got on his feet, he leapt out into a great pool and swam across the river there and came at night to a farm called Hrossholt and by then was quite exhausted. He stayed in bed there for a week and his body was all inflamed. After that he went to his lodging. Grettir went back and picked up the things that Gisli had thrown down and took them back with him to his hide-out, and Gisli got none of them back afterwards. Many thought Gisli had got his just deserts for his over-reaching himself and the boasts that he had made about himself. Grettir composed this about their encounter:

> The horse that can scratch really little with its teeth
> when it should be biting, runs hardest from another horse
> and is not the first to stop from weariness.
> But from me over Myrar that day
> the enterprising Gisli ran farting;
> he left behind all honour and respect.

The following spring Gisli got ready to go to the ship and gave firm instructions that none of the goods that were his were to be taken south past the mountain, saying they would find the devil himself there. Gisli rode south along by the sea all the way to the ship and he and Grettir never met again, and no one thought he amounted to anything thereafter, and he is out of the story. Things got still worse between Thord Kolbeinsson and Grettir. Thord made many attempts to get Grettir away from there or to get him killed.

60

Now when Grettir had been two winters on Fagraskogafiall and the third had come, then Grettir went south to Myrar to a farm called Lækiarbug and he took six wethers without the permission of the owner. From there he went down to Akrar and drove off two cattle to slaughter and many sheep and went up on the south side of Hitara. And when the farmers found out where he had gone, they sent word to Thord at Hitarness and asked him to take charge of getting rid of Grettir, but he declined. But in response to people's entreaties he got his son Arnor, who later on was known as Earls' poet, to go with them and told them not to let Grettir get away. Men were then sent through the whole district.

There was a man called Biarni who lived at Iorvi in Flysiuhverfi. He got men together from the other side of Hitara. Their plan was that the two troops should approach from different sides of the river. Grettir had two men with him. There was Eyiolf, son of a farmer from Fagraskogar, and a sturdy man, who went with him, and there was a third man with them. It was Thorarin from Akrar and Thorfinn of Lækiarbug that got there first, and they were a party of about twenty men. Grettir was then going to make for the other side of the river. Then Thorgeir[60] and Arnor and Biarni arrived on the other side of the river. A narrow ness went out into the river on the side that Grettir was. He had driven the animals to the end of the ness when he saw the approach of the men, for he never wanted to give up what he had got his hands on. The men of Myrar started the attack straight away and were going to it valiantly. Grettir told his companions to see that they didn't get behind him. Not very many could come at him at once. There was a sharp exchange between them. Grettir struck on both sides with his *cutlass* and they didn't find it easy to get at him. Some of the men of Myrar fell and some were wounded. They took a long time on the other side of the river because the ford was not very close. They had not been fighting for long before they drew back. Thorarin from Akrar was a very old man, so he took no part in the attack.

[60] This Thorgeir has not been introduced into the story, but is presumably Thorgeir Thorhaddsson of Hitardal, father of the Finnbogi who appears later in the chapter.

And when the fighting was over, then Thorarin's son Thrand and Thord's[61] nephew Thorgils Ingialdsson and Thorgeir Thorhaddsson of Hitardal's son Finnbogi and Steinolf Thorleifsson of Hraundal arrived. They strongly urged men to the attack. They had another hard fight. Grettir now saw that he must do one of two things: flee, or not spare himself. He now went forward so hard that no one could withstand him, for there were such a lot of men that he thought there was no prospect of getting out of it except to do as much as he could before he fell. He also wanted to get someone in exchange for himself who had some fight in him. He leapt then at Steinolf of Hraundal and struck at his head and clove him down to the shoulders and immediately struck another blow at Thorgils Ingialdsson and hit him in the middle and nearly cut him in two. Then Thrand was going to leap forward and avenge his kinsman. Grettir struck at him on the right thigh so that it cut off all the muscle and he was immediately disabled. After that he gave Finnbogi a great wound. Then Thorarin shouted and told them to withdraw, 'for you will suffer worse from him the longer you fight, and he is picking men off from your troop.'

They did so and turned back. Five men were fallen there, and five mortally wounded or crippled, but most had some cuts who had been at the encounter. Grettir was exceedingly tired but not much wounded. The men of Myrar made off then and had suffered great losses, for many doughty men had fallen there. But those who had been the other side of the river took a long time and didn't arrive until the engagement was over. And when they saw how badly their men had fared, Arnor did not want to expose himself to danger and he was greatly criticised by his father and many others. People think that he did not behave like a hero. It is now called Grettir's Point, where they fought. And Grettir's party got themselves horses and rode up under the mountain, for they were all wounded. And when they got to Fagraskogar Eyiolf stayed behind there. The farmer's daughter was outside there and asked for news. Grettir gave a detailed account and uttered a verse:

> It will not easily, horn-flood keeping Saga [lady],
> heal, Steinolf's great head-scratch,

[61] Thorarin's in other manuscripts, which is more in conformity with *The Book of Settlements*, ch. 67, according to which Ingiald and Thorarin were the sons of Thorgils Knappi.

though others plunged down too.
Heavy hope remains of Thorgils's life,
as his bones burst.
Men speak of eight other dead wealth-breakers there.

After this Grettir went to his hide-out and stayed there for the winter.

61

And when Biorn and he met, he told Grettir that he felt things had now really gone wrong, 'and it will not be possible for you to go on staying here. You have now killed both relatives and friends of mine, though I will not go back on what I agreed with you, for as long as you stay.'

Grettir said he had had to defend himself and his life, 'but I am sorry that you are upset about it.'

Biorn said there was nothing could be done about it. A little later people came to Biorn who had lost their relatives at Grettir's hands and asked him not to let this ruffian stay there any longer as a torment to them. Biorn said it should be done as soon as the winter came to an end.

Thorarin of Akrar's son Thrand was healed. He was a well-to-do man. He was married to Hrut of Kambsness's daughter Steinunn. Steinolf's father Thorleif at Hraundal was an important man. From him are descended the Hraundalers. Nothing further is told of dealings between Grettir and the people of Myrar while he was on the mountain there. Biorn also stayed friends with him though Biorn lost some of his friends because he let Grettir stay there, for people were not content to have their relatives unatoned for. At the time of the *assembly* Grettir set off from Myrar. He then went again to Borgarfiord and saw Grim Thorhallsson, and asked for advice about what he should do next. Grim said he had not the means to keep him and so Grettir went to see his friend Hallmund and stayed there during the summer until towards the end of it.

In the autumn Grettir went to Geitland and stayed there until bright weather came. Then he went up onto Geitland glacier and made for the south-east along the glacier and took with him a pot and materials for making a fire. It is thought that he was following directions given by Hallmund, for he knew about all sorts of places. Grettir went until he found a valley in the glacier, long and rather narrow, and enclosed by ice on all sides so that it overhung the valley. He got down in a certain place. He saw then fair slopes grown with grass and brushwood. There were hot springs there and he thought it must be because of the subterranean heat that the ice did not close in over the valley. A small river flowed along the valley with smooth gravel banks on both sides. There was not much sun there, but it seemed to him beyond counting how many sheep there were there in the valley. These animals were much better and fatter than he had seen the like of before. Grettir now fixed himself up there and made himself a hut with the wood he found there. He used the sheep for food. One sheep provided more meat than two elsewhere. There was a fawn-coloured, hornless ewe with a lamb, which he thought most exceptional because of its size. He was very interested in catching the lamb, and he did this and then slaughtered the lamb. There was half a hundredweight of suet in the lamb and it was better than anything. But when Mokolla found her lamb gone, she went up onto Grettir's hut every night and bleated so that he could not sleep at all at night. Because of her distress he felt the greatest regret for having slaughtered the lamb. Every evening when it was half dark he heard calls up in the valley and then all the animals ran to the same place to sleep every evening. According to Grettir the valley belonged to a giant, half man, whose name was Thorir, and Grettir stayed there under his protection. Grettir named the valley after him and called it Thorisdal. He said Thorir had daughters, and they provided Grettir with entertainment, and they were glad of this, for there was not much company there. And during the fasts Grettir made this observance that suet and liver should be eaten during Lent. Nothing noteworthy happened during the winter. Then Grettir found it was so dull there that he could stay no longer. He then went away from the valley and walked south straight across off the glacier and arrived on the north side of the middle of Skialdbreid. He raised a slab of rock up and knocked a hole in it and said if you put your eye to the hole in the slab, that then you could see the gully that comes down from Thorisdal. Then he went south across the country and on to the Eastern Fiords. He was on this journey during the summer and the winter and met all the important people, and he got such a poor reception that nowhere did he get food or lodging. So he went back northwards and stayed in various places.

62

Soon after Grettir left Arnarvatn Heath, a man came onto the heath called Grim. He was son of the widow at Kropp. He had killed Eid Skeggiason of As's son and for that had been outlawed. He now established himself there where Grettir had previously been and had good catches from the lake. Hallmund resented it that Grim had taken Grettir's place and decided that he should get no benefit from it, even though he had caught a lot. It happened one day that Grim caught a hundred fish and took them back to the hut and stowed them outside, but the next morning when he got to them every fish had gone. He thought this was strange and went to the lake and now caught two hundred fish, took them back and stowed them, and it all went the same as before, that they were all gone in the morning. Now it seemed to him that there was something abnormal about this. The third day he caught three hundred fish, took them back and kept watch over his hut. Grim watched through the eye hole in the door to see if anyone came to the hut. So passed a part of the night. And when less than a third of the night had gone by he heard someone walking past outside and stepping rather heavily. And when Grim heard this he took an axe that he had. It was a very sharp weapon. He wanted to know what the person was up to. The visitor had a great creel on his back and put it down and looked around and saw no one outside. He investigated the fish and thought they were worth getting his hands on, pulled all the fish down into the creel. Then the creel was full. There was so much fish that Grim thought that a horse would not be able to carry more. The other now set to and got himself under the load, and just when he was going to stand up, Grim leapt out and struck with both hands at his neck to that the axe sank in up to its back. The other man pulled hard away and set off at a run with the creel south onto the mountain. Grim went after him and wanted to find out whether he had got him. They went all the way south under Ball-glacier. There this man went into a cave. There was a bright fire in the cave. There sat a woman by it, of huge size and yet comely. Grim heard her greet her father and call him Hallmund. He threw down his load hard and sighed heavily. She asked why he was covered in blood. He answers and spoke this:

It is clear to me
that no man

can rely on his own strength
for so fails
on the day of their death
heroes' heart
when fortune fails.

She asked then in detail about their dealings and he told all that had happened.

'You shall now listen,' he said, 'and I shall tell of my doings, and I shall recite a poem about them, and you shall cut what I say on a stave.'

She did so. Then he recited Hallmund's Poem, and this is part of it:

I thought I was doughty
when I stroked Grettir
pretty hard
down from the reins.
I saw that
how he stood and gazed
a good while
into his palms.

That was next
when Thorir came
to Arnarvatn
up on the heath,
and we two
against eighty
point-play [battle]
went and held.

They seemed doughty
of Grettir's hands
the glancing blows
on their shields.
Yet I have heard
far greater
my edge-tracks [wounds]
seem to men.

I made arms
and heads fly
from fighters
when they came round the back
so that warriors
of Kelduhverfi
eighteen there
lay behind.

I have giants
and their kin
harshly treated
and crag-dwellers
but evil beings
thrashed many
and of half-men
been the death.

Also elf-kin
and monsters
to nearly all
I've done harm.

Hallmund referred to many deeds of his in the poem, for he had travelled over the whole country. Then his daughter said:

'This man has not been one to let anything slip out of his grasp, and it is not surprising, for you did act badly towards him. But who will now avenge you?'

Hallmund answers, 'It is not certain that anyone can. I am sure that Grettir would avenge me if he had an opportunity, but it will not be easy to combat this man's success, for he is destined for great things.'

After this Hallmund's strength ebbed away in proportion as the poem went on, and it was at about the same time that the poem ended and Hallmund died. This was hard for her to bear and she wept very bitterly. Then Grim came forward and bade her pull herself together.

'And "everyone has to go when their time comes". It was to a large extent his doing. I could scarcely sit by and watch him rob me.'

She said there was much in what he said, 'and "bullying has a bad end".'

She then began rather to cheer up in conversation. Grim stayed there many nights in the cave and memorised the poem and then they got on tolerably well. Grim stayed on Arnarvatn Heath during the winter after Hallmund's death. After that Thorkel Eyiolfsson went against him on the heath and they fought. Their engagement ended with Grim having Thorkel at his mercy and he decided not to kill him, but Thorkel took him in and got him abroad and gave him a lot of goods and each was considered to have done well by the other. Grim afterwards became a trader and there is a great tale told about him.[62]

63

Now we must take up the story where Grettir came back from the Eastern Fiords and now travelled in disguise and kept hidden, for he did not want to meet Thorir, and he lived in the open during the summer on Modrudal Heath and in various places. Some of the time he was also on Reykiaheid. Thorir found out that Grettir was on Reykaheid and got men together and rode onto the heath and was determined that he should not escape. Grettir hardly noticed before they were almost upon him. He was then by a *shieling* which stood a little way off the road. He was with one other person. And when they saw the bands of men and had to decide quickly what to do, then Grettir said they should fell the horses and drag them into the *shieling*, and they did so. Thorir rode past north along the heath and failed to meet the friend he was expecting and found nothing and now turned back. And when the party had ridden over to the west, then Grettir said:

'They will not be pleased with their trip if we do not meet. Now you shall look after our horses, and I shall go up to them. It will be a fine trick on them if they don't recognise me.'

His companion was against this, but still he went and put on different gear and had a long hood down over his face and had a staff in his hand, then went down the road in front of them. They greeted him and asked whether he had seen any men ride over the heath.

'I saw those who must have been the ones you are looking for. You weren't far off meeting them, for they were here to the south of the marshes which are on the left hand side.'

[62] See *Laxdæla saga*, chs 57–8.

And when they heard this, they rushed out onto the marshes. There were such great bogs there that they got stuck and had to drag their horses out and they floundered about in it for a good part of the day. They called down curses on him, this tramp who had made such fools of them. Grettir went straight back towards his companion, and when they met Grettir uttered a verse:

I ride not towards
the trees that tend shield's threat [warriors].
Trouble is the lot of this man.
I go away alone.
I do not want to meet
the keen wielders of Vidrir's wall [warriors].
You will not think me mad.
I look for a better chance.

I shrink back where Thorir's
very great bands go.

They now rode off down as fast as they could to the front of the farm at Gard before Thorir came off the mountain with his band. And when they got near the farm a man came up with them. He did not recognise them. They saw a woman standing outside, young and in fine clothes. Grettir asked who this woman would be. The stranger said it was Thorir's daughter. Then Grettir uttered a verse:

Wise gold-dweller's seat Sol [lady],
you will be able to tell your father,
though my words often do not signify,
where I ride past the broad farm
and near Gard with a third man.
The supporters are few
of the prow-land-horse adorner [seaman, i.e. Grettir].

From this the stranger realised who it must be, and rode to the farms and said that Grettir had ridden by. And when Thorir got home, many thought Grettir had pulled the wool over their eyes. Thorir now put men on the watch for Grettir wherever he went. Grettir then decided to send his companion to the western districts with the horses, and he went up into the mountains and was in disguise and so went about in the north there in the first part of the winter without being recognised. Everyone now thought Thorir had fared the same or worse than before in their dealings.

64

There was a priest called Stein who lived at Eyiardalsa in Bardardal. He was a good farmer and wealthy. His son was called Kiartan, a man with plenty of vitality and sturdy. There was a man called Thorstein the White who lived at Sandhaugar, south of Eyiardalsa. His wife was called Steinvor, young and cheerful. They had children, and they were young at this time. This place was believed to be badly haunted because of the visitation of trolls. It happened two years before Grettir came to the northern districts that Steinvor, the lady at Sandhaugar, went to the Christmas service at Eyiardalsa as usual, but the farmer stayed at home. People lay down to sleep in the evening. And in the night a great crash was heard in the room, coming from the farmer's bed. No one dared to get up to investigate, for there were very few people there. The lady came home the next morning and the farmer had disappeared and no one knew what had become of him. So the next seasons passed.[63] And the next winter the lady decided to go to the service. She told her workman to stay at home. He was reluctant, but said he would do as she said. Everything went the same way as before, so that the workman disappeared. This was thought very strange. Then they saw some gouts of blood in the main doorway. They then felt certain that monsters must have taken both of them. This was reported all over the surrounding districts. Grettir got to hear of this, and because he was very good at getting rid of hauntings and the activities of revenants he made his way to Bardardal and arrived on Christmas-eve at Sandhaugar. He concealed his identity and called himself Guest. The lady saw that he was astonishingly large in size, and the household were very afraid of him. He asked for lodging there. The lady said he was welcome to food.

'But it is at your own risk.'

[63] The Icelandic year had two seasons, winter and summer. 'The seasons' therefore usually means a year.

He said it should be so. 'I shall stay in,' he says, 'and you go to the service if you want to.'

She answers, 'I think you are bold if you dare to stay in the house.'

'I am used to a variety of things,' he said.

'I don't like staying at home,' she said, 'but I can't get across the river.'

'I'll help you over,' says Guest.

Then she got ready to go to the service and her daughter with her, very small. There was a great thaw outside and the ice on the river was melting. There were ice-floes on it. Then the lady said:

'The river is uncrossable for both people and horses.'

'There will be places to cross,' said Guest, 'and do not be afraid.'

'Take the girl first,' said the lady, 'she is lighter.'

'I don't care to make two journeys of it,' says Guest, 'and I'll carry you on my arm.'

She crossed herself and said, 'It is impossible to get across; but what will you do with the girl then?'

'I know what to do,' he says, and picked them both up and put the younger one on her mother's knee and bore them thus on his left arm, keeping his right arm free, and so stepped out into the crossing-place. They didn't dare cry out, they were so afraid, and the river crashed straight up against his chest. Then a great ice-floe was driven at him, but he flung out his free arm against it and pushed it away. It then got so deep that the current was breaking against his shoulder. He waded strongly until he got to the bank the other side and flung them ashore. Then he turned back and it was then half dark when he got back to Sandhaugar and called for food. And when he was fed he told the household to go in to the back of the room. He then took tables and some loose beams and fixed them across the room and made a great partition so that none of the household could get out over it. No one dared object and no one was allowed to grumble. The entrance was through the side wall of the room at the end by the gable wall and there was a *platform* across the room by it. Guest lay down there and didn't take off his clothes. A light was burning in the room opposite the doorway.

The lady arrived at Eyiardalsa for the service, and people were amazed about her travelling across the river. She said she didn't know whether it was a man or a troll that had carried her across. The priest said it must certainly have been a man.

'Though there are few equal to him, and let's keep quiet about it,' he said, 'maybe he is destined to bring about a cure for your troubles.'

The lady stayed there overnight.

65

Now this is to be told about Grettir, that when it got close to midnight he heard great clatterings outside. Next there came into the room a great trollwife. She had a trencher in her hand, and in the other rather a big machete. She looked round when she got in and saw where Guest was lying and leapt at him and he up against her and they attacked each other fiercely and fought for a long time in the room. She was the stronger, but he gave ground cleverly and everything that got in their way they broke, even the cross-partition at the end of the room. She dragged him out past the doorway and so into the farm-house entrance. There he resisted strongly. She was trying to drag him out of the farm-house, but she could not do this until they had pulled down all the door-frame and carried it out on their shoulders. She struggled then down to the river and right out to the edge of the gorge. By now Guest was enormously tired, but he had to do one of two things, make an effort, or else she would pitch him into the gorge. All night they fought. He thought he had never engaged with such a monster as far as strength was concerned. She had been holding him so firmly to herself that he could not use either arm for anything except to hold her round the middle, the woman. And when they got to the river gorge, he swung the giantess round off her feet. At that moment he got his right arm free. He then grasped quickly for the *cutlass* he was girded with and drew it, and struck then at the troll's shoulder so that it took off her right arm, and so he got free, and she threw herself into the gorge and so into the waterfall. Guest was then both stiff and tired and lay there for a long time on the cliff edge. Then when it began to get light he went back to the house and lay down in bed. He was all swollen and *blue*.

And when the lady got back from the service she thought there had been a bit of a disturbance in her home. She went then to Guest and asked what had happened that everything was broken and crushed. He related all that had happened. She was very impressed and asked who he was. He then told the truth about himself and told her to get the priest and said he wanted to see him. This was done. And when the priest Stein came to Sandhaugar, he soon discovered that it was Grettir Asmundarson who had come there under the name of Guest. The priest asked what he thought would have become of the people who had disappeared from there. Grettir said he thought that they must have disappeared into the gorge. The priest said he would not be able to put any faith in his account if there was no evidence for it to be seen. Grettir said that later they would be convinced. The priest went home. Grettir lay in bed for many nights. The lady looked after him very well; so Christmas went by. Grettir's story was that the troll-wife had thrown herself down into the gorge on receiving the wound, but the people of Bardardal say that she was turned to stone by the dawn while they were wrestling, and collapsed when he cut off her arm, and that there is still the image of a woman standing there on the crag. The inhabitants of the valley concealed Grettir there during the winter.

It was one day after Christmas that Grettir went to Eyiardalsa, and when they met, Grettir and the priest, Grettir said:

'I can see, priest,' he said, 'that you put little faith in my account. Now I want you to go with me to the river and see what probability there seems to you to be in it.'

The priest did so. And when they got to the waterfall they could see a hollow up under the cliff. This was a sheer rock-face so huge that there was no way to get up it, and it was nearly ten fathoms down to the water. They had a rope with them. Then the priest said:

'It looks far beyond your capability to go down there.'

'Certainly it is possible, but it is best attempted by men of merit [daring]. I shall investigate what is in the waterfall, and you shall watch the rope.'

The priest told him to do as he wished and drove a stake into the cliff-top and piled stones against it [and sat down beside it].

66

Now it is to be told about Grettir that he put a stone in the loop at the end of the rope and let it drop down to the water.

'How are you planning,' said the priest, 'to get down?'

'I shan't want to be tied,' said Grettir, 'when I get to the waterfall. I have a premonition about it.'

After this he got ready for his expedition and was lightly clothed and girded himself with his *cutlass*, but took no other weapons. Then he leapt off the cliff and down into the waterfall. The priest saw the soles of his feet and knew nothing of what happened to him afterwards. Grettir dived under the waterfall and this was difficult to do, for there was much turbulence and he had to dive right down to the bottom before he could get up under the waterfall. There was a great jutting rock and he managed to get in up onto it. There was a great cave there under the waterfall and the river fell in front of it off the cliff. He then went into the cave and there was a great fire on a pile of burning logs. Grettir saw a horribly big giant lying there. He was terrifying to see. And when Grettir approached him the giant leapt up and grasped a long weapon and struck at the intruder, for one could both strike and thrust with it. It had a wooden shaft. It was known as a haft-knife[64] when it was made like that. Grettir struck back with his *cutlass* and it hit the shaft so that it went in two. The giant was then about to reach back behind himself for a sword that was hanging there in the cave. At that moment Grettir struck him from the front in the chest so that it practically took off all the ribs and belly so that his innards were flung out of him down into the river, and they were swept down along the river. And while the priest was sitting by the rope he saw some shreds being carried down along in the current, all bloody. He was then no longer rooted to the spot and felt certain that Grettir must be dead. He ran then from the holdfast and went home. Evening had then come and [the priest] said for certain that Grettir was dead and said that such a man was a great loss.

Now it is to be said about Grettir, that he struck one blow after another until the giant was dead. Then Grettir went further in along the cave. He lit a lamp and explored the cave. It is not told how much wealth he got in the cave, but people think it must have been a great deal. He was occupied there on into the night. He found there the bones of two men and put them in a bag. He then made his way out of the cave and swam to the rope and shook it and was expecting the priest to be there, but when he realised that the priest had gone home

[64] *heptisax;* cf. Old English *hæftmece* in *Beowulf*, line 1457, the one supposed verbal parallel between the two stories.

he had to haul himself up the rope and so got up onto the cliff. Then he went back to Eyiardalsa and put the bag with the bones in in the porch of the church together with a rune-stave on which these verses were extremely well carved:

> I went into the dark gorge;
> the stone-churning flow yawned with wet-cold mouth
> for the empowerer of sword-storm pole [warrior, i.e. Grettir].
> The flying stream pressed forward
> hard on my breast in Nauma's hall [cave];
> the rather harsh hostility of Bragi's wife[65]
> came at the poet's shoulders.

And this too:

> Ugly troll-wife's friend [giant] came against me from the cave;
> Truly rather tough to deal with,
> he fought long with me.
> I caused the hard-edged haft-knife
> to be cut from its shaft;
> bright battle-flame clove Gang's breast
> and black chest.

It [also] said on it that Grettir brought these bones from the cave. And when the priest came to the church in the morning he found the rune-stave and what was with it and read the runes. But Grettir had gone back to Sandhaugar.

67

And when the priest saw Grettir, he asked in detail about what had happened, and he told the whole story of his exploit and said the priest had been unreliable in looking after the rope. The priest admitted this. People felt sure that it must have been these monsters that had been responsible for the disappearance of people there in the valley, and

[65] Another pun: Bragi's wife was Iðunn; *iðunnar* would mean 'of the turbulent water'.

there was never any harm done afterwards by revenants or hauntings there in the valley. Grettir was considered to have carried out a great cleansing of the land there. The priest buried the bones in the churchyard.

Grettir stayed the rest of the winter at Sandhaugar and yet kept himself hidden from the general public. But when Thorir of Gard heard a rumour that Grettir was in Bardardal, then he set men on to get rid of him. He was then advised to find somewhere else to go and he went to the [districts to the] west. And when he got to Modruvellir to Gudmund the Great he asked Gudmund for help, but he said it was not possible for him to take him in.

'And the only thing for you,' said Gudmund, 'is to get you somewhere where you need not fear for your life.'

Grettir said he did not know where that could be. Gudmund said:

'There is an island lying out in Skagafiord called Drangey. It is such a good stronghold that it is impossible to get up onto it anywhere without using ladders. If you could get there, I don't know where the man is to be found who could attack you there with weapons or tricks if you guard the ladder well.'

'It shall be tried,' says Grettir, 'but I'm getting so afraid of the dark that to save my life I cannot bring myself to be on my own.'

Gudmund said, 'Maybe that is so, but trust no one so well that you do not trust yourself best of all. But "many are difficult to beware of".'

Grettir thanked him for his good advice. He then went away from Modruvellir. He did not stop until he got to Biarg. His mother welcomed him, and so did Illugi. He stayed there a few nights. There he learned of the killing of Thorstein Kuggason.[66] This had happened in the autumn before Grettir went to Bardardal. He felt now that the blows were falling all around him. Grettir then rode south across Holtavarda Heath and planned to avenge Hallmund if he could find Grim, but when he got to Nordrardal he found out that Grim had gone from there two or three winters before, as was said above. The reason Grettir had heard this news so late was that he had been going in disguise for the two winters and the third, while he was in Thorisdal, and had met no

[66] See *Laxdæla saga*, ch. 75. According to Icelandic annals he was killed in 1027, but the circumstances are not known.

one who would tell him any news. Then he went on to Breidafiardardalir and waylaid people travelling over Brattabrekka. He then again let his hands sweep over the property of small farmers. This was about the time of high summer. That summer, towards its end, Steinvor at Sandhaugar gave birth to a baby boy, and it was called Skeggi. He was at first said to be son of Kiartan, son of the priest Stein at Eyiardalsa. Skeggi was different from his other brothers and sisters as regards his strength and size, and when he was fifteen years old he was the strongest there in the north and was then put down to Grettir's account. It was thought that he would turn out to be an outstanding man, but he died at the age of sixteen and there is nothing to tell of him.

68

After the killing of Thorstein Kuggason, Snorri *Godi* fell out with his son Thorodd and Bork the Stout's son Sam, but it is not specified what in particular they had done to earn this, except that they had refused to carry out some great deed that Snorri had asked them to do, and so Snorri *Godi* drove Thorodd away from him and told him not to come back until he had killed some outlaw, and he had to put up with it. Thorodd then went across to Dalir.

At that time there lived at Breidabolstad in Sokkolfsdal a widow called Geirlaug. She kept a shepherd who had been outlawed for injuring some one. He was a lad scarcely adult. Thorodd Snorrason heard about this and rode to Breidabolstad. He asked where the shepherd was. The lady said he was with the sheep.

'And what do you want with him?'

'I intend to have his life,' said Thorodd, 'for he is a condemned outlaw.'

She answers, 'That will do you no good, killing him, poor fellow, such a great hero as you think yourself. I can direct you to a greater achievement if you have such a great mind to prove yourself.'

'What is that?' says he.

She answers, 'Up in the mountain here Grettir Asmundarson is staying. Tackle him, that is more in your line.'

Thorodd was pleased at this suggestion, 'and I shall do that.'

He then spurred on his horse and rode up along the valley. And when he got onto the hills below Austra he saw where there was a pale dun-coloured horse with a saddle on. He saw there too a big man with weapons and went straight up to him. Grettir greeted him and asked who he was. Thorodd gave his name and said:

'Why don't you ask me rather about my purpose than about my name?'

'Because,' said Grettir, 'it can only be something of little importance, but are you Snorri *Godi*'s son?'

'That's right,' said Thorodd, 'but now we shall see which of us is the stronger.'

'By all means,' said Grettir, 'but have you not heard that I have not been a source of much profit for most people to meddle with?'

'I know that,' says Thorodd, 'and yet we shall have a bit of a try,' and drew his sword and attacked Grettir vigorously, and he defended himself with his shield. But he did not use weapons on Thorodd, and so it went on for a while. He was not wounded. Grettir said then:

'Let's stop this game, for you will gain no victory in our engagement.'

Thorodd then went on striking furiously. Grettir got tired of dealing with him. He took hold of Thorodd and set him down beside himself and said:

'I am in a position to do anything I like with you, and I am not afraid of your killing me, but I'm afraid of the old grey-locks Snorri *Godi*, your father, and his counsels. They have brought most men to their knees. And you should limit yourself to undertakings that are within your power. It is no job for an infant to fight with me.'

And when Thorodd saw that he was going to achieve nothing, he calmed down a bit, and they parted thus.

Thorodd rode home to Tunga and told his father of his encounter with Grettir. Snorri *Godi* smiled at this and said:

'"Many are deceived about themselves", and you were not equally matched. You were striking up at him and he could have done anything he liked with you. And yet Grettir acted wisely in not killing you, for I would not have been happy for you not to be avenged. I will do what I can to help him if I am in a position to do anything in his case.'

It was clear to see in Snorri that he thought Grettir had acted well towards Thorodd, and he was always afterwards his friend in what he proposed.

69

Grettir rode north to Biarg soon after he and Thorodd separated and hid himself there for a while yet. Then there came such a great increase in his fear of the dark that he dared go nowhere as soon as night began to fall. His mother suggested he should stay there, but said she realised that this would not work because he had committed offences all over the country. Grettir said she should have no trouble because of him.

'But I am not going to put up any longer with being on my own,' he says, 'in order to stay alive.'

His brother Illugi was then fifteen years old and the ablest of men. He was present at their conversation. Grettir told his mother what Gudmund the Great had suggested to him, and said he would see whether there was any way of getting onto Drangey, though he said he would not be able to stay there unless he got some reliable person to stay with him. Then said Illugi:

'I will go with you, brother, but I don't know whether my company will be any good to you, except that I will be true to you and not run from you while you stand on your feet, and I will know better how you are getting on if I am with you.'

Grettir answers, 'You are the sort of person who gives me most joy, and if it were not against my mother's wishes I would be very keen for you to go with me.'

Asdis said then, 'Now it has reached the point that I can see that there are two evils to choose from. I feel I cannot do without Illugi, but I know that Grettir's problems are so great that he has to find some solution. And though I find it very hard to lose both of you my sons, yet I am willing to put up with that so that Grettir could then be better off.'

Illugi was glad at this, for he thought it would be fine to go with Grettir. She gave them a lot of money. They then set out on their way. Asdis went a little way down the road with them, and before they parted she said as follows:

'Now you are both going there, my two sons, and your death together will be the hardest thing, and "no one can escape what has been fated for him". I shall not see either of you ever again. Now stay together until the end. I do not know what fortune you will find out there on Drangey, but there you will lay down your bones, and there are many that will resent your staying there. Beware of treachery, but weapons will pierce you. My dreams have been very strange. Be on your guard against witchcraft. "Little is stronger than sorcery".'

And when she had said this, she wept bitterly. Then said Grettir:

'Do not weep, mother. It shall be said that you had sons, not daughters, if we are attacked with weapons, and fare well and happily.'

After that they parted. They now went through the districts to the north and went to see their relatives. So they spent the autumn and on until winter. Then they made their way to Skagafiord and went north over Vatnsskard and so to Reykiaskard and so down Sæmundarhlid and on to Langholt. They got to Glaumbæ late in the day. Grettir had thrown back his hood onto his shoulder. That was how he always went in the open whether it was better or worse weather. They went on from there, and when they had gone a little way past, a man came towards them with a large head, tall and thin and ill-clad. He greeted them and each asked the other their names. They said who they were, and he said his name was Thorbiorn. He was a solitary wanderer and did not care to work and chattered a lot, and for some people was a source of much mirth and ridicule. He behaved very friendly towards them and told much from up in the district about the people of the neighbourhood. Grettir found him very amusing. He asked whether they didn't feel they needed someone to work for them.

'I would happily go with you,' he says.

He managed to convince them, so that they let him go with them. There was driving snow and it was cold. And because this man was a very rowdy person and a great buffoon he had a nickname and was called Glaum (Merryman).

'They wondered greatly in Glaumbæ, when you went there by the farm with no hood in such bad weather,' said Glaum, 'whether you would be the tougher for being more impervious to the cold, and there were the two farmer's sons, very exceptional men for strength, and the shepherd called on them to go with him for the sheep and they thought they could hardly clothe themselves against the cold.'

Grettir saw a young man inside the doorway pulling on his gloves there, and another walking between the cowshed and the midden.

'And I shall be afraid of neither of them.'

After that they went down to Reyniness and stayed the night there. From there they went out onto the shore to a farm called Reykir. A man called Thorvald lived there and was a good farmer. Grettir asked him for help and told him his plan, that he wanted to get out onto Drangey. The farmer said that the people of Skagafiord would not take kindly to that, and would not agree. Grettir then took out the purse of money his mother had given him and gave it to the farmer. He brightened up when he saw the money and got his workmen then to take them out at night by moonlight. From Reykir is the shortest crossing to the island, and it is a sea-*league*'s distance.[67] And when they got to the island, Grettir thought it was a pleasant sight, for it was covered with grass and steep down to the sea so that one could not get up anywhere except where the ladders had been put, and if the upper ladder was pulled up then it was within no one's capability to get onto the island. There was a great nesting site on the cliffs there for birds in the summer then. There were at that time eighty sheep there on the island that belonged to the farmers. They were mostly rams and ewes that were intended for slaughter. Grettir now settled himself down there peacefully. By now he had been fifteen or sixteen winters in outlawry, according to what Sturla Thordarson has said.

70

When Grettir went to Drangey, there were these leading men of the area in Skagafiord. Hialti lived at Hof in Hialtadal, son of Thord, son of Hialti, son of Thord Skalp. Hialti was a leading figure and a very distinguished man and well-liked. His brother was called Thorbiorn Ongul (hook). He was a big man and strong and tough and difficult to deal with. Their father Thord had married in his old age and this woman was not the mother of the brothers. She did not get on with her step-children, and worst of all with Thorbiorn, for he was ill-natured and thoughtless. It happened once that Thorbiorn Ongul was playing a board-game. His stepmother went past and saw that he was playing *hneftafl*. They were large pieces standing on pegs. She thought he was wasting his time and let fly some words at him, and he answered bad-temperedly. She then snatched up one of the pieces and stuck the point in Thorbiorn's cheek and it glanced off into his eye so that it came out

[67] The distance is about 6 $^1/_2$ km.

onto his cheek. He leapt up and grabbed at her mercilessly so that she took to her bed as a result and she died from it later, and they said that she had been pregnant. Afterwards he became a most uncontrolled person. He took over his share of the property and lived to begin with in Vidvik.

Halldor son of Thorgeir, son of Thord of Hofdi, lived at Hof on Hofdastrond. He was married to Thordis Thordardottir, sister of the brothers Hialti and Thorbiorn Ongul. Halldor was a worthy farmer and well off. There was a man called Biorn who lived on Haganess in Fliot. He was a friend of Halldor at Hof. They worked together in every affair. There was a man called Tungu-Stein who lived at Steinsstadir. He was son of Biorn, son of Ofeig Thunnskegg (thin-beard), son of Kraku-Hreidar, [son of][68] the one to whom Eirik of Guddalir gave the tongue of land down below Skalamyr. Stein was a renowned man. There was a man called Eirik, son of Holmgongu-Starri, son of Eirik of Guddalir, son of Hroald, son of Geirmund Ordigskeggi (rough-beard). He lived at Hof in Guddalir. These were all men of high standing. Two brothers lived at a place called Breida on Slettahlid, and they were both called Thord. They were mighty in strength and yet gentle people. These all owned shares in Drangey. They say that there were no fewer than twenty people had shares in the island and none of them was willing to sell his share to anyone else. The sons of Thord had the greatest stake in it, for they were the richest.

71

Now time passed until the solstice. Then the farmers got ready to fetch their sheep from the island for slaughter. They made a crew for a sailing boat and each of the farmers provided one member, some of them two. But when they got near to the island they saw people about there on it. They were surprised at this, and supposed that some men must have wrecked their ship there and got ashore there. They now rowed up to where the ladders were, and the people who were already there

[68] These words are not in some manuscripts, which then correspond with *The Book of Settlements*, ch. 197.

drew up the ladders. This seemed a strange reaction to the farmers, and they called to them and asked who it was that was there. Grettir gave his name and those of his companions. The farmers asked who had taken him out to the island. Grettir answers:

'He brought me who was the owner of the vessel and had arms and was more a friend of mine than a friend of yours.'

The farmers answered, 'Let us get our animals, then come to the mainland with us and you can have what you have used of our animals for nothing.'

Grettir answers, 'That is a kind offer, but still each shall now keep what they have taken, and to put it briefly, I shall not go from here unless I am dragged away dead. I will not give up what I have got my hands on.'

Now the farmers were silent and felt that a real plague had arrived on Drangey. They offered him many alternatives, accompanied both by gifts of money and fair promises, but Grettir refused them all and the farmers went away with matters thus and were very unhappy with their lot. They told the people of the area what a plunderer had gone onto the island. This was a great surprise to them, and it did not seem easy to do anything about it. They had long discussions about it during the winter and could not think of any way to get Grettir off the island.

72

Now time passed until people were going to the Hegraness *Assembly* in the spring. A large number of people attended from all the areas that belonged to the *assembly*. People stayed there for a long time in the spring both for lawsuits and entertainments, for there were at that time many people in these areas who liked entertainments. And when Grettir learned that the general public had gone to the *assembly* (he had made an arrangement with his friends, for he was always on good terms with those who were closest by, and was never miserly towards them with whatever he got hold of) he said that he wanted to go ashore to get supplies, but that Illugi and Glaum were to stay behind. This seemed inadvisable to Illugi, and yet he agreed to what Grettir wanted. He told them to guard the ladder and said this was very important. After that he went ashore and got together what he felt he needed. He disguised himself now wherever he went and no one realised that he had come ashore. He got news from the *assembly* that there was much entertainment there. Grettir had a great desire to go the *assembly*, and he put on old clothes, rather shabby, and got to the *assembly* just when everyone was leaving the legal meeting and returning to their *booths*. Then some of the young men suggested that the weather was good and fine and now it would be good for the youngsters to have some wrestling and games. They said that was a very good idea. People then went and sat down in front of the *booths*. The sons of Thord were the ones who mostly organised the games. Thorbiorn Ongul was very officious and was eagerly making arrangements for the entertainment. Everyone had to take part whom he wished. He took everyone by the shoulders and pulled them out onto the grass. Now the first people to wrestle were those who were least strong, and then each in turn, and this was a source of great entertainment. And when most had taken part in the wrestling except those who were strongest, the farmers had a discussion about who could be got to take on one or other of the Thords who were mentioned above, but there was no one forthcoming. They then went up to various men and challenged them, but the more they called on them the less they were willing. Thorbiorn Ongul then looked round and saw where a man was sitting, huge in size, and his face could not be seen clearly. Thorbiorn took hold of him and pulled at him hard. He sat still and did not move at all. Then said Thorbiorn:

'No one has sat as firmly before me today as you; and who is this man?'

He answers, 'My name is Guest.'

Thorbiorn said, 'No doubt you will be willing to provide some entertainment, and you are a welcome guest.'

He answers, 'Things have a habit of changing very quickly, and I am not going to rush into a tournament with you, I don't know how things are here.'

Then many said that he deserved good treatment if he was willing to provide people with some entertainment, being an unknown person. He asked what they wanted from him. They asked him to wrestle with someone. He said he had given up scrapping.

'But there was a time when I thought it fun.'

And since he didn't refuse absolutely, they urged him the more. He said:

'If you think it important that I be drawn into it, then you will grant me this to obtain it, to give me safe-conduct here at the *assembly* and until I get back to my abode.'

Then they all leapt up and said they were very happy for that to be. The man's name was Hafr who was most eager for this person to be given safe-conduct. He was son of Thorarin, son of Hafr, son of Thord Knapp, who had taken possession of land from Stifla in Fliot as far as Tungua. He lived at Knappsstadir and was a very eloquent man. He pronounced the terms of the truce with great emphasis, and it begins like this:

'Here I establish a truce,' he says, 'between all men, especially as regards this same specified person Guest, who is sitting here, and including all *godord*smen and worthy farmers and all the population of fighting men and those capable of bearing arms and all the other people of the area at the Hegraness *Assembly*, or from wherever each of them has come, named people and unnamed: we establish truce and absolute peace to the unknown stranger who calls himself Guest, for games, wrestling and all kinds of entertainment, for the duration of his stay here and for his journey home, whether he needs to travel by sea or by land, [by ship] or other conveyance. He shall have truce in all places, named and unnamed, as long as he needs until his safe return home with unbroken pledges. I establish this truce for us and our families, friends and connections, women as well as men, women and men bondservants, workmen and independent persons. Let him be known as a recreant truce-breaker who violates the truce or breaks the pledges, outcast and banished from God and good people, from the kingdom of heaven and from all the saints, and allowed to be nowhere among men and thus driven away from everyone as far and wide as they drive wolves or Christian people go to church, heathen people sacrifice in temples, fire burns, earth grows, children with speech call mother and mother gives birth to child, men kindle fire, ship passes, shields glint, sun shines, snow lies, the Lapp skies, fir grows, falcon flies the spring-long day if there comes a fair wind under both wings, sky turns, the world is inhabited and the wind brings waters to the sea, slaves sow corn. He shall shun churches and Christian people, heathen men, houses and caves, every world except hell.

'Now shall we all be at peace and in agreement one with another with good thoughts whether we meet on mountain or shore, ship or ski, earth or ice, on ocean or on horseback, just as when one meets one's friend in water or one meets one's brother on the road, just as much at peace one with another as son with father or father with son in all dealings. Now let us clasp hands, all of us and keep the truce well and all the words spoken in these pledges, in the presence of God and good men and all those who hear my words or are at all close by.'

Then many spoke up, that quite something had been said. Guest then said:

'Well have you spoken and presented it, if you do not spoil it later. I shall now not delay what I have to present.'

Then he threw off his hooded cape and after that all the covering on his body. Then they all looked at each other and their faces fell. They realised that this was Grettir Asmundarson, for he was not like other men as regards size and strength of body, and they were now all silent, and Hafr looked rather foolish. They now walked around in twos, the men of the area, and they all blamed each other, especially the one who had pronounced the truce. Then said Grettir:

'Be straightforward with me, as to what your intentions are, for I am not going to go on sitting here with no clothes on. You have much more at stake than I, whether you keep your truce or not.'

They made little answer and sat down. The sons of Thord and their brother-in-law Halldor now held a discussion. Some wished to keep the truce, and some didn't. They all wagged their heads at each other. Grettir uttered a verse:

> Many a neck-ring bush [man] has
> failed to recognise his acquaintance this morning.
> The fray-house bushes [men] are in a quandary.
> The word-sharp men have been dealt a difficult hand.
> Folk are failing to keep their word.
> "Hafr's chatter has dried up".

Then said Tungu-Stein, 'Do you think so, Grettir? and what are they going to decide, these leaders? But true it is that you are a paragon for courage. And don't you see how they are all nosing at each other?'

Grettir then uttered a verse:

Hlokk's hangings' raisers [shield-raisers, warriors]
put their noses together
and Hild's wall's storm-Niords [warriors]
poked each other with their beards.
Mind-firm they went,
they began to repent their truce,
serpent's lair robbers [generous men], into groups
when they recognised me.

Then said Hialti Thordarson:

'That shall not be,' he says, 'we must keep our truce, even though we have been shown to be so inferior in judgement. I do not want people afterwards to use it as a precedent that we have ourselves gone back on the truce which we ourselves established and made. Grettir shall go freely wherever he will, and have safe-conduct until he gets back from this expedition. Then the truce will have expired, whatever takes place between us.'

Everyone thanked him for what he had said, and he was thought to have shown true leadership, the situation being what it was. Thorbiorn Ongul said nothing. Then it was suggested that one or other of the Thords should take on Grettir, and he said it was up to them. Now one of the brothers came forward. Grettir faced him squarely and the other leapt at him without hanging about but Grettir did not budge. Grettir reached over Thord's back and took hold of his breeches and jerked his feet off the ground and threw him back over his head so that he came down on his shoulders and it was a very heavy fall. Then people said that both the brothers should go up together, and they did so. Then there was a very great deal of pulling and pushing and it went now one way and now the other, and yet Grettir always had one of them down, but one after another was forced to his knees or to bite the dust before the other. They went at it so hard that they were bruised and bloody all over. Everyone was greatly entertained by this. And when they stopped, everyone thanked them for their wrestling, and it was the judgment of those who were there that the two of them were not stronger than Grettir on his own, but each of them had the strength of two men of full power. They were so matched in strength that neither of them was superior to the other when they tried with each other. Grettir did not stay long at the *assembly*. The farmers asked him to give up the island, but he refused and the farmers could do nothing about it. Grettir went back to Drangey and Illugi welcomed him warmly. They stayed there peacefully. Grettir told them about his expedition.

Time passed through the summer. Everyone thought the men of Skagafiord had behaved very decently in keeping their truce so well, and one can see from this what real gentlemen there were at that time, considering what offences Grettir had committed against them. The farmers who were less wealthy said among themselves that it was of no advantage to them to own a small share in Drangey and offered now to sell to the sons of Thord, but Hialti said he did not want to buy. And the farmers stipulated that he who wished to buy must either kill Grettir or get him away. Thorbiorn Ongul said he would not hold back from taking on responsibility for an attack on Grettir if they would give him money to do so. His brother Hialti gave up to him his share in the island, for Thorbiorn was the harsher of the two and unpopular. Other farmers did the same. Thorbiorn then gained a large part of the island at a low price, and he undertook to get Grettir away.

73

About the end of summer Thorbiorn Ongul went with a fully manned sailing boat to Drangey, and [Grettir and his companions] went to the edge of the cliff. They then exchanged words. Thorbiorn asked Grettir to accede to his request to leave the island. Grettir said there was no hope of that. Thorbiorn said:

'It may be that I shall be able to do you an equivalent favour, if you did this, but now many farmers have given up to me the part of the island that they owned.'

Grettir answers, 'Now you have let something out that makes me still determined never to leave here, when you said you owned the greatest part of the island. "That is fine, that we should pick a bone with each other". It was quite true that I found it hard to have all the people of Skagafiord against me, but now there's no need for either of us to hold back, for we shall not be smothered in brotherly love. You may as well give up coming here, for as far as I am concerned our negotiations are finished.'

'"There is a time for everything",' said Thorbiorn, 'and you have got something coming to you.'

'I'll have to risk that,' said Grettir, and they parted with matters thus. Thorbiorn went back home.

74

It is said that when Grettir had been on Drangey for two winters they had slaughtered nearly all the sheep that had been there. But they kept one ram alive, according to the story. It was grey-bellied in colour and with large horns. They got a great deal of fun from it, because it was so tame that it waited for them outside and ran after them wherever they went. It went back to the hut in the evenings and rubbed its horns against the door. They liked being on the island for there was plenty of food because of the birds and eggs. But there was very little store of firewood to be found there and Grettir made the servant always examine what washed up on the shore, and often pieces of wood washed up and he carried them back for the fire. The brothers did not need to do any work except to go collecting on the cliffs when they felt like it. The servant began to get very lazy about his work. He began to grumble a lot and to be more careless than he had been. He was supposed to look after the fire every night, and Grettir made a point of warning him about this, because there was no boat with them. Now it so happened that the fire went out on them one night. Then Grettir was very annoyed at this and said it was fitting that Glaum should be flogged. But he, the servant, said he was living a poor sort of life, to be lying here in outlawry and being abused and beaten if anything went wrong. Grettir asked Illugi what they were to do, and he said he could think of nothing except that they would have to wait for a boat to turn up. Grettir said there was little prospect of that.

'Rather I shall take the risk of whether I can get ashore.'

'I am very worried about that,' said Illugi, 'for we shall have had it, if anything happens to you.'

'I shall not drown while swimming,' said Grettir, 'but I shall not so readily trust the servant from now on, when we depended on this so much.'

It was a *league* across the sea where the distance from the island to the shore was shortest.

75

Grettir now got ready for swimming and had on a homespun cloak and girded it into his breeches; he made his fingers webbed. The weather was good. He set out from the island towards the end of the day. Illugi was very worried about his expedition. Grettir now swam in along the fiord and the current was with him and it was completely calm. He swam hard and got in to Reykianess after sunset. He went to the farm at Reykir and went into the hot pool, for he had become pretty cold. He basked for a long time in the hot water during the night and then went into the *living-room*. It was very warm in there because there had been a fire there during the evening and the room had not cooled down much. He was very tired and fell fast asleep. He lay there right on into the day. And when the morning drew on the people of the household got up and two women were the first to go into the *living-room*. These were a serving-girl and the farmer's daughter. Grettir was asleep and the clothes had tumbled off him down onto the floor. They saw a man lying there and recognised him. Then the serving-girl said:

'My goodness, sister, this is Grettir Asmundarson come here, and he looks really big about the ribs, lying there with nothing on. But it seems to me very strange how little he has developed between the legs, and it is not in keeping with his size elsewhere.'

The farmer's daughter answers, 'Why do you chatter on so? And you are a more than average fool, and be quiet.'

'I cannot be quiet about this, dear sister,' says the serving-girl, 'because I wouldn't have believed if anyone had told me.'

She now went over to him and peered at him, and now and again ran up to the farmer's daughter and burst out laughing. Grettir heard what she was saying, and when she ran back again across the floor he took hold of her and uttered a verse:

A caution is the scatterbrain's behaviour.
Arrow-wind desiring bushes [warriors]

cannot usually see the sword in another one's hair properly.
This I bet, they do not have bigger balls than I
even if the spear-storm trunks [warriors] have larger cocks.

Then he snatched her up onto the bench, and the farmer's daughter ran out. Then Grettir uttered a verse:

Seam-prop spinster said I had got small in the sword.
The boastful balls-branch Hrist [servant-girl] is telling the truth.
My low maned-horse can grow quite long
in my young man's thigh forest,
island-bone Freyia [servant-girl];[69] wait a moment.

The maid shrieked at the top of her voice, but they parted with her no longer taunting Grettir by the time it was finished. A little later he got up and went to farmer Thorvald and told him of his problem and asked him to ferry him out and he did so and made a boat available to him and ferried him out and Grettir thanked him for this kindness. And when it became known that Grettir had swum a *league* across the sea, everyone thought his prowess was surpassing both on sea and on land. The people of Skagafiord criticised Thorbiorn Ongul greatly because he didn't get Grettir away from Drangey, and they said they would each take back their share. He found himself in a spot, and told them to be patient.

76

That summer a ship came out to Gonguskardsos. On this ship there was a man called Hæring. He was a young man and so good at climbing that there was no cliff he couldn't get up. He went to stay with Thorbiorn Ongul and was there on into the autumn. He kept pressing Thorbiorn to go to Drangey, and said he wanted to see whether it was such a steep rock that there was nowhere one could get up. Thorbiorn said he wouldn't be wasting his time if he got up onto the island and managed to give Grettir a wound or to kill him. He made this sound

[69] Island-bone = jewel, precious stone.

tempting to Hæring. And after this they went to Drangey and put him, the *Easterner*, up in a certain spot and he was to steal up on them, if he got up onto the island, but they went round to the ladder and started talking to Grettir and his companions. Thorbiorn asked Grettir whether he had made up his mind not to leave the island. He said there was nothing on which he was so determined.

'You have really led us a dance,' says Thorbiorn, 'whether we are ever able to get our own back or not, but there's not much that worries you.'

They went on with this for a long time, and they reached no agreement. But of Hæring there is this to tell, that he climbed back and forth over the cliff and managed to get up in a certain place where no one has been able to go either before or since. And when he got up onto the rock he saw where the brothers were with their backs to him. He thought that he would now within a short time be winning both fame and fortune. They had no suspicion about his movements, for they thought that it was impossible to get up anywhere except where the ladders were. Grettir was then busy with Thorbiorn and there was no lack of sharp words on both sides. Then Illugi happened to glance round and saw a man had come very close upon them. He then said:

'A man has come here upon us wielding an axe and he doesn't look too friendly to me.'

'You go against him then,' says Grettir, 'and I shall guard the ladder.'

Illugi made at Hæring, and when the *Easterner* saw this he set off somewhere along the island. Illugi chased him as far as the island went, and when he got to the edge of the cliff Hæring leapt off over it and broke all his bones. So his life came to an end. That has since been called Hæring's leap where he perished. Illugi came back and Grettir asked how he had parted from the one that he had been assigned to.

'He wasn't content,' says Illugi, 'to let me sort things out for him, and he broke his neck down over the cliff, and the farmers should pray for him on the assumption that he is dead.'

And when Ongul heard this, he told them to row away.

'I have now made two trips to meet Grettir, and I shall not come a third time unless I find out something new. But now I think it most likely that they can stay on Drangey as far as I am concerned. But I think that Grettir's time here from now on will be shorter than the time he has been here.'

Now they went home. This expedition was considered to be even worse than the previous one, and Grettir stayed that winter on Drangey, and there was no meeting between him and Thorbiorn that winter.

In that year *Lawman* Skapti Thoroddson died. This was a great loss to Grettir, for he had promised to press for his release as soon as Grettir had been twenty winters in outlawry, and this was the nineteenth winter of his outlawry of which we have just told. In the spring Snorri *Godi* died, and there were many things happened during this year which don't come into this story.

77

That summer at the Althing, Grettir's family discussed his outlawry a great deal, and some were of the opinion that he had worked out his outlawry if he had done part of the twentieth year. But those who had charges against him would not agree and claimed he had committed many deeds deserving of outlawry since, and so thought his outlawry ought to be even longer. Then a new *lawman* was chosen, Stein, son of Thorgest, son of Stein the Great Traveller, son of Thorir Autumndark. The mother of *Lawman* Stein was Arnora, daughter of Thord Gellir. Stein was a wise man. He was asked to give a ruling and he told them to work out whether it was the twentieth summer since he had been made outlaw, and it turned out to be the case. Then Thorir of Gard interposed and sought to bring forward all possible objections, and he was able to show that Grettir had been out here one winter when he was not an outlaw, so that it was then nineteen winters that he had been in outlawry. Then the *lawspeaker* said that no one should be longer in outlawry that twenty winters in all, even if he had committed deeds deserving of outlawry during that time.

'But until that time is up I will release no one from outlawry.'

As a result his release came to nothing for the time being, but it was now thought to be certainly going ahead that he would be released the next summer. The people of Skagafiord did not like the idea of Grettir getting out of outlawry, and now demanded that Thorbiorn Ongul should now either hand back the island or kill Grettir. He now thought he had a problem on his hands, for he saw no way of defeating Grettir, and yet he wanted to keep the island. He searched through all the possible ways of getting the better of Grettir, either by force or trickery or by whatever means he could get it done.

78

Thorbiorn Ongul had a nurse called Thurid. She was very old and not able to do much, so people thought. She had been very skilled in magic and had great knowledge of sorcery when she was young and people were heathen. Now it looked as though she must have forgotten it all. But though Christianity ruled in the land, there were yet many sparks of heathendom remaining. It had been the law in this country that it was not forbidden to sacrifice in secret or to perform other pagan rites, but the penalty was lesser outlawry if it was discovered. Now it was for many people that "the hand was most inclined to habit", and "it came most naturally to do what had been learned in youth". And when Thorbiorn Ongul had run out of ideas, he turned there for help where most would have thought it least likely to be found, and that was to his nurse, and he asked what sort of advice would be available from her. She answers:

'Now it seems to have come to this, as they say, that "many go to the goat-shed to ask for wool". And the last thing I want is that I should regard myself as superior to all the people of the area, and then turn out to be a useless person as soon as it is put to the test. Now I do not see that I could fare worse than you have done, even though I can scarcely rise from my bed. If you want to take my advice, then I shall tell you how to go about it.'

He agreed to this and said that her advice had proved helpful to him for a long time. So time passed until *Double-month* in the summer. It was one fine day that the old woman said to Ongul:

'Now it is calm weather and bright. I wish you now to go to Drangey and pick a quarrel with Grettir. I shall go with you and see how watchful he is of his words. I shall be able to get some certain knowledge, if I see them, as to how long their luck will last, and then I shall pronounce over them whatever words I please.'

Ongul answers, 'I'm getting tired of visits to Drangey, because I'm always in a worse mood when I come away from there than when I arrive.'

Then said the old woman, 'I shall not make any suggestions to you if you won't ever do as I say.'

'We don't want that, my dear,' he says, 'but I have declared that when I went there for the third time, something should come out of it for us.'

'You will have to risk it,' says the old woman, 'and it is going to cost you a great deal of trouble before Grettir is laid low, and it will often seem to you uncertain how it is going to turn out for you, and you will suffer for it when it is finished. And yet you are so committed to all this that something has to be done.'

After this Thorbiorn Ongul has a ten-oared boat launched and went aboard in a party of twelve. The old woman was along with them. They set to rowing out to Drangey. And when the brothers saw this, they went out to the ladder and they again began to discuss their affairs, and Thorbiorn said that he was again come to raise these questions, whether Grettir was willing to go away, and said he would still make a small issue of his loss of produce and their squatting there if they parted without trouble. Grettir said he would not accept or offer any terms for his leaving there.

'I have said this often before, and there is no point in your discussing it with me,' he says. 'You can do what you like, but here I shall stay and face whatever comes.'

Now Thorbiorn realised that his errand was going to be fruitless for the time being, and said:

'I felt I knew what accursed men we had to deal with here, and it is most likely that it will be a few days before I come here again.'

'I don't consider that one of my misfortunes, even if you never come here again,' says Grettir.

The old woman was lying back in the stern and clothes had been laid over her. She then stirred and said:

'These men seem to be tough and not prone to success. You and they are not of a kind. You make them many good offers, and they refuse them all, and there is little that more surely leads to misfortune than not being able to accept a good offer. Now I pronounce this upon you, Grettir, that you shall be bereft of success, all good fortune and luck and all defence and sense, ever the more the longer you live. It is my expectation that your days of joy here from now on will be fewer than those you have had up to now.'

And when Grettir heard this, he was very taken aback, and he said: 'What sort of devil is on the boat with them?'

Illugi replies, 'I think it is the old woman, Thorbiorn's nurse.'

'To hell with that sorceress,' says Grettir, 'and there was nothing worse to have been expected, and there are no words that have more taken me aback than those which she spoke, and I know that from her and her magic something evil will come to me. She is also going to have something from me to remind her of her visit to us.'

And he took up a pretty large stone and threw it down onto the boat, and it landed on the heap of clothes. Yet it was a longer throw than Thorbiorn had thought that any man could do with a stone. At that there was heard a great shriek. The stone had hit the old woman's thigh so that it broke. Then said Illugi:

'I would rather you hadn't done that.'

'Don't criticise it,' says Grettir, 'but I'm afraid that it has achieved too little, for it wouldn't have been too much in exchange for the two of us, if just one old woman had been the price of us.'

'Why should she be the price of us?' said Illugi, 'and we would not be making much of a showing then.'

Thorbiorn now went home, and there were no farewells when they parted. He then said to the old woman:

'Now it went as I expected, that you have not come back from your expedition to the island covered with glory. You have been maimed, and we are no closer to a proper solution than we were before, and we are forced to put up with one disgrace on top of another with no redress.'

She answers, 'This will be the beginning of their misfortunes, and I am sure that from now on things will take a turn for the worse for them. I am not worried that if I live I shan't be able to take vengeance for the treatment that has been given to me.'

'You really have raised your spirit, my dear,' said Thorbiorn.

So they came home, and the old woman took to her bed and remained there nearly a month. Then her injured leg had mended. She then began to get about on her feet. People made a great joke of Thorbiorn and the old woman's trip, and they thought there had been a lot of points scored in his exchanges with Grettir, to begin with at the spring *assembly* with the granting of the truce, secondly when Hæring was killed, and now the third when the old woman's thigh was broken, and there had been no points scored back. Thorbiorn Ongul found these comments very trying.

79

Now time passed on into the autumn, until it was three weeks before the beginning of winter.[70] Then the old woman asked to be carted to the sea. Thorbiorn asked what she intended to do.

'I haven't got a great deal of business, though it may be,' she says, 'that it will be the beginning of things of greater significance.'

It was done as she asked, and when she got to the shore, she limped along by the water as if she was being guided. There lay before her a log of wood with its root as big as one could carry on one's shoulder. She looked at the log and told them to turn it over for her. It looked as though it had been scorched and rubbed on one side. She had a little flat bit carved where it had been rubbed. Then she took her knife and cut runes on the root and reddened them with her blood and recited spells over them. She walked backwards withershins round the log and spoke over it many powerful formulas. After that she had the log pushed into the sea and made this pronouncement that it was to drift out to Drangey and be a source of every evil to Grettir. Thereupon she went back to Vidvik. Thorbiorn said he had no idea what this would achieve. The old woman said he would find out later. The wind was blowing in along the fiord and the old woman's root moved off against the wind and seemed not to travel too slowly.

Now Grettir was on Drangey, as was said above, with both his companions, and they were quite happy. The next day after the old woman had cast her spell on the piece of wood, Grettir and his companions went down over the cliff and looked for firewood, and when they got to the west side of the island they found a log with its roots washed ashore. Then said Illugi:

'That is a huge log for the fire, brother, and let's take it home.'

Grettir kicked it with his foot:

'An evil piece of wood, and sent by someone evil, and we shall use some other firewood,' and threw it out into the sea, and told Illugi he was not to bring it home, 'for it has been sent to cause us harm.'

After that they went to the hut and said nothing of this to the servant. The next day they found the log and it was closer to the ladders than the previous day. Grettir pushed it out to sea and said it must never be taken home. So that night passed. Then came windy weather

[70] See *Winter Nights* in Glossary.

with rain and they didn't feel like going out and told Glaum to look for firewood. He was cross at this and said he was being treated badly when he had to suffer outside in all the bad weather. He went down the ladders and found the old woman's root there and thought things had turned out well, lifted it up and struggled back to the hut and threw it down, and it made a great bang. Grettir heard it:

'Glaum has found something and I'll go out and see what it is,' and he takes up a wood-axe and goes out. Glaum then said:

'Make as good a job of cutting it up as I have of bringing it home.'

Grettir was not pleased with the servant and hit the root with the axe with both hands without noticing what log it was. And as soon as the axe touched the log it turned flat and glanced off the log and into Grettir's right leg above the knee so that it cut to the bone, and this was a great wound. Then he looked at the log and said:

'That which was more inclined to evil has proved more powerful, and this will not be the only misfortune. Now that same log that I threw away for two days has found its way here. Two accidents have now befallen you, Glaum, the first when you let our fire go out, and now this, that you have brought home this disastrous log, but if you have a third accident it will mean death for you and for all of us.'

Then Illugi went and dressed Grettir's wound, and it bled little, and Grettir slept well during the night, and so three nights passed without any pain coming into the wound. And when they unwrapped it the wound had closed across so that it was nearly healed. Then Illugi said:

'I really think that you are not going to have much trouble from this wound.'

'That would be a good thing, then,' says Grettir, 'but this is a strange business, however it turns out, and my feeling about it is quite different.'

80

Now they go to bed in the evening. And when it reached midnight Grettir began to toss about violently. Illugi asked why he was so restless. Grettir said that he had got a pain in his leg.

'And it would seem most likely to me that there has been some change in its colour.'

They then kindled a light. And when they unwrapped it the leg looked swollen and black as coal and the wound had broken open and was much worse-looking than before. At the same time it gave him a great deal of pain so that he couldn't put up with it without moving and he got not a wink of sleep. Then said Grettir:

'We must be prepared for this illness that I have got not being without consequences, for this is sorcery, and the old woman will have hoped to avenge the blow with the stone.'

Then Illugi said, 'I told you that no good was to be got from that old woman.'

'It will all come to the same thing,' says Grettir, and uttered five verses:[71]

Oft did the blade's edge
determine fates in battle,
when I defended the birch-dwelling
strongly from the attack of *berserks*.
Hrist's defender [warrior], Hiarrandi also
lost strong tree of hands [arm];
Biorn and Gunnar both soon lost
life and peace.

Also I came once out
on broad ferry to Dyrholmar,
spear-man [warrior, i.e. Grettir] long on boat.
Torfi, Vebrand's fine son
then challenged well-disposed man
to heavy spears' tumult [battle]
with a great force.

So was tough tree of Mimir's wall [warrior, i.e. Torfi]
parted from the poet [Grettir]
though many men stood in weapons' quarrel [battle]
so that oar-maple [sailor, Torfi] once was disabled
by Grettir's hand in storms of wounds [battles];
a horse he gave me in conclusion.

[71] Some of these verses refer to events not recounted in the saga; with the fourth, compare *Ljósvetninga saga*, ch. 1. They are not in all manuscripts of the saga, and may have been composed after the saga was first written.

I have heard that Thorfinn Arnor's son
was widely thought a man strong in dangerous deeds.
Point-tree [warrior, Thorfinn] said he would keep me from old age.
Determination failed the headstrong
scatterer of serpents' lairs [gold]
though he met me alone in the open;
I was not the more ready.

I was able to keep my life from spear-wielders [warriors],
for I trusted my might against men's sieges;
it was not a rare occurrence.
Now has a powerful ancient stone-land [woman, Thurid]
defeated battle-fire tree [warrior, Grettir] by charms.
These grim undertakings are mighty.

'Now we must be on the watch,' said Grettir, 'for it will be Thorbiorn Ongul and his people's intention that this will not be the only thing. I want you, Glaum, to guard the ladder every day from now on, and pull it up in the evening, and do this faithfully, as if a great deal depended on it. But if you betray us, you will not be long in getting something unpleasant.'

Glaum made fair promises about this. Now the weather began to worsen, and a great north-easterly blew up with cold weather. Grettir asked each evening whether the ladder had been pulled up. Glaum said:

'It really is most likely that people will come! And is anyone so determined to have your life, that to gain it he would kill himself? For this weather is quite beyond travelling in. And I think your great heroism is now extinguished when you are expecting death for yourselves at every moment.'

'You will put up with it even worse than either of us,' said Grettir, 'whatever has to be faced. But even so you must now guard the ladder, if you have to be forced.'

They drove him out every morning. He made a great fuss about it. The pain in the wound began to get worse, so that the whole leg swelled up and the thigh then began to fester both above and below and it spread over the whole wound so that Grettir became mortally ill. Illugi watched over him night and day so that he took no notice of anything else. The second week had now passed since Grettir had wounded himself.

81

Thorbiorn Ongul was now staying at home in Vidvik and was dissatisfied that he was unable to defeat Grettir. And when a good week had passed since the old woman had cast her spell on the root, she came to talk to Thorbiorn and asked whether he didn't plan to go and see Grettir. He said there was nothing he was more determined against.

'But do you want to see him, my dear?' says Thorbiorn.

'I shall not go to see him,' says the old woman, 'but I have sent him my greeting, and I am sure it will have reached him. And I think it would be a good thing for you to jump to it quickly and go soon to see him, otherwise you will have no chance of defeating him.'

Thorbiorn answers, 'I have gone there on so many disastrous trips that that is somewhere I am not going. That alone is a good enough reason, that there is such a storm raging that it isn't possible to go anywhere, whatever urgency there may be.'

She answers, 'You really are lacking in initiative, if you can see no way to go about it. Now I shall again tell you what to do. First, go and get hold of some men and ride out to Hof to your brother-in-law Halldor and get his advice. But if I have some power over Grettir's health, why should it be thought unlikely that I am responsible for the breath of wind which has been playing over us for a time?'

Thorbiorn realised that it could be that the old woman could see further than he had thought and immediately sent for men round in the district. There was a quick response, that none of those who had given up their share were willing to do anything to help, said that Thorbiorn could keep both the share in the island and the attack upon Grettir. Tungu-Stein provided him with two of his supporters, his brother Hialti sent him three men, Eirik of Guddalir sent him one man; he also had six men from his own house. These twelve rode from Vidvik out to Hof. Halldor invited them to stay and asked what was their purpose. Thorbiorn gave a most clear account. Halldor asked whose idea it was. He said that his nurse had urged him greatly.

'That will lead to no good,' said Halldor, 'for she is a sorceress, and that is now forbidden.'

'We can't take account of all that,' says Thorbiorn, 'but a conclusion shall be reached somehow if I have anything to do with it. But how shall I go about getting onto the island?'

'I can see,' says Halldor, 'that you are putting your trust in something, but I am not sure how good it is. Now if you want to go ahead, go out to Haganess in Fliot to my friend Biorn. He has a good boat. Tell him it is my wish that he lend you the ship. From there it should be possible to sail in to Drangey, but I am not confident about your trip if Grettir is not ill and in good health. And you can be sure of this, that if you don't defeat him in a decent way, he has plenty of people to bring a suit on his behalf. Don't kill Illugi if you can avoid it. But I feel sure that not everything is Christian in this enterprise.'

Now Halldor gave them six men to go with them. One was called Kar, the second Thorleif, the third Brand. More are not named. And from there the eighteen of them went out to Fliot and came to Haganess and gave Biorn Halldor's message. He said he felt obliged to comply on his account, but said he owed Thorbiorn no favours and thought this trip was a crazy idea, and was much against it. They said they would not turn back, went down to the sea and launched the boat, and the gear was near by in the boat-shed. They now got ready to sail. Everyone standing on the shore thought it would be an impossible trip for them. Now they hoist the sail. The boat got under way quickly and speedily out into the fiord. And just as they got pretty well out into the fiord and into the deep water, the wind moderated so that it never seemed too strong. In the evening when it had grown dark, they got in to Drangey.

82

Now it is to be told that Grettir was so ill that he could not stand on his feet. Illugi stayed with him, and Glaum was supposed to keep guard. He was still full of objections and said that they were afraid they would drop dead even though nothing was happening. Now he went out of the hut and very unwillingly. And when he got to the ladders he went over it in his own mind and decided that he would not pull up the ladder. He now began to get very sleepy and lay down and slept the whole day and right on until Thorbiorn got to the island. They now saw that the ladder was not drawn up. Then spoke Thorbiorn:

'Things are different,' he said, 'from what is normal, in that there are no people about, while their ladder is up. Maybe more will happen on our trip than we thought to begin with. Now we must hurry to the hut and let there be no lack of determination. We can be sure of this, that if they are in full form we shall need everyone to do the best they can.'

Then they went up onto the island and looked around and saw where a man was lying a little way from the way up and he was snoring hard. Thorbiorn recognised Glaum and went up to him and knocked him on the ear with his sword-hilt and told the bugger to wake up.

'And truly he is in a bad way whose life depends on your good faith.'

Glaum sits up and said, 'Now they are going on as usual. And do you think I have too much freedom, by lying out here in the cold?'

Ongul said, 'Are you mad, that you don't realise that your enemies are here and are going to kill you all?'

Then Glaum didn't say anything, but began to howl as loud as he could when he realised who the men were.

'Make your choice,' said this Ongul, 'either be quiet at once and tell us about your living quarters, or else I shall kill you.'

Then Glaum went silent as if he had been plunged in water. Thorbiorn said:

'Are they at the hut, the brothers, and why are they not about?'

'They have no choice,' says Glaum, 'for Grettir is ill and nearly dead, and Illugi stays with him.'

Ongul asked what was wrong with him and what had caused it, and then Glaum said how it had come about with Grettir's wound. Then Ongul laughed and said:

'The ancient saying is true, that "old friends stick together longest", as is the other one, that "it is bad to make a slave your best friend", in your case, Glaum, and you have shamefully betrayed your master, even if he was a bad lot.'

Many of the others attacked him for his bad behaviour and beat him almost past healing and left him lying there. And they went up to the hut and banged at the door with some force. Then said Illugi:

'Grey-belly is knocking at the door, brother,' he says.

'And knocking rather hard,' said Grettir, 'and not very kindly.'

And at that moment the door gave way. Then Illugi leapt to his weapons and defended the door so that they could not get in. They kept up the attack for a long time, and could not get at him except with spear-thrusts, and Illugi struck them all off their shafts. And when they saw they were not achieving anything, they leapt up on top of the hut and tore off the roof. Then Grettir got on his legs and grasped a spear and thrust it out between the rafters. It was Halldor of Hof's man Kar that it got, and it passed straight through him. Ongul spoke and told them to mind how they went and take good care of themselves.

'For we can defeat them if we act wisely.'

They now stripped away round the ends of the roof-beam and then pushed at the beam until it broke in two. Grettir could not rise from his knees. He then grasped the *cutlass* that had been Kar's. At that moment they jumped down into the remains of the building and there was now a hard battle between them. Grettir struck with the *cutlass* at Hialti Thordarson's man Vikar and hit his left shoulder just as he jumped into the building and it sliced across his shoulders and out under his right side and took the man straight across in two, and the body plunged down on top of Grettir in two pieces. Then he was not able to straighten up the *cutlass* as quickly as he hoped and at that moment Thorbiorn Ongul thrust between Grettir's shoulders, and this was a great wound. Then said Grettir:

' "Everyone's back is bare unless he has a brother".'

Illugi then threw a shield over him and defended Grettir so stoutly that everyone acknowledged how splendid his defence was. Then Grettir said to Ongul:

'Who directed you to the island?'

Ongul said, 'Christ directed us.'

'But it's my guess,' said Grettir, 'that it was the wretched old woman, your nurse, who directed you, for it is her counsel you will have relied on.'

'It will make no difference to you now,' said Ongul, 'whoever it is we have relied on.'

They attacked hard, but Illugi fought very valiantly to defend them both, but Grettir was entirely disabled from fighting both by his wounds and his illness. Then Ongul ordered that they should bear down on Illugi with shields.

'For I have never met his like, a man no older than him.'

They now did so and hemmed him in with planks and weapons so that he could make no defence. Then they managed to capture him and held him. He had given most of them some wounds, those who had been in the attack, and had killed three of Ongul's men. After that they approached Grettir. He had fallen forward. There was then no defence from him, for he had already come to be on the point of death from the leg-wound. His thigh was all festered right up to his groin. They then gave him many wounds without him bleeding hardly at all. And when they thought he must be dead, Ongul took hold of the *cutlass* and said he had borne it long enough. But Grettir had clenched his fingers hard round the handle and it would not come free. Many of them went up and could do nothing. Eight of them were pulling at it by the end, and they still got nowhere. Then said Ongul:

'Why should we hold back with the outlaw? Put the hand down on the block.'

And when that was done they hacked off his hand at the wrist. Then the fingers straightened out and released the handle. Then Ongul took the *cutlass* in both hands and struck at Grettir's head. It was a very great blow so that the *cutlass* could not withstand it and a piece broke off in the middle of the edge. And when they saw that they asked why he was spoiling such a fine article. Ongul answers:

'Then it will be easier to recognise if anyone asks about it.'

They said there was no need for this, since the man was already dead.

'There is more to be done about it, though,' says Ongul.

He then struck two or three blows at Grettir's neck before it took off his head.

'Now I know for certain, that Grettir is dead,' said Ongul.

Thus Grettir ended his life, the most valiant man there has been in Iceland, one winter short of forty-five when he was killed, and he was fourteen years old when he killed Skeggi, his first killing, and then everything went towards increasing his honour and fortune until he came up against the villain Glam, and he was then twenty years old. And when he fell into outlawry he was twenty-five, and he was a good nineteen years in outlawry and frequently got into great trials of his manhood and always kept his faith well as far as circumstances allowed. He had foreknowledge of most things, though he was unable to do anything about them.

'It is a great fellow we have laid low,' said Thorbiorn. 'We shall now take his head with us to the mainland, for I don't want to lose the price that has been put on his head. They will then not be able to dispute that I have killed Grettir.'

They told him to do as he liked, but were not very pleased, for they all thought what he had done was disgraceful. Then Ongul said to Illugi:

'It is a great shame for such a brave man as you are, that you have landed in such foolishness as to engage in criminal deeds with this outlaw and as a result be subject to killing without redress.'

Illugi answers, 'You will only then know, when the Althing is over in the summer, who the outlaws will be. And neither you nor the old woman your nurse will be judges in this business, for your sorcery and witchcraft have killed Grettir, even though you used weapons on him when he was at the point of death, and you thus added a deed of baseness to your black magic.'

Then said Ongul, 'You speak boldly, but it will not turn out so. I will demonstrate that I would be sorry to lose you, and I will give you your life if you will swear on your honour an oath to us, to take no vengeance on those who have been on this expedition.'

'That would seem to me worth considering if Grettir had been able to defend himself and if you had defeated him honourably and bravely. But there is now no chance that I will do that to save my life, to be such a vile person as you. But to give you a straight answer, no one shall be less on your side than I, if I live, for I shall never forget how you have treated Grettir. I would much rather die.'

Then Thorbiorn had a discussion with his companions about whether they should let Illugi live or not. They said it was up to him to decide what was done, since he had been in charge of the expedition. Ongul said he could not have this man hanging over him who would make no promises to them. And when Illugi saw that they were going to execute him, he laughed and said:

'Now you have decided on what was closer to my wishes.'

They took him then, when it got light, to the east of the island and dispatched him there, and they all praised his courage and all thought he was unlike anyone of his age. They buried both the brothers there on the island, but after that took Grettir's head and carried it with them together with everything there that was worth anything in weapons and clothes. Ongul would not allow the good *cutlass* to be included in the share-out, and carried it long after. They took Glaum with them, and he took it very badly. The wind had dropped already during the night. They rowed to land during the morning. Ongul went ashore at the most convenient place for him and sent the boat out to Biorn. And when they got nearly in to Osland, Glaum began to make such a fuss that they didn't feel like taking him any further and killed him there, and he wept at the top of his voice when he was about to be killed.

Ongul went home to Vidvik and thought he had done well on this trip. They put Grettir's head in salt in a storehouse that they called Grettir's store, there at Vidvik. It stayed there the winter. Ongul was thought very ill of because of these deeds as soon as people knew that Grettir had been defeated with the help of witchcraft. Ongul stayed put until after Christmas. Then he rode to see Thorir of Gard and told him of these killings and this too, that he thought himself entitled to the price that had been put on Grettir's head. Thorir said that he would not deny that he had been responsible for Grettir's outlawry.

'I have often suffered harshly at his hands, but I would not have done that to get his life, to make myself a criminal or sorcerer as you have done. I am so far from handing you the money, that it seems to me that you deserve to lose your life for witchcraft and black magic.'

Ongul answers, 'I think it is more that you are motivated by tight-fistedness and meanness than that you care by what means Grettir was defeated.'

Thorir said that the solution for them was simple, they should wait for the Althing and accept what the *lawman* thought was most just. They parted with nothing but bad feeling between Thorir and Thorbiorn Ongul.

83

Grettir and Illugi's family were very angry when they learned of the killings, and interpreted it that Ongul had done an act of baseness in killing a man at the point of death and secondly in his sorcery. They consulted the most learned men about it and Ongul's affairs came in for a lot of criticism. He now rode west to Midfiord when four weeks of the summer had past. And when news got about of his movements, Asdis called on people to come to her and many of her friends were there, her sons-in-law Gamli and Glum and their sons Skeggi, who was known as Short-Arm, and Ospak who was mentioned above. Asdis was so well liked that all the people of Midfiord joined to help her, and even those who previously had been enemies of Grettir. The foremost of these people was Thorodd Poem-bit and most of the people of Hrutafiord. Ongul now got to Biarg with twenty men. They had Grettir's head with them. All the people who had promised her help had not yet arrived. They went into the *living-room* with the head and put it down on the floor. The lady was in the room and many other people. There were no greetings between them. Ongul then uttered a verse:

I carried up from the island
Grettir's unsated head;
brooch-Nauma [Asdis] is forced to weep
for this red-haired one.
Here you can see on the floor
the head of the truce-breaker;
it will all rot for the Frid of the sea's bright flame [Asdis]
unless she salt it.

The lady sat still while he uttered the verse. After that she uttered a verse:

You would no less than sheep
before a wild animal have leapt into the sea—
new laughing-stock is come north
to Syr's tear-Niords [men]—
if war-trees [warriors] had faced, weapon-Frey [Ongul],
an unsick Grettir on the island.
I have been quick in praise of men.

Then many said it was not surprising that she had had brave sons, a brave one like her, having to put up with such provocation. Ospak was outside and had a talk with Ongul's men, those who had not gone inside, and asked about the killings, and everyone praised Illugi's stand. Then they told how hard Grettir had held the *cutlass* when he was dead. This men thought amazing. Then the approach of many men riding up from the west was seen. It was many of the lady's friends who had come there and Gamli and Skeggi from Melar in the west. Ongul had been planning to hold a court of confiscation after Illugi, for they were laying claim to all his property. But when this great crowd came, Ongul saw that he could do nothing. It was Ospak and

Gamli who were fiercest and wanted to make an attack on Ongul, but those who were wiser told them to accept the advice of their kinsman Thorvald and other leading men and said that Ongul's position would be the more condemned the more wise men there were considering it. With this intervention, Ongul rode away and took Grettir's head with him, for he planned to take it to the Althing. He now rode home, and things began to look bad for him, for nearly all the leading men in the land were related either by blood or marriage to Grettir and Illugi. That summer Skeggi Short-Arm married Thorodd Poem-bit's daughter [Valgerd].[72] Thorodd then allied himself with Grettir's family's case.

84

Now people rode to the Althing and Ongul's supporters turned out to be fewer than he expected, for his case was widely condemned. Then Halldor asked whether they were to take Grettir's head with them to the Althing. Ongul said he planned to take it.

'That is unwise,' says Halldor, 'for there will be plenty of opponents for you without your giving such reminders calculated to revive people's griefs.'

Then they were on the road and were about to ride south across Sand. Ongul had the head taken and buried down in a mound of sand. It is called Grettir's mound. At the Althing it was crowded, and Ongul brought forward his case and boasted greatly about his deeds in having killed the greatest outlaw in the land and laid claim to the price that had been put on his head. But Thorir made the same reply as was said above. Then the *lawman* was asked for a ruling. He said he wished to hear whether any counter-charges were to be brought as a result of which Ongul should lose the outlaw-price, otherwise he should get what had been put on his head. Then Thorvald Asgeirsson called upon Short-Arm to bring forward the charges, and charged Thorbiorn Ongul on one charge of sorcery and the black magic which had also caused Grettir's death, and on another of their having attacked him when he was a man half dead, and declared the penalty to be full outlawry.

[72] The name is in some manuscripts and also in *The Book of Settlements*, ch. 173.

Now there was a great split into two parties, and there were few who stood by Thorbiorn. Now it turned out differently from what he had thought, for Thorvald and his son-in-law Isleif believed it was a capital crime to cast spells to bring about a man's death. But at the suggestion of wise men the conclusion of the case was that Thorbiorn was to sail the same summer and never return to Iceland as long as those were still alive who were responsible for prosecutions on behalf of Illugi and Grettir. It was then made law that all sorcerers were declared outlaws. And when he realised how things were likely to turn out for him, he took himself off from the *assembly*, because it looked as though Grettir's family were going to go for him. He also got nothing of the money that had been put on Grettir's head, for *lawspeaker* Stein would not agree to that being paid for a deed of baseness. No compensation was paid for the men with Thorbiorn who had fallen on Drangey. This was to be balanced against the killing of Illugi. His family, however, did not like this at all. Now people rode home from the *assembly*, and all charges that people had against Grettir were made void.

Gamli's son Skeggi, who was Thorodd Poem-bit's son-in-law and Grettir's nephew, went north to Skagafiord with the support of Thorvald Asgeirsson and his son-in-law Isleif who later became bishop of Skalaholt and the agreement of all the people and got a boat and went to Drangey to fetch the bodies of the brothers Grettir and Illugi and took them out to Reykir on Reykiastrond and buried them there at the church. And there is this evidence that Grettir lies there that in the time of the Sturlungs, when the church at Reykir was moved, Grettir's bones were exhumed and they were thought to be enormously big and surprisingly so. Illugi's bones were afterwards buried to the north of the church, and Grettir's head was buried at the church at home at Biarg. The lady Asdis remained at Biarg and was so much liked that no trouble was ever offered her, and had not been even while Grettir was in outlawry. Skeggi Short-Arm took over the farm at Biarg after Asdis and became a great man. His son was Gamli, father of Skeggi at Skarfsstadir and of Asdis, mother of the monk Odd. Many people are descended from him.[73]

[73] I.e. Skeggi Short-Arm.

85

Thorbiorn Ongul got a passage on a ship at Gasir taking everything of his possessions he could get onto it with him, and his brother Hialti took over his land. Ongul also gave him Drangey. Hialti afterwards became quite a leading man and he is not mentioned any further in connection with this story. Ongul went to Norway and still threw his weight about. He believed he had achieved a very mighty deed in the slaying of Grettir. Many of those who were unacquainted with how it had come about were of the same opinion, and there were many who knew how renowned a man Grettir had been. He related only those parts of their dealings that were to his credit, but he suppressed what in the story was less to his renown. This story came in the autumn east to Tunsberg. When Thorstein Dromund learned of the killings he was very silent about it, because he was told that Ongul was very powerful and tough. Thorstein called to mind what he had said when he and Grettir once long before had been talking about their arms. Thorstein now kept informed of Ongul's movements. Both of them were in Norway during the winter and Thorbiorn was in the north of the country and Thorstein in Tunsberg, and neither had ever seen the other. And yet Thorbiorn found out that Grettir had a brother in Norway and felt it was risky in a country he didn't know, and so he cast about for some idea as to where he should go to. At that time many Norwegians were going out to Constantinople and becoming mercenaries there. So Thorbiorn found it quite an attractive idea to go there and so win fame and fortune for himself, but to keep out of Scandinavia because of Grettir's family. So he set out from Norway and travelled far abroad and didn't stop until he got out to Constantinople and there became a mercenary. [He stayed there for a time.]

86

Here begins the episode of Spes and Thorstein

Thorstein Dromund was a rich man and stood in the highest regard. He now learned that Ongul had left the country and gone out to Constantinople. He responded quickly and put his property into the charge of his relations and set off and pursued Ongul and kept arriving where Ongul had just left. Ongul knew nothing of his travels. Thorstein Dromund got out to Constantinople soon after Ongul and was determined by all means to kill him, but neither could recognise the other. Now they wanted to join the Varangian guard, and this was welcomed as soon as it was known that they were men from Norway. At this time Michael Catalactus was king over Constantinople. Thorstein Dromund now kept on the watch for Ongul to see if he could in some way recognise him, and he couldn't manage this because of the crowds. He continually lay awake and was very unhappy about his situation. He felt he had had a great loss.

Now the next thing was that the Varangians had to go on some military expedition to free the country from an invasion. And before they set out it was their custom and rule to have an inspection of weapons, and they did so now too. And when the weapons-inspection had been arranged, all the Varangians had to go to it, including those who were then intending to join with them on the expedition, and show their weapons. Both of them attended, Thorstein and Ongul. Thorbiorn presented his weapons; he still had the *cutlass* that had been Grettir's. And when he showed this, many admired it and said that it was a very fine weapon, and said it was a great pity that there was the notch in the middle of the edge, and asked him how it had come about. Ongul said it was worth recounting.

'For this is the main thing to say about it, that out in Iceland,' he says, 'I slew the warrior called Grettir the Strong, who was the greatest champion there and hero, for no one was able to defeat him until I came along. And since it was granted to me to defeat him, I got the better of him, and yet he had many times my strength. I then struck at his head with the *cutlass* and then it broke the notch in the edge.'

Those who were standing nearest said that he must indeed have had a hard skull, and they showed it to one another. From this Thorstein realised who Ongul was, and asked if he could look at the *cutlass* like the others. Ongul made no objection, for most were praising his valour and prowess. He thought that this person would do the same, and he was not expecting that Thorstein or any member of Grettir's family would be there. Dromund now took hold of the *cutlass* and at the same time raised it up and struck at Ongul. The blow struck his head and was so hard that it came to rest in his teeth. Thorbiorn Ongul ingloriously fell dead to the ground. At this everyone was struck dumb.

The sheriff of the place immediately arrested Thorstein and asked for what cause he committed such a wicked deed there at a solemn assembly. Thorstein said he was brother of Grettir the Strong and also that he had never been able to carry out the vengeance until then. Then there were many who agreed that this strong man must have been very important for Thorstein to have had to travel so far across the world to avenge him. The governors of the city thought this might well be true, but because there was no one there who was able to confirm what Thorstein said, their law was that anyone who killed a man should be subject to no other forfeit than his life. Thorstein was given a quick sentence and rather a harsh one. He was to be put in a dungeon in a prison and suffer death there if no one redeemed him with money. And when Thorstein got into the dungeon there was a man there. He had been there a long time and was on the point of death from neglect. It was both foul and cold there. Thorstein said to this man:

'How do you find your life?'

He answers, 'Very bad, for there is no one who will help me and I have no relations to redeem me.'

Thorstein said, 'There is much one can do in a difficult situation, and let's be cheerful and do something to entertain ourselves.'

The other said there was nothing could cheer him up.

'Yet we shall try,' says Thorstein. He started then and chanted a poem. He was a man with a very good voice, so that one could hardly find his equal. He did not hold back. There was a public street a little way out from the dungeon. Thorstein chanted so loudly that it resounded in the stonework and the other, who previously was half dead, found it very entertaining. So he continued on into the evening.

87

There was a noble lady with an establishment there in the city called Spes, very rich and of great family. Her husband was called Sigurd. He was wealthy and of a less noble family than she. She had been given to him for his money. There was no great love between the couple, and she felt she had married very much beneath her. She was a high-spirited and very self-willed person. It so happened that while Thorstein was giving his performance in the evening, Spes was walking along the street near the dungeon and heard from it such a beautiful voice that she said she had never heard the like. She was walking with a large number of servants and told them to go over there and find out who it was that had this splendid voice. They called now and asked who it was that was so harshly confined there. Thorstein gave his name. Then said Spes:

'Are you an accomplished man at other things besides reciting?'

He said he was no great shakes.

'What have you done wrong,' she says, 'that you should be tortured to death here?'

He said he had killed a man to avenge his brother.

'But I was unable to prove it with witnesses,' said Thorstein 'and so I was put in here,' said he, 'unless someone is willing to redeem me. But I think there is no hope of that, for I have no connections here.'

'It will be a great loss if you are killed. But was your brother as outstanding a man, whom you avenged?'

He said that he was more than twice the man he was. She asked what evidence there was of that. Then Thorstein uttered this verse:

> Eight edge-moot's makers [warriors] could not,
> rings' Grund [lady, i.e. Spes], from bold-spirited
> Grettir's hand take the *cutlass*,
> until all-virtuous fasteners of sword-belt's girding [warriors]
> struck shoulder-leg from courage-bold
> wave-horse urger [warrior, i.e. Grettir].

'Such a thing is very splendid,' said those who understood the verse. And when she knew what it meant she said:

'Will you accept your life from me, if it is offered you?'

'Very happily,' said Thorstein, 'if this companion of mine is redeemed with me, who is sitting here. Otherwise we shall both stay here.'

She answers, 'I think you are a better bargain than he.'

'However that may be,' said Thorstein, 'we shall either come out of here together or neither of us.'

She then went to where the Varangians were and asked for Thorstein's release and offered the money for it. They were very glad to do this. She then brought it about by her influence and wealth that they were both released. And as soon as Thorstein got out of the dungeon he went to see Spes. The lady took him in and kept him secretly, though sometimes he was on military expeditions with the Varangians and proved to be a most courageous man in all enterprises.

88

At that time Harald Sigurdarson was in Constantinople and Thorstein became friends with him. Thorstein was now considered a man of some consequence, for Spes did not let him go short of money. They now fell in love, Thorstein and Spes. She was very impressed by his accomplishments. Her expenses now became rather large, for she devoted herself a great deal to her friendships. Her husband also felt he noticed that she had changed her ways, both in character and various kinds of behaviour and especially in spending money; he found both gold and precious objects missing which disappeared from her keeping. And on one occasion her husband Sigurd spoke to her and said that she was starting to behave in a strange way.

'You pay no regard to our goods and squander it in various ways; and you seem to me to be as if in a dream, and you never want to stay put where I am. Now I am quite sure that something is the matter.'

She answers, 'I told you and also my family, when we joined together, that I wanted to be independent and have freedom with everything that it was proper for me to dispose of, and it is for these reasons that I do not spare your money. But are there other things you want to discuss with me which I ought to be ashamed of?'

He answers, 'I am not without the suspicion that you are keeping some man that you like more than me.'

'I do not know,' she says, 'that there is much reason for that, but yet I would think that you cannot support what you say with any proofs. But the two of us are not going to talk together alone if you are accusing me of this perfidy.'

He dropped the conversation for the moment. She and Thorstein continued in the same way and paid no attention to what evil people might say, for she trusted her cleverness and influence. They often sat in conversation and entertained each other. There was one evening when they were sitting in an upstairs room where she kept her jewels. She asked Thorstein to recite something, for she thought her husband was sitting drinking as was his custom. She fastened the doors to. And when he had been reciting for a while, there was a knocking at the door and a shout that it should be opened. It was her husband with many servants who had come. The lady had opened a large chest and was showing Thorstein her jewels. And when she recognised who it was she did not want to open the doors. She spoke to Thorstein:

'I have a quick idea; jump down here into the chest and keep quiet.'

He did so. She closed the lock on the chest and sat up on it. At that moment her husband came into the upstairs room, and they had just broken into the room. The lady said:

'Why are you coming with such a great clatter, are there attackers after you?'

Her husband answers, 'Now it is a good thing that you yourself provide the proof of what you are. But where is the man who was most letting himself go with his voice just now? I expect you think he has a better voice than I.'

She said, '"No one looks entirely foolish if he can keep his mouth shut". That's how it is with you. You think you're clever and expect you can make your lies stick on me, and here is the proof of it. If what you say is true, then take him, for he won't jump out through the walls or the roof.'

He searched the building and found nothing. She said:

'Why don't you take him now, if you're so sure you are in the right?'

He was silent then and felt he didn't know what tricks he was up against, and asked his companions whether they hadn't heard the same as he had. But when they saw that the lady was annoyed, nothing came of their witness, and they said that what one heard could always be deceptive. Her husband then went out and felt he knew the truth even though he couldn't find the man. He then stopped his inquisition of his wife and her affairs for a long time.

It happened again another time much later that Thorstein and Spes were sitting in a store-room for clothes. In there there was cloth both cut and uncut which belonged to her and her husband. She was showing Thorstein many pieces of cloth and they were opening it out. And when they least expected it, her husband came upon them there with a lot of men and broke into the upstairs room. While they were doing that, she threw the cloth down over Thorstein and was leaning against the pile of cloth when they came inside.

'Are you again going to deny,' says her husband, 'that there was a man here with you? There will be people here now that saw you both.'

She told them not to be in such a rush.

'You cannot fail now, but let me be and don't push me about.'

They now searched through the building and found nothing. In the end they gave up. Then the lady said:

'It is always a good thing when one turns out better than many expect, and it was predictable that you wouldn't find what wasn't there. So will you now, husband, admit your foolishness and free me from this slander?'

He said, 'So far from freeing you, I feel convinced that you are guilty of what I have accused you of. And you will have to do your best in this matter to see if you can clear yourself of it.'

She said she had no objection to that. With that they ended their talk.

After this Thorstein stayed the whole time with the Varangians, and they say that he asked for advice from Harald Sigurdarson, and it is thought that they would not have found a solution without the benefit of him and his cleverness. And when some time had passed, her husband Sigurd announced that he was going away on certain business of his. The lady did not try to stop him. And when her husband had left, Thorstein went to see Spes and they were then continually in each other's company. Her establishment was so arranged that it was built out over the sea, and there were some buildings where the sea flowed up underneath. That was where Spes and Thorstein usually sat. There was a small trapdoor in the floor there which only they two knew about. They kept it standing open in case it was necessary to use it in a hurry. Now this is to be told about the husband, that he didn't go away at all, instead he hid and tried to spy on his wife. So it came about that when they were least expecting it one evening, and they were sitting in the room over the sea and enjoying themselves, that the husband with a large number of people surprised them there and took some people to the window that was in the building and told them to see whether it was as he had said. They all said that he had been correct, and that it must have been the same before. They burst now into the room. And when they heard the clatter, she said to Thorstein:

'You will have to go down here, whatever the risk. Send me some sign if you get away from under the buildings.'

He said all right and threw himself down through the floor, and the lady kicked the trapdoor with her foot. It fell then back into place and there was no sign of any alteration to the floor. The husband came into the room with his men. They now went searching and found nothing, as was to be expected. The room was empty, so that there was nothing inside there except a smooth floor and the *platform*-seats. The lady sat there playing with [the rings on] her fingers. She took no notice of them and went on quite unconcernedly. Now the husband found it very strange and asked his companions whether they had not seen the man. They said they had indeed seen him. Then said the lady:

'Now we shall see another example of what they say, that "everything has always happened in threes in days gone by". It has been so with you, Sigurd,' she said. 'Three times you have caused me annoyance, it seems to me. Are you now any wiser than at the start?'

'This time I was not the only witness,' says the husband. 'You shall submit to proof of your innocence of all this, for I am in no way going to accept this humiliation without reparation.'

'I think,' said the lady, 'what you are demanding I am going to offer, for I shall be very pleased to clear myself of this charge. It has got about so much that it will bring me great dishonour if I don't refute it.'

'At the same time you must make a formal denial,' says the husband, 'to the effect that you haven't given away our goods or treasures.'

She answers, 'At the time I submit to the proof, I shall altogether clear myself of all the items that you are complaining of about me. But take note of what the outcome will be. I intend straightway tomorrow to go before the bishop and he shall appoint me an absolute proof of innocence regarding everything that has been said concerning this accusation.'

Her husband said this would quite content him and went away with his men. Now this is to tell of Thorstein that he swam out from under the buildings and went ashore at a convenient place and got a piece of wood with a burning flame and held it up so that it could be seen from the lady's establishment. She stayed outside for a long time during the evening and in the night, for she wanted to know whether Thorstein had got ashore. And when she saw the flame, she knew for certain that he had got ashore, for they had made this arrangement between themselves. The following morning Spes suggested to her husband that they should discuss their affairs in front of the bishop, and he was in full agreement. They now come before the bishop and the husband brings the same charges against her that were detailed above. The bishop asked whether she had been involved in this in the past, and no one said they had ever heard of that. Then he asked what reasons he had for accusing her of this. He then produced men who had seen her sitting in a locked building with a man with her. The husband said he had suspicions that this man must have seduced her. The bishop said that she could easily clear herself of this accusation if she wanted to. She said she wanted to very much.

'I believe,' said Spes, 'that I shall easily find women to vouch for me in this matter.'

Now the oath was prescribed for her and a day fixed for when it should be performed. After that she went home and expressed her satisfaction. Thorstein and Spes had a meeting and laid their plans.

89

So that day passed and so on until the day came that Spes was to perform the oath. Then she invited to it all her friends and relations and fitted herself out in the best clothes she had. Many fine women walked alongside her. It was very wet weather. The path was wet and there was a great ditch to cross before they got to the church. And just as Spes and her party came up to the ditch, there was facing them a great crowd and a large number of poor people who were begging for alms, for it was a public street. They all felt obliged to greet her warmly, those who knew her, and wished her well in return for her often having been kind to them. There was one beggar among the other poor people, of great size and he had a long beard. The procession of women stopped at the wet spot, for courtly people found the ditch dirty to cross. And when this great beggar saw the lady, that she was better dressed than the other women, he spoke to her thus:

'Good lady,' he said, 'be so condescending as to let me carry you across this ditch, for we beggars have a duty to serve you to the best of our ability.'

'How can you carry me properly,' said she, 'when you cannot carry yourself?'

'Yet it would be a proof of your humility,' he says, 'and I cannot offer more than I have got, and things will turn out better for you in every way if you don't show pride towards a poor man.'

'You can be sure of this,' she says, 'if you don't carry me properly you will earn yourself a flogging or other worse disgrace.'

'I will gladly risk that,' he said, and got onto his feet out in the ditch. She appeared to feel very averse to his carrying her, and nevertheless got on his back. He shuffled very slowly and walked with two crutches. And when he got to the middle of the ditch he swayed from side to side. She urged him to pull himself together.

'And this will be the worst trip you have ever undertaken if you drop me in here.'

The poor fellow struggled on and made an extra effort, put himself out to the utmost and got very close to the side, and then caught his foot and plunged forward so that he threw her up on the bank and himself fell into the ditch up to his armpits. And as he lay thus he grasped at her, the lady, and could not get a hold on her clothes. He then put his dirty hand up on her knee and right up onto her bare thigh. She leapt up and swore, saying that trouble always came from wretched beggars.

'And it would be right for you to lie dead if that didn't seem to me shameful in view of your wretchedness.'

He said then, '"Various are the fortunes of men". I thought I was doing you a good turn and was hoping for some alms from you but I get from you threats and abuse and no benefit,' and he went on as though he was really upset. Many felt sorry for him but she said he was a real rogue. But when many pleaded for him, she took out her purse and there were many gold coins in it. She shook out the coins and said:

'Take this now, old man. It can never be right that you don't get full payment for my abusing you, and so it is now settled, in accordance with your deserts.'

He collected up the gold and thanked her for her kindness. Spes went to church, and there was a very large crowd there. Sigurd set about it heatedly and urged her to clear herself from the accusation which he had brought against her. She answers:

'I care nothing for your accusation. But which man is it you claim to have seen in the house with me? For there always has to be some able-bodied man about me, and I declare that to be without reproach. But I will take my oath upon it that to no man have I given gold and by no man have I been physically soiled except by my husband and that evil beggar who put his dirty hand on my thigh when I was carried over the ditch today.'

Now there were many who agreed that this was a valid oath and that it was no blot on her character though the old man had defiled her accidentally. She said that whatever there was had to be mentioned. After that she swore an oath in the terms that have just been specified. Many said that she was demonstrating, as they say, that "nothing must be left out of an oath". She said she was sure that it would be seen by wise men that this had been made beyond suspicion. Then her family put in that this was a great vexation to a noblewoman to have to put up with such slander without reparation, for it was a capital offence there if a woman was found out in sexual intercourse with other than her husband. Spes then asked the bishop to arrange a divorce of herself and Sigurd, for she said she could not suffer his slanders. Her family supported her in this. It then came about thus as a result of their pressure and payments that they were divorced, and Sigurd got little of the property. He was banished from the land. In this it came about, as often happens, that "those who are lower have to submit", and he couldn't do anything about it, even though he had a just case. Spes now took over all their money and was considered a most remarkable woman. When people thought about the terms of her oath, people thought there was something suspicious in it, and thought that clever people must have prescribed this wording for her. Then people managed to bring it to light that the beggar who had carried her was Thorstein Dromund, and even so Sigurd got no redress in this affair, [and he is out of the saga].

90

Thorstein Dromund stayed with the Varangians while there was most talk going on about this affair. He became so renowned that it seemed that there had hardly such an accomplished man come there as he. He was held in the greatest honour by Harald Sigurdarson, for he gave him credit for his being related to him, and the plan that Thorstein had carried out was in people's opinion his. Soon after Sigurd was driven from the land, Thorstein asked for Spes's hand. She responded favourably, but deferred to her family. Then meetings were held; agreement was reached between them that she should have the greatest say in the matter. Then a contract was made between them with the consent of her family and their marriage turned out well, and they had plenty of wealth. Thorstein was considered a very successful man, the way he had solved his difficulties. They lived together for two years there in Constantinople. After that Thorstein told his wife that he wanted to go and see to his property back in Norway. She said it was up to him. He then sold the property he owned and they got from it a good deal of money. They then made their way back from those foreign lands with a fine retinue and went all the way until they got to Norway. Thorstein's family welcomed them both very warmly, and it was soon seen that she was generous and munificent. She soon became very well liked. They had children together and lived on their property and were very content with life. Then King Magnus the Good was king over Norway. Before long Thorstein went to see him and was well received there, for he was greatly renowned for having taken vengeance for Grettir the Strong. Hardly a case is known of any person from Iceland having been avenged in Constantinople other than Grettir Asmundarson. It is said that Thorstein entered the service of King Magnus. Thorstein stayed put for nine years after he came to Norway, and they were both considered most distinguished people. Then King Harald Sigurdarson came back from Constantinople and King Magnus gave him half share of Norway with himself. They were both kings of Norway for a while. [The following summer King Magnus the Good died and then King Harald took sole power in Norway.] After King Magnus's death many were discontented, those who had been his friends, for everyone loved him. People found King Harald's temper hard to cope with, for he was harsh and severe. Thorstein Dromund was by this time getting on in life but was still a most vigorous man. There had now passed sixteen winters since the slaying of Grettir Asmundarson.

91

Then many urged Thorstein to go and see King Harald and become one of his men, but he would not agree. Then said Spes:

'It is my wish, Thorstein,' she said, 'that you do not go to see King Harald, for there is another king that we owe something more to, and we need to give some thought to that. But we are now both getting old and have passed our period of youth and we have been led more by our desires than by Christian teaching or the authority of righteousness. Now I know that this debt of ours cannot be redeemed either by our relatives or by gifts of money unless we ourselves pay what is proper. Now I wish to change our way of life and go from this country and to the Pope's palace, for I believe that then my affairs may be put right.'

Thorstein answers, 'I am as much aware of these things you speak of as you. It is proper that you should determine this, which can lead to so much good, when you let me decide what tended in a much less satisfactory direction, and it shall all be arranged as you dictate.'

This took people very much by surprise. Thorstein was now two years less then sixty-five and yet vigorous in everything he undertook. He now invited all his family and relations to his house and revealed to them his intention. Wise people approved of this, and yet their departure was greatly regretted. Thorstein said that nothing was certain about his return.

'I wish now to thank you all,' says he, 'for how you looked after my goods while I was out of the country last time. Now I wish to invite and ask you to take charge of my children's money and of them themselves and bring them up in accordance with your own humanity, for I have reached such an age that it is an even chance whether I come back or not, even if I live. You must see to everything that I leave behind here on the assumption that I shall not return to Norway.'

Then people answered that it would be easier for many things to be well looked after if the lady remained behind to see to it. Then she said:

'It was for this reason that I travelled from foreign lands and from Constantinople with Thorstein and gave up both family and wealth, that I wished that we might always be together. Now I have found it very pleasant here. But there will be nothing to tempt me to stay here long in Norway or here in Scandinavia if he goes away. We have always got on well together, and there has been nothing to cause differences. Now we shall both go together, for it is we who know best about the many things that have taken place since we met.'

And when they had thus made arrangements for their affairs, then Thorstein asked men of integrity to divide up their property into two equal parts. Thorstein's family took the part that the children were to have, and they were brought up with their father's family and became afterwards the most splendid people and a great family is descended from them there in Oslofiord. But Thorstein and Spes divided up their share of the money and gave some to churches for their soul, and some they took with them. They set off now on their journey to Rome and many wished them farewell.

92

They now went all the way until they came to the city of Rome. When they came into the presence of the one who was appointed to hear people's confessions, they told everything truly, how it had gone and with what trickery they had arranged their marriage. They submitted themselves humbly to whatever penance to make amends that he wished to impose upon them. But because they had themselves on their own initiative taken steps to make amends for their offences without any compulsion or persecution by the church authorities, then they were excused from all impositions as far as might be, and were urged with kindliness that they should now provide as sensibly as possible for their soul and live in purity from then on, having received absolution for all they had done. They were considered to have acted well and wisely. Then said Spes:

'Now I think things have gone well and well have our affairs been settled. We have now suffered not only misfortune together. It may be that foolish people will take our former life as something to imitate. We must now make such a conclusion to our life that it may be something for good people to imitate. Now we shall hire some men who are good at building in stone to make a cell for each of us, so that we can atone for our offences against God.'

Now Thorstein had money paid out for building cells for them both and for such other things that they needed and could not do without to survive. And when the building was finished, and at a suitable time and when all the arrangements had been made, they ended their temporal life together of their own free will so that they might rather come to enjoy sacred life together in the next world. Each of them then took their place in their own cell and lived for such a length of time as God wished to allot, and so ended their lives. Most people have said that

Thorstein Dromund and his wife Spes seem to have been most successful people considering how they had started out. But neither his children nor descendants have come to Iceland so as to have any story told of them.

93

Lawman Sturla has so said that he thought no outlawed man had been as great a man as Grettir the Strong. He brings forward three reasons for this. First, he thought he was the cleverest, for he was longest in outlawry of any man and was never defeated while he was in health. Second, that he was the strongest in the land for his age and had greater ability in getting rid of revenants and hauntings than other men. The third, that he was avenged out in Constantinople, as was no other Icelandic person, and in addition, what a successful person Thorstein Dromund became in his latter days, the same person who avenged him.

Here ends the saga of Grettir Asmundarson, our countryman. Thanks to those who have listened and little thanks to him who scribbled the story. Here is the work's end, may we all God-wards wend. Amen.[74]

[74] The colophon is clearly by the scribe rather than the author, since he complains about the hand-writing of his exemplar.

THE SAGA OF HORD

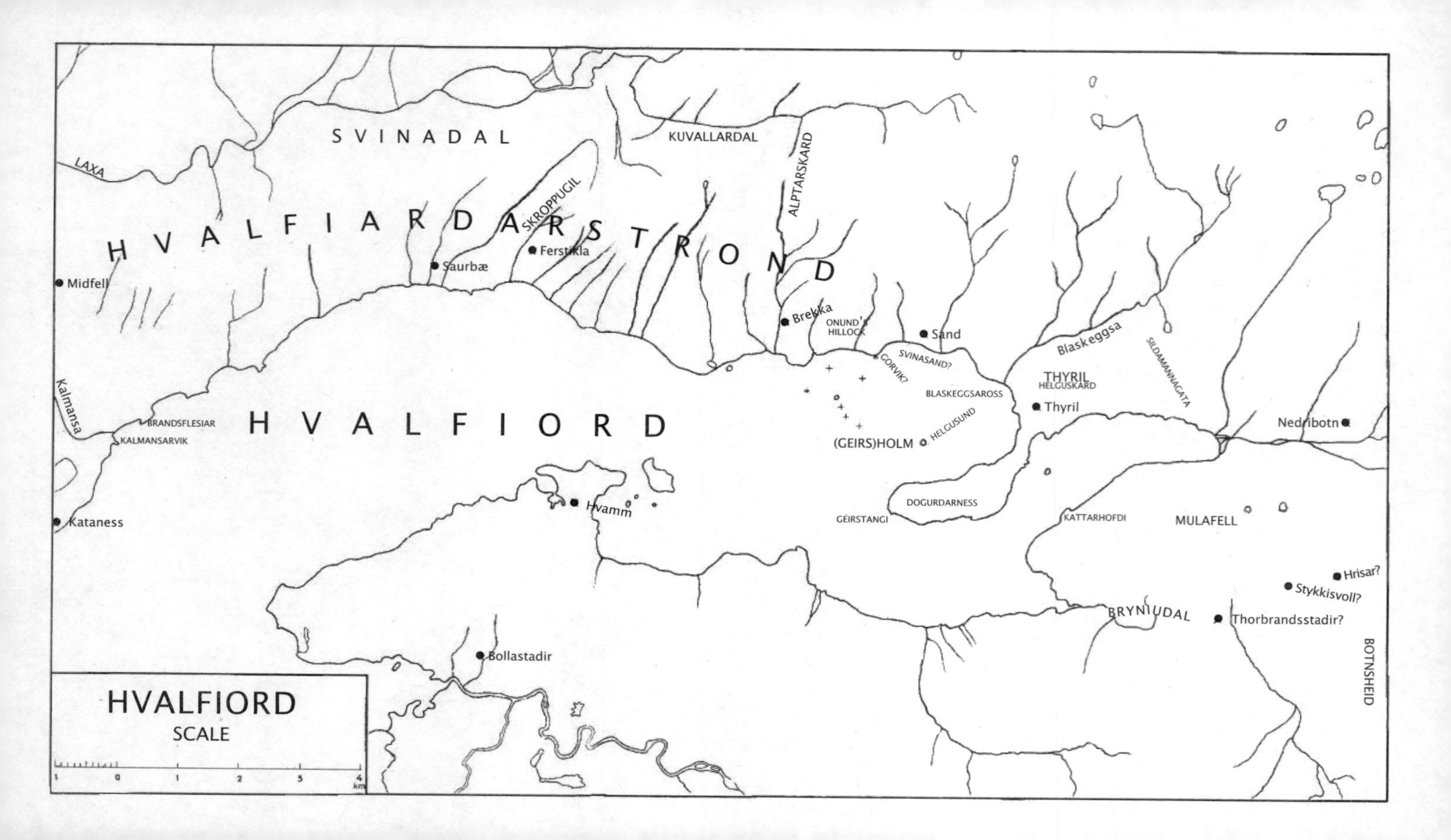

HVALFIORD
SCALE
1 0 1 2 3 4 km
SVINADAL
LAXA
HVALFIARDARSTROND
KUVALLARDAL
ALPTARSKARD
SKROPPUGIL
Saurbæ
Ferstikla
Midfell
Brekka
ONUND'S HILLOCK
Sand
SVINASAND?
GORVIK?
BLASKEGGSAROSS
HELGUSUND
(GEIRS)HOLM
Blaskeggsa
THYRIL
HELGUSKARD
Thyril
SILDAMANNAGATA
Nedribotn
HVALFIORD
Kalmansa
BRANDSFLESIAR
KALMANSARVIK
Kataness
Hvamm
DOGURDARNESS
GEIRSTANGI
KATTARHOFDI
MULAFELL
Hrisar?
Stykkisvoll?
BRYNIUDAL
Thorbrandsstadir?
BOTNSHEID
Bollastadir

1

It was in the days of Harald Finehair that Iceland was largely settled, because people could not put up with his oppression and tyranny, particularly those who were of great descent and proud mind and had good means, and they preferred to abandon their possessions than suffer aggression and injustice, whether from the king or from anyone else. One of these was Biorn Gullberi (gold-bearer). He went from Orkadal to Iceland and settled the southerly Reykiardal from Grimsa to Flokadalsa and lived at Gullberastadir. Svarthofdi, Geirmund, Thiostolf were his sons; and they do not come into this story.

The eldest of Biorn's sons was called Grimkel. He was both big and strong. Biorn Gullberi became an important man and of great property. Biorn's son Grimkel asked for the hand of Rannveig, daughter of Thorbiorn of Arnarholt—Thorbiorn was brother of Lyting, father of Geitir of Krossavik—and married her, and they were together no longer than three winters, and she died of sickness. A daughter survived who was called Thurid. She was brought up with a man who was called Sigurd Muli (snout). He lived under Fell. She was a handsome woman and skilled with her hands and of a somewhat harsh disposition. Nevertheless she was popular.

2

Grimkel lived to begin with south at Fioll, not far from Olfusvatn. It is now called Grimkelsstadir, and it is now a sheep-shed. Grimkel had an extensive *godord*. He was a wealthy man and a very great leader and said not to be in all respects a just man. He moved his farm after his wife's death to Olfusvatn, for he thought the qualities of the land were better there. Thereafter he dwelt there always, as long as he lived. He was known as Grimkel *Godi*.

There was a man called Hogni and he lived in Hagavik, a little way from Olfusvatn. His wife was called Thorbiorg. They had a daughter who was called Gudrid. She was a handsome woman and popular. Hogni was of an insignificant family and was nevertheless an accomplished person, but his wife Thorbiorg was of considerably greater family, and yet they got on well together. Hogni had great property.

There was a man called Valbrand who lived at Breidabolstad in the northerly Reykiardal. He was son of Valthiof the Old. Valbrand's son was called Torfi. Father and son owned a *godord*. Torfi was a clever man and widely known. A man grew up there with the father and son who was called Sigurd and he was son of Gunnhild. He was related to Torfi. He was known as Sigurd Torfi's foster-brother. He was a most promising man and able in most accomplishments. Valbrand had a second child. It was a daughter who was called Signy. She was married to Thorgeir, son of Finn of Midfell the Wealthy, son of Halldor, son of Hogni. He was dead when this story took place. Their son was called Grim, a promising man, and he grew up with his mother. Signy lived at Signyiarstadir a little way from Breidabolstad. She was a very outstanding person, ready of tongue and of proud mind and harsh-spirited in everything. A man grew up with her there who was called Grim. He was known as Grim the Small. He was Signy's foster-son and an important man, swift in his movements and intelligent about most things.

Koll son of Kiallak was living then at Lund in the southerly Reykiardal. He was a great leader.

3

There was a man called Thorvald who lived at Vatnshorn in Skorradal, a big man and strong. His wife was called Thorgrima and she was known as Smith-woman, very skilled in magic. Their son was called Indridi, a big man and promising. Thorgrima lived the longer of the pair, and when she had become a widow, she lived at Hvamm in Skorradal. She became a wealthy woman and one of importance.

It is said that one summer as on other occasions, Grimkel *Godi* rode to the *assembly*, and one day he went from his *booth* with a great troop of men to Valbrand's *booth* and went straight into the *booth*. Valbrand welcomed him, for Grimkel was already known to him. They sat down and began to talk together. Grimkel said:

'I have been particularly told, Valbrand, that you have a daughter who is called Signy, and that she is a very outstanding person. I wish to ask for her hand, if you are willing to marry her to me.'

Valbrand replied, 'It is known to us that you are of good family and have much wealth and are yourself a very fine fellow. I would like to give a favourable response to this.'

Their talk ended with Valbrand betrothing his daughter Signy to Grimkel *Godi*, and the wedding was to be in *Double-month* south at Olfusvatn.

Torfi son of Valbrand was not at the *assembly*, and when Valbrand came home from the *assembly*, he told his son Torfi the news. Torfi replied:

'Very little do you value my opinions, when I am not asked about such a matter, and moreover I do not consider this match that you have arranged for your daughter as advantageous as it seems to you to be. Signy will not get much out of it when the man is both old and harsh.'

Torfi then uttered a verse:

> Old demander of mail-coat-strap wound-storm [warrior, Valbrand]
> —thane [Torfi] has learned this—
> has given brooch-prop [woman] to Grimkel.
> The simple one has deprived jewel-Niorun
> of wealth, pleasure and happiness; I guess
> the old fellow will provide her with little of that.

Signy now learned of her proposed marriage and made little response. And when the brother and sister, Torfi and Signy, meet, he expresses his disapproval of the match.

'There is great love,' he says, 'between us; I am not pleased that you should move away from the district with your wealth.'

She replies, 'I have thought of a good plan to deal with this, brother. Do not change this arrangement, but I will make over to you all my wealth on these terms, that you are to pay my *dowry*, as much as my father has agreed to, and that will certainly amount to no less than twenty *hundreds*. I will give you this back in token of our friendship, excluding my two treasures, the ones I place greatest store by. One is my fine necklace, and the other is my horse Svartfaxi (black-mane).'

Torfi expressed his satisfaction with this and spoke kindly to her.

4

Now people got ready to go to the wedding. Koll from Lund was invited to the wedding as one of the most honoured. Father and son asked him to lead the guests, for Valbrand was so old that he did not feel like going, and Torfi did not wish to go. Koll set out on the journey with the bride, and they were thirty people in all. They lodged at Thverfell in the southerly Reykiardal.

Grim the Small, Signy's foster-son, was to look after the horses at the lodging, and in the morning, when he looked for them, he could not find Signy's horse Svartfaxi. Grim then went to search north over the ridge to Flokadal. He followed a track in the dew. He found the horse dead in a landslide there in the valley. He took off the hobble that it had had on it during the night, and then went back and told Signy that that fine horse of hers was dead and how it had come about. She replies:

'That is a bad omen and bodes no good. I shall turn back and go no further.'

Koll said that was impossible and it would not do to alter her plans of this kind for this reason, and it had to be as Koll wished; and they all travel on together and they come to Olfusvatn and Grimkel had there a large number of guests from his side to meet them. There was a most magnificent feast there. It all went forward satisfactorily and splendidly.

After the feast had finished Koll went away, and the other guests, but Signy stayed there and her nurse who was called Thordis, and Grim the Small. Grimkel had given Koll good gifts and had spoken friendly words to him, but the father and son were considered to have treated the business with clear contempt, when they did not attend the wedding. He also heard about Torfi's verse and could do nothing about it. There was now no warmth between them. Grimkel was unbending in mood, while Signy was quiet, and there was little warmth between them, for they could not have any friends in common, except for Grim the Small. He managed to go on so that they were both happy. So the first year passed.

5

Grim the Small came to talk with Signy in the spring, he said he wanted to leave.

'I find it hard to go between you,' he says, 'and it is best to part while both still feel well-disposed.'

Signy said, 'Discuss it first with Grimkel and take his advice, for then you will be better off, and I am very keen that you should be well off, and I think he is well disposed towards you.'

Now Grim does this, he speaks to the farmer, says he wants to leave if he will agree to it. Grimkel replies:

'My advice is that you should stay put. You shall also be better off than before, because you depend greatly on Signy, and we depend on you very much to compensate for our tempers.'

And Grim did this, he stayed put that year and they were both pleased with him. But the following spring Grim spoke to the farmer, that he did indeed want to leave, but Grimkel was rather against it.

'Then ask for the hand of Gudrid, Hogni's daughter, on my behalf,' says Grim, 'if you want me to stay with you.'

Grimkel replies, 'You are putting a high price on yourself now, for there is a great difference of rank here; you are of small means, while Hogni is very rich.'

Grim said, 'Nevertheless you can arrange this.'

Grimkel replies, 'I can try.'

He now goes to Hagavik and he is well received there. He now asks for the hand of Gudrid on Grim's behalf.

'There is this to be said of the man, that he is an intelligent person and well endowed with skills. He will also be very helpful on the farm and be able to achieve a great deal that will be of benefit to it, while you are getting on in years, and such a connection seems to me to be very advantageous for you.'

Hogni replies, 'You have often tried to bring about things of greater honour to me than anything of this kind; but mother and daughter shall have the greatest say in this.'

Grimkel said they would not need to lay out a great deal of money.

'And nothing is of greater importance than that you should yourself persuade your daughter for me; but I am confident about Grim, that he will turn out well.'

There is no need to make a long tale about it; the outcome of their talk was that Grim got Gudrid. Their wedding was at Olfusvatn and this went off satisfactorily. They got on well together. They were there for the winter, and they were happy with each other.

But in the spring Grim and his wife wanted to leave. He told Signy, but she said he must tell Grimkel and said everything would turn out for the best if he let Grimkel decide. Now he raised it with the farmer that he wanted to leave. Grimkel replies:

'I think it now right to do what is best for you and let you have your way, because it is likely that you will turn out well.'

Grim then bought land south from Kluptir which he called Grimsstadir and lived there from then on. Grimkel provided all the stock, and Hogni paid for the land. Grim quickly piled up wealth; there were two heads on everything that he had.[1] He was soon reckoned among the best farmers.

6

It is said that Signy daughter of Valbrand dreamed a dream. She seemed to see a great tree in her and Grimkel's bed, very beautiful and with such large roots that the roots of the tree reached all the buildings at home there on the farm, but the blossom on it did not seem to her to be as great as she wished. She told the dream to her nurse Thordis, and she interpreted it that she and Grimkel would have a child and it would be great and honourable. She said she thought it was a boy.

'And many will be very impressed by him because of his achievements, but I wouldn't be surprised if his circumstances did not flourish with the greatest blossoming by the end, since that great tree did not seem to you to have as great blossom as you wished, and it is not certain that he will enjoy much affection from most of his kinsmen.'

7

Soon after Signy gave birth to a baby boy. He was called Hord. He was at an early age of great size and handsome in appearance, but not

[1] I.e. all his animals seemed to double in number.

all that precocious in this respect, that he could not walk on his own when he was three years old. People thought this strange and not a sign of early development, he being an outstanding person in everything else.

And on the day when a temple festival was being held at Olfusvatn, Grimkel being a great man for heathen sacrifices, Signy was sitting on her seat in the middle of the living-room floor. She was then adorning herself, and her fine necklace was lying on her knees. The boy Hord was standing by the foot of the *platform* and walked now for the first time from the *platform* to his mother and stumbled onto her knees. The necklace was flung down onto the floor and broke apart in three pieces. Signy was very angry and said:

'Evil were your first steps, and many other evil ones will follow this one, but your last ones will be worst.'

She uttered a verse:

> Broke asunder for lady
> good Sirnir's voice[2] necklace.
> I believe that none of mankind will repair
> this again for wealth-slope [lady, Signy].
> The first walk of the young gold-desirer [man, Hord]
> was not good. Each hereafter will be worse.
> Yet meanest will be the last.

Grimkel came into the living-room at that moment and heard what she said. He grabbed up the boy in silence and was very angry at these words and uttered a verse:

> Wealth-seeker [man, Hord] has got himself a no good mother.
> He was first of the woman's children, having just begun to walk,
> to hear temper-words from which sea-fire demander [man, Hord]
> will suffer. "People's judgement lives longer than any man."

Grimkel had become so angry that he did not want the boy to stay at home there. He went and saw Grim and Gudrid and asked them to take Hord in and bring him up there. They said they would be very

[2] The story of how gold came to be called 'giants' words' is told in Snorri Sturluson's *Edda*, p. 61.

pleased to do so and took him in joyfully and thought it to be a blessing. The previous year[3] Grim and Gudrid had had a son whom they named Geir. He was early large and good-looking and well endowed with skills, only that he fell short of Hord in everything. They now grew up both together, and there soon came to be great affection between them.

Signy was now even less content after this than before, and there was now considerably less warmth between her and Grimkel than previously. Again she dreamed a dream, that she saw a great tree as before, greatest in its roots, with many branches and there came a great deal of blossom on it. This dream was again interpreted by her nurse as about a child being begotten between them, and it would be a daughter and much progeny would live after her, as the tree had seemed to her to have many branches.

'And your thinking it had much blossom must mean the change of religion which will come about, and her descendants will hold that faith which is preached then, and it will be a better one.'

8

After the *assembly* in the summer Signy asked Grimkel to let her go north to her relations. He said he would let her do that, but said that she should not stay longer than a fortnight. Two servants went with her, and her nurse Thordis. They rode north into Reykiardal. Torfi received them very warmly and invited her to stay for the winter, and said that otherwise he would feel that he had lost her affection. She said she had been permitted to be away a fortnight and no longer. Torfi said that was not important. She then gave in to his request and urging. They went then on some visits during the winter and when they were on a visit down in Bæ, Signy's nurse died suddenly and is buried at Thordisarholt. This is a little way from Bæ. Signy was greatly affected by this. Then they went back to Breidabolstad.

And soon afterwards Signy was taken ill with childbirth labour, and her illness was looking very serious. Torfi spoke to her, said he had

[3] This conflicts with other chronological indications in the saga and probably ought to read 'the year before Hord was born'.

never felt happy about her marriage, declared that he had always been very much against Grimkel. She said it was not unlikely that it would have grave consequences. She gave birth to a girl-child, large and healthy. Torfi would not have the child sprinkled with water[4] until Signy's fate was clear. She died straight away without getting up from childbirth. Then Torfi got so angry that he wanted to have the child exposed to die. He told his foster-brother Sigurd to pick up the child and take it to Reykiardalsa and destroy it there. Sigurd said that was a very bad thing to do, but yet did not care to disobey Torfi in this. Sigurd now picked up the child and went on his way. He thought the child looked pretty and so did not feel like throwing it out into the river. He set off now up to Signyiarstadir and put the child down in the farmyard gateway and felt sure it would soon be found. Farmer Grim was standing out under the gable of the house, Signy's son. He saw this, went up and picked up the child and took it home with him and made his wife Helga pretend to be ill and say that she had given birth to this girl. He had her sprinkled with water and named her Thorbiorg.

Grim set out for Breidabolstad. He saw a large number of people coming out of the farm. Signy's body was being taken to burial. Torfi told Grim of his mother's death.

'And I will hand everything over to you, and yet we ought to pay this wealth to Grimkel, but we want to do the best we can by you.'

Grim said he spoke well. Then they buried Signy and left afterwards.

Now Sigurd and Grim meet. Sigurd says he knows that Torfi will be angry with him when he knows that he has allowed the child to live.

'I know how to deal with this,' says Grim, 'I shall get you abroad and thus reward you for the chance that has befallen you.'

And he did so. He sent Sigurd south to Eyrar and gave him two horses, and there were packs on one of them. From there he went abroad.

The next day Torfi came to Signyiarstadir and asked why Helga was in bed, for he did not have any previous knowledge of her sickness. He now recognised the child that lay by her and said:

'This is a very bold thing to do, that you dare to nurture a child that I had had exposed to die.'

[4] Many sagas record that in heathen times there was a ceremony used similar to Christian baptism.

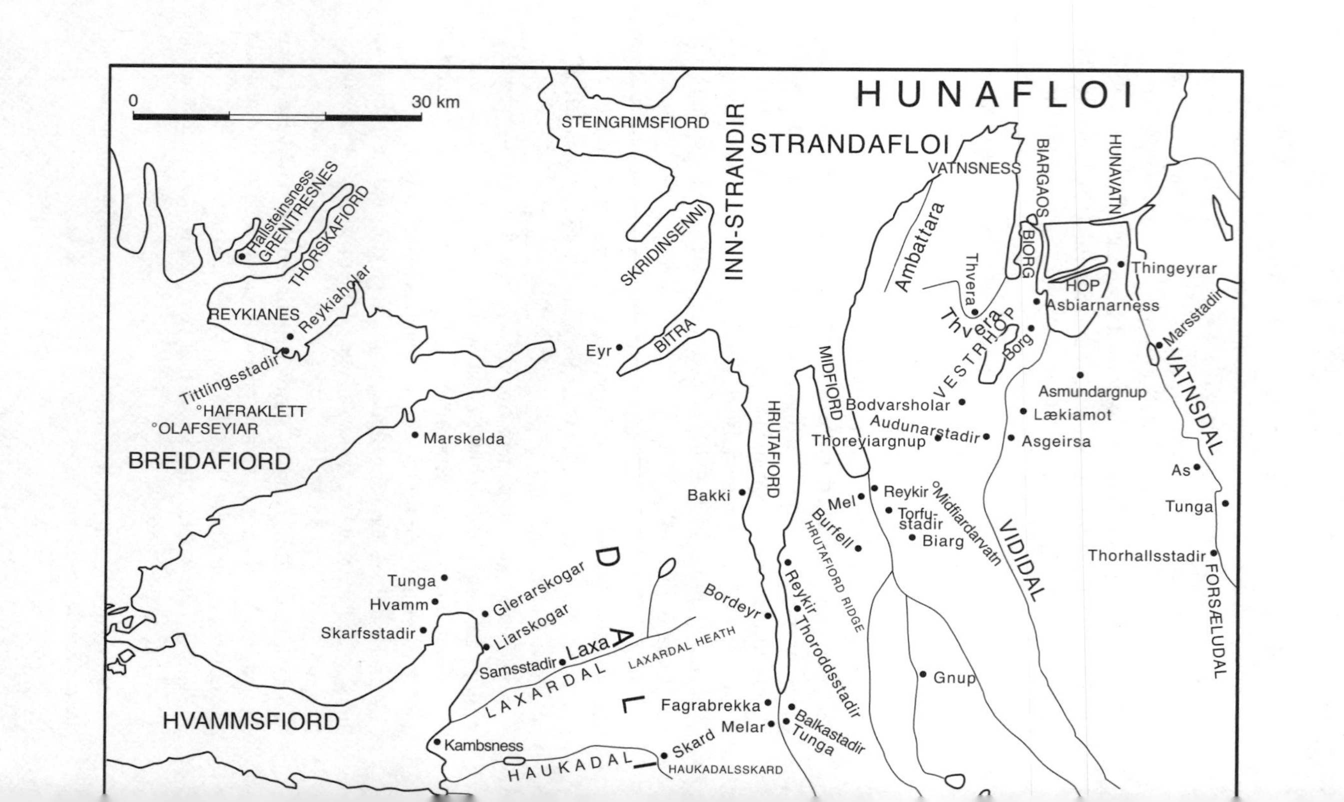
0
30 km
HUNAFLOI
STEINGRIMSFIORD
INN-STRANDIR
STRANDAFLOI
VATNSNESS
BIARGAOS
HUNAVATN
BIORG
Ambattara
Thvera
Thingeyrar
HOP
Asbiarnarness
Marsstadir
VATNSDAL
Borg
VESTRHOP
Hallsteinsness
GRENITRESNES
THORSKAFIORD
SKRIDINSENNI
REYKIANES
Reykiaholar
Eyr
BITRA
Tittlingsstadir
HAFRAKLETT
OLAFSEYIAR
Marskelda
BREIDAFIORD
MIDFIORD
HRUTAFIORD
Bodvarsholar
Asmundargnup
Lækiamot
Audunarstadir
Asgeirsa
Thoreyiargnup
As
Tunga
Bakki
Mel
Reykir
Midfiardarvatn
Torfu-stadir
Biarg
Burfell
HRUTAFIORD RIDGE
VIDIDAL
Thorhallsstadir
FORSÆLUDAL
D
A
L
Tunga
Hvamm
Skarfsstadir
Glerarskogar
Liarskogar
Samsstadir
Laxa
LAXARDAL
LAXARDAL HEATH
Bordeyr
Reykir
Thoroddsstadir
Gnup
Fagrabrekka
Melar
Balkastadir
Tunga
HVAMMSFIORD
Kambsness
HAUKADAL
Skard
HAUKADALSSKARD

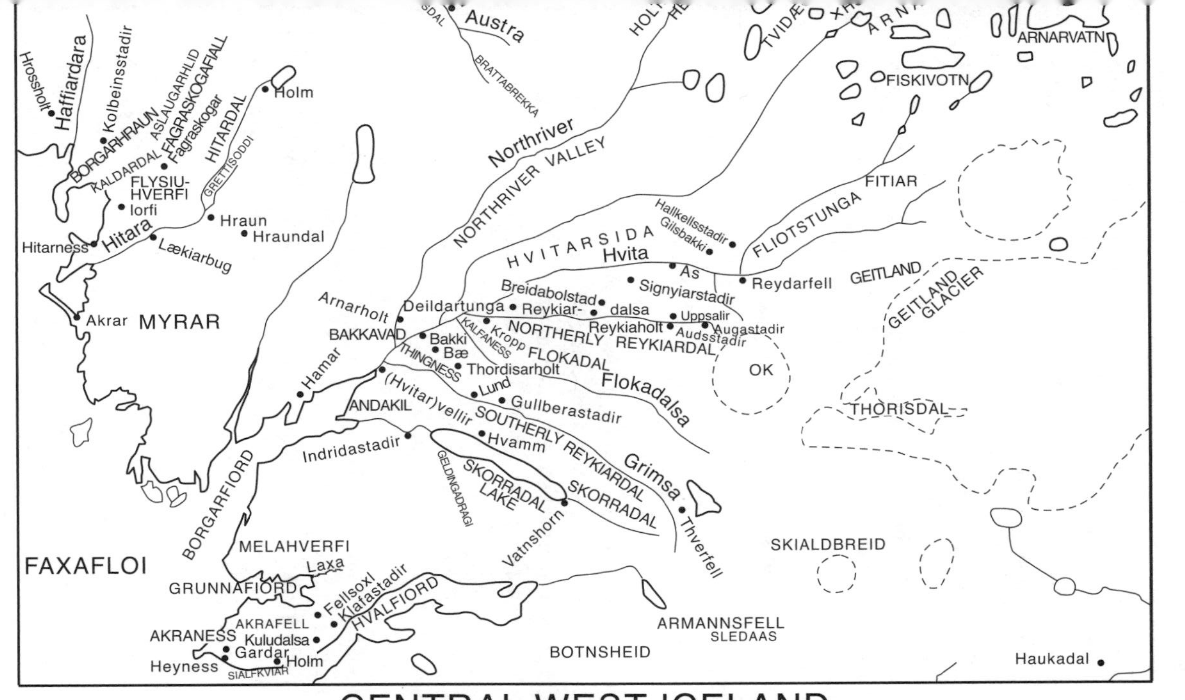

CENTRAL WEST ICELAND

Helga replied, 'This child was very closely related to Grim, and he is justified in saving it.'

Then Torfi asked where Grim was. She said he had gone to see the farm-workers. Torfi went there and saw Grim. Torfi went on in the most awful manner and said Grim was acting towards him with extraordinary boldness and asked what he knew of Sigurd, said he deserved to be punished for having broken his orders, declared that Grimkel had deserved to be treated in this insulting way by him. Grim said he had sent Sigurd to the Western Fiords to a ship. Torfi was angry at this. He took the girl and did not feel like having her killed, for it was said to be murder to kill children once they had been sprinkled with water. He took the girl home and gave it for fostering to a certain slave-woman, and provided nothing for its clothing and would not remit any of the slave-woman's labour.

9

There was a man called Sigmund. He went around begging from house to house and his wife and son who was called Helgi. Usually they stayed in guests' quarters wherever they arrived, unless Sigmund was let inside to provide entertainment. That same autumn Sigmund and his family came to Breidabolstad. Torfi welcomed them and said to them:

'You are not to stay in the guests' quarters, for I like the look of you, Sigmund, and you seem to promise well.'

He replies, 'You would not be mistaken if this was your opinion.'

Torfi said he wanted to do him an honour, 'for I shall accept the fostering of a child from you.'

Sigmund replies, 'There is a difference of rank between us, if I foster a child for you, for it is said that he is a lesser man who fosters a child for another.'

Torfi said, 'You shall take the child to Olfusvatn.'

Sigmund agrees to this. He now picks Thorbiorg up and ties her on his back and then goes off. Torfi was intending all this as an insult to Grimkel, and thought this man the right person to take the girl into beggary; he also did not want to risk a better person for it than Sigmund, for he thought there was nothing that Grimkel might not do if someone had brought the child to his house whom he would have thought worth taking vengeance on.

Sigmund now found himself well off for lodging-places, for everyone felt themselves obliged to treat the girl well and those who travelled with her, wherever she went, and so Sigmund decided to take the longest way round. He went out round Andakil and Melahverfi and all along the coastal route round the Nesses and round past Grindavik and Olfus.

One day in the evening Sigmund and his family arrived at Olfusvatn. Sigmund was wet and very frozen. He sat out near the door, but Grimkel sat in his place and had a sword across his knees. He asked what sort had come. Sigmund replies:

'It is Sigmund, fosterer of your child, who has come, my dear sir, and your daughter Thorbiorg. She is the very best of children.'

Grimkel said, 'Listen to what this beggar says. You, to be fosterer of my child, the most miserable of vagrants? And Torfi's enmity towards me is not all of a piece. First he caused the mother's death, and now he has driven the child into beggary.'

Grimkel then uttered a verse:

> Torfi did not hold back from killing
> thread and embroidery prop [woman, Signy].
> He acts insultingly indeed towards sword-harmer [warrior, Grimkel]
> in all this. Sword-snatcher sent this silver bowl Gna [woman, Thorbiorg]
> into beggary wrongfully. It is time to pay back this suffering.

Grimkel knew all about what Torfi was planning and so did not want the girl to be left there. Grimkel told Sigmund to be off as quickly as he could if he did not want to be beaten up and then suffer worse. They now had to go straight off with the child. They went over Grimsness and across Laugardal and began to neglect the child, for they felt uncertain whether they would ever get rid of it. They now found it hard to get lodging. Sigmund felt he had just snapped up a fly when he took the girl from Torfi.

They arrived at Grimsstadir one day for breakfast. They tell Grim that they had with them a young child. Grim says he wants to see this young child that people are now talking so much about.

Sigmund said it was a lot of trouble to unwrap the child, and said that even then it would not be easy to quieten her down again. Grim said no one would bother about that. The child was now unwrapped and shown to Grim. He then said:

'This is truly Signy's child; it has her eyes and she would expect this of me, that I would not let her child go from house to house if I could do anything about it. But Torfi wants to bring great shame upon all this child's relations and even on himself. I shall now, Sigmund, take off you this child and dependant.'

He was very pleased at this. They stayed there that day and then went down over Botnsheid. There were many who said that Grim would be putting himself at risk from Grimkel *Godi* in this affair with his temerity.

10

About the time of the *moving-days* Grimkel *Godi* set out to Olfus past Hialli and out round Arnarbæli and up along Floi to Oddgeirsholar, from there into Grimsness, and stayed in Laugardal and so back home. He summoned all the farmers to a meeting with him at Midfell, those he had just met, after an interval of two nights, for Grimkel had the *godord* over all these areas. To Midfell came sixty of his *assembly-men*. Grimkel told them of his need to take up a suit against Torfi and declared his intention of going to serve a summons on Torfi. They all thought this was justified. They rode past Giabakki, so to Kluptir and round Ok, so the lower route down by Augastadir and so to Breidabolstad. Torfi was not at home and had gone up into Hvitarsida. Grimkel summonsed Torfi for plotting the death of Thorbiorg and for Signy's *dowry*. He referred the cases to the Althing and afterwards rode home, and there was now hardly anything that was more talked about than the case of Grimkel and Torfi.

And when Grim the Small heard about this, he set off out to Reykiarvik to see Thorkel Mani (moon) the *lawspeaker*. They came to discuss the case of Grimkel and Torfi. Grim asks what he thinks about how this will be concluded between them. He says he thinks it does not look good, since it was very contentious people that were involved. Grim said:

'I would very much like you to do what you can to bring about a settlement between them, for you are both clever and well-disposed.'

Thorkel replies, 'Your request becomes you well and shows your good nature, and I will do what I can to reconcile them.'

Grim said, 'I will give you money to bring about a settlement between them.'

He poured into his lap a *hundred* of silver and thanked him for his promise to try to reconcile them. Thorkel said he was acting nobly.

'But understand this, that I am giving you prospect of a settlement, but I do not promise it.'

Grim replies, 'Your offering a prospect is more valuable than when most other men promise absolutely.'

Grim left after that.

Time passed until the *assembly*. Both sides came with great followings. Grim was at the *assembly*. He went to see Thorkel Mani and asked him to seek a settlement. He said he would gain great honour from this if he was able to reconcile the leaders. Thorkel now did this. He went first to see Grimkel *Godi* and raised the question of the case with him. Grimkel replies:

'I can tell you in brief that in relation to all our dealings as well as Torfi's enmity towards me I shall accept no one's adjudication but my own, except only if it is stipulated as a basis that he pay no less than twelve *hundred* triple units of cloth.'

Thorkel then offered to arbitrate between them.

'But you can see what is at stake here, for there will be open hostility if you do not reach a settlement, and we shall support the side that acts more in accordance with our words and that is willing to respect our decision, and that is more important than what is causing the difference between you.'

Then Grimkel said, 'I agree that Thorkel shall adjudicate in the case. He is known for consistently correct judgements.'

Now Torfi sees that this alone is acceptable. He says now that he too agrees to this.

Thorkel said, 'This is my decision and judgement, that Torfi shall pay Grimkel six *hundred* triple units of cloth and have it on loan for six winters and then pay twelve *hundred*.'

He said that he had now adjudicated as seemed to him most just. Grimkel replies:

'I shall accept this arbitration because I have myself proposed it, but it seems to me the matter has been greatly diminished. Hord, my son, shall have this money, and have it as his inheritance from his mother.'

Torfi said he would not pay Hord this money unless he did not turn out a worse man than his father. Grimkel said that to be sure it was impossible to know this, how it would turn out, but said that Hord would be no better off if the saying proved true that "men take most after their maternal uncles".

'For you are a shape-changer, and I think it would be worse for him to inherit that from you than not.'

Then there was a great outcry. Neither side was pleased with the judgement, yet it was abided by more or less.

This year passed and then another. Then Grimkel proposed a wife for himself, Sigrid daughter of Thorbiorn of Skalmarness. This suit was given a good response, for the man was considered noble and of great family, even though he was rather past his prime. She was married to him. Their wedding was at Olfusvatn, at Grimkel's home. It went forward satisfactorily and splendidly. They got on very well together. Grimkel now kept to himself.

11

There was a man called Illugi who lived at Holm on Akraness. He was son of Hrolf the Geitlander, son of Ulf, son of Grim the Halogalander. Illugi's brother was Solvi, father of Thord, father of Magnus, priest at Reykiaholt. Illugi's sister was Halldora (who was married to Gizur the White), mother of Vilborg, mother of Iorun, mother of Gudrun, mother of Einar, father of Bishop Magnus. Illugi was a big man and strong and had great wealth. He went to Olfusvatn on a wooing journey and asked for the hand of Thurid, Grimkel's daughter by his first marriage. Grimkel responded well, for Illugi was known to him. This engagement took place there. Hord was not present when this match was arranged. The wedding was to be in *Double-month* at home at Olfusvatn.

And when the time arranged for this came, Illugi set out from home with thirty people for his wedding. With him was Thorstein Oxnabrodd (oxen-goad) of Saurbæ, a great farmer, and Thormod of Brekka from Hvalfiardarstrond. They went over the fiord to Kialarness and to the north of Mosfell and so up by Vilborgarkelda, on to Iorukleif and so to

Hagavik and so in to Olfusvatn and they arrived early in the day. Illugi said:

'Where is Hord, as I do not see him, or has he not been invited?'

Grimkel said he was invited as a matter of course.

'But I have not named him in particular for this.'

Illugi replies, 'That is not proper, however.'

He rides to Grimsstadir. The doors there were closed. They knocked on the doors. Geir went to the door and asked who had come. Illugi said who he was and asked for Hord. Geir said he was inside. Illugi said:

'Ask him to come out, for I wish to see him.'

Geir went in and came out, said Hord was in bed and was ill. Illugi went in, as Hord would not come out. Illugi said:

'Of what nature is your sickness, Hord?'

He said it was nothing much. Illugi said:

'I would very much like you to come to my wedding with me and make friends with me.'

Hord said he might have said this before if he thought it was very important.

'I am going nowhere, for you have not involved me much in this business.'

Illugi gets nothing from Hord but strong words. He rides away without achieving anything further.

A little later Geir said to Hord:

'It is more seemly that we go to the wedding. I shall fetch us some horses.'

Hord said he did not much care to. Geir said:

'Do it for the sake of my asking, and your honour.'

Hord now did so. They then rode after them, and when they met, Illugi was very glad and disregarded Hord's strong words. They now rode to the wedding and they were welcomed. Hord sat on one side of Illugi. The wedding went forward satisfactorily and splendidly.

They all rode from the wedding together, right to Vilborgarkelda. There the paths divided. Then said Illugi:

'Now, Hord we shall part here, and I would like us to be good friends, and here is a shield that I would like to give you.'

Hord replies, 'My foster-father Grim has got plenty of bits of wood,' and uttered a verse:

A shield gave me the generous weapon-reddener [warrior, Illugi],
and not a good one. He will need this thane [shield]
in Hild's rain [battle].
Let him keep his treasure himself, this sharp one,
who desires my land-thong-slope Aud [woman, Hord's half-sister],
breaker of oaths and rings.[5]

Then Illugi said, 'Accept this ring from me, then, as a token of friendship, if you do not want the shield.'

Hord took the ring. It was a fine treasure.

'I do not know,' says Hord, 'why I have the feeling that you will not be a good brother-in-law to me, but yet we shall find out later on.'

Then they parted, and there were few expressions of goodwill, but yet they separated on good terms for the time being. But when Hord got home, he spoke to Thorbiorg:

'I would like to give you this ring, which Illugi gave to me, because I love you best of everyone. But you remember this gift when I am dead, for I know that you will live longer than I.'

Thorbiorg replies and uttered this:

If you are, to my certain knowledge,
slain with weapons, or felled in battle,
to that man shall my bitter designs
for sure cause death.

Hord was now twelve years old when the saga had reached this point. He was then equal in strength to the strongest men in the area. So time passed until Geir was sixteen years old and Hord fifteen. He was then a full head higher than most other men. His eyes could never be deceived by false appearances, for he saw everything as it was. His hair was the finest of anyone's and he was of mighty strength, the best of swimmers and in every respect well endowed with skills. He was white of skin and light of hair. He was broad-faced and full-faced, with a bend in his nose, blue-eyed and keen-eyed and rather wide-eyed, broad-shouldered, thin-waisted, broad under arm, with slender extremities

[5] Breaker of rings (i.e. of swords) means warrior; or spender of rings, generous man, i.e. Illugi.

and in every way well grown. Geir was rather less strong, and yet there were almost none his equals. He was one of the greatest men of skills though he did not come up to Hord.

12

That same summer a ship came from the sea to Eyrar. It was owned by a man called Bryniolf, son of Thorbiorn, son of Griotgard, a man from Oslofiord. There were thirty men on the ship. They arrived before the *assembly*. Bryniolf rode to the *assembly* and stayed in Grimkel *Godi*'s *booth*. He often said that he had a desire to see Hord.

'For much has been told me,' he says, 'of his good looks and abilities.'

And now it happened that Hord came to the *assembly*, he and Geir too, for they were never apart. There was amazing affection between the foster-brothers, for neither word nor deed ever came between them. They and Bryniolf now met. They got on well together. Bryniolf said that there had been no exaggeration about Hord as to his size and good looks.

'You seem to me, Hord,' says Bryniolf, 'a very good person to go abroad and be among noblemen. I would like to be your friend and give you half share in my ship with me.'

Hord said, 'You are taking on a great deal with an unknown person, but yet I will give a good response to your proposal, and yet I shall not promise to go away until I know what I shall have to take with me, for I have not got much so far.'

Geir said, 'This is a good suggestion, foster-brother, and it seems to me a promising plan. I shall be much in favour of it.'

Hord said, 'I am not keen to ask Grimkel to provide for me.'

Geir told him not to be like that, 'for he is very fond of you. Now I would like you to be straightforward in these plans, and also that you should accept gratefully what Bryniolf is offering you.'

They now travel home from the *assembly*, and when Hord got home, he told his sister Thorbiorg. She said Bryniolf must be a good fellow. Geir then again urged the journey abroad.

'I would like,' he said, 'you to take Helgi son of Sigmund as your servant.'

Thorbiorg answers, 'I would be rather against that, because all Sigmund's people seem to me prone to disaster. The grief will never leave my breast which I got from when they took me begging from house to house.'

Hord answers, 'I am not very keen on Helgi, for they have been the cause of the greatest disgrace to us,' and he uttered a verse:

> This grief in Thorbiorg's Hlokk's storm [mind]
> that I tell of is the greatest in many men's memory
> when destroyer [warrior, Torfi] of sleeve-plain brands [swords],
> her mother's brother, asked Sigmund to bring her up in beggary.

Helgi was very persistent in asking, and Geir supported his suit very much. The conclusion was, by the time they had finished, that Helgi should go with them, and Hord said that they would find out rather more clearly how mistaken it was.

After this Hord asked Grimkel for capital and requested sixty *hundreds*, and of this twenty *hundreds* was to be brown-striped. Grimkel said:

'Your arrogance and greed is clearly apparent in this.'

He went away in silence. Grimkel's wife Sigrid said this was equivalent to consent.

'For this will be more or less what he had intended for trading in.'

Grimkel handed over the capital, and they transported all the wares under Fell to Sigurd Muli,[6] went abroad after that with Bryniolf straight away that summer and reached Bergen with ship unscathed.

13

King Harald Greycloak was then ruling over Norway. They straight away looked for private lodgings for themselves and found them with Bryniolf's help, for he did the best he could for them in everything.

There was one day when Bryniolf had ridden up into the country, that Geir was walking out on his own. He had a furry homespun cloak on. Then Geir sees where a troop of men was going and one of them

[6] I.e. so as to be close to the ship and ready to load; Fell is near the south coast of Iceland, on the Olfus river.

was in a *blue* cape. They soon meet. They ask him his name. Geir tells them what it is and asks who they are. Their leader says his name is Arnthor, and that he is the treasurer of Gunnhild Mother of Kings. They asked to buy Geir's cloak, but he was not willing to sell. Then one of them snatched the cloak from him. Geir was left standing with his hand on his sword. They laughed then a great deal and mocked him, saying that the landsman[7] had not held on to his cloak very hard. Both these things then made him angry, their mockery and losing the cloak. He then grasped hold of the cloak, and they jerk at it for a while. Arnthor then reached for the cloak and tried to wrench it from him. At this Geir drew his sword and struck at Arnthor's arm above the elbow, cutting it off. He then got hold of his cloak and after this went back to his lodging, for he had taken them aback. His scabbard was left behind. They attended to Arnthor, for he was weak from loss of blood. Hord asked, when Geir came back, why there was blood on his sword. Geir said what had happened. Hord answers:

'What you did was quite proper. Now we must waste no time.'

Now Arnthor was overcome from loss of blood and he collapsed in the arms of those who were with him, and died a little later from loss of blood. Hord now sent for the Icelanders who were there. There was Tind son of Hallkel, brother of Illugi the Black. They quickly responded and came to meet Hord and numbered twenty-four in all. Then a horn was blown in the town and the king was sent for and told that one of the king's men was slain. The king came quickly and ordered Geir to be handed over.

'For he has killed a friend of mine and my mother's treasurer.'

Hord answers, 'It is not right for us to surrender our man to your weapons. We are willing to offer you *self-judgement* for the man as long as Geir keeps life and limb unscathed.'

Just then Bryniolf came back, while they were discussing this, and said:

'Lord, be so good, take payment for the man, and pay regard to your honour and my friendship, for many a man will lose his life before Geir is killed.'

The king replies, 'I shall do that, Bryniolf, at your request, make a settlement with Geir and accept compensation for my part, but not on my mother's part.'

[7] I.e. Icelander.

Bryniolf thanked him. He paid over all the money for Geir and furthermore gave the king good gifts, for he had plenty of wealth and was the most decent person.

But when the king had gone away, Bryniolf said:

'I am not confident that I can keep you here because of Gunnhild. I shall send you east into Oslofiord to my father Thorbiorn for safety and protection.'

Hord replies, 'I shall rely on your guidance, for you are a decent person.'

They now went quickly east to Oslofiord. Thorbiorn welcomed them because of his son's recommendation. They were well treated there and were considered to be splendid men. Most people did not think Helgi was any compensation for Hord's character. Early in winter Bryniolf came there to the east. They all stayed there together in friendship.

In the spring Thorbiorn discussed with Hord and his friend that he wanted to send them east to Gautland 'to see my friend Earl Harald with unequivocal tokens, for I know that Gunnhild will come here soon and then I shall not be able to protect you from her.'

Hord said that the father and son should decide. They now prepared their ship.

14

When they were ready the foster-brothers and the father and son parted in great friendship. They now make east for Gautland, go to see Earl Harald. He received them well as soon as he saw his friend Thorbiorn's tokens. The earl had a son who was called Hroar, and he was out raiding, and a daughter who was called Helga, the most handsome of women. Earl Harald made Hord sit next to himself, in his son Hroar's seat. They stayed there the summer.

In the autumn Hroar came back from raiding. He was made welcome. Hord gave up his place to Hroar. So time passed until Yule, and when people had taken their places on the first evening of Yule, Hroar stood up and said:

'Here I step on the stock[8] and make this vow, that I shall have broken open the *viking* Soti's grave-mound by next Yule.'

[8] Probably one of the supports for the edge of the side-*platforms* of the hall.

The earl said, 'A great vow, and you will not have the power to fulfil it on your own, for Soti was a great troll in his life and has been twice as great a one since he died.'

Hord then stood up and said, 'Will it not be proper to follow your customs? I make this vow to go with you into Soti's mound and not to leave it before you.'

Geir made a vow to accompany Hord, whether he wanted to go there or anywhere else, and never to part from him unless Hord wished it. Helgi also made a vow to accompany Hord and Geir wherever they went if he could, and to value no one more highly while they both lived. Hord replies:

'It is not certain that there will be long between us, and take care that you are not the cause of both our deaths, or even of other people's too.'

'I would hope to do so,' says Helgi.

The earl was well disposed to Hord and said he looked chiefly to where Hord was for facilitating his son Hroar's advancement.

15

And when spring came, Hroar set out in a party of twelve for Soti's mound. They rode through thick forest, and in one place Hord saw where a small hidden path led off the forest road. He rode this path until he came into a clearing. There he saw a building standing, both large and splendid. A man was standing outside in front of the building in a *blue*-striped hooded cape. He greeted Hord by name. He responded well and asked what he was called.

'For I do not recognise you, though you behave as if you know me.'

'My name is Biorn,' says he, 'and I recognised you when I saw you, even though I have not seen you before. But I was friend of your kinsmen, and I will let you benefit from this. I know that your party is planning to break into the *viking* Soti's mound and you will not easily manage this if you are left to your own devices. But if it goes as I suspect, that you do not manage to break into the mound, then come and see me.'

Now they part. Hord rides now to meet Hroar. They get to the mound early in the day and begin to break into it and in the evening reached the timbers. But the following morning the mound was undisturbed as before. So it went the second day. Then Hord rode to see Biorn and told him how far they had got.

'And it went,' said Biorn, 'as I expected, for it was not unknown to me what a troll Soti was. Now here is a sword that I shall give you, and you stick it into the opening in the mound and then see whether the mound closes up again or not.'

Now Hord goes back to the mound. Hroar says then he wants to give up and not struggle with this devil any longer. Others were in favour of this. Hord replies then:

'It does not do to fail to fulfil one's vow. We shall have another go.'

The third day they set about breaking into the mound. They again reached the timbers as before. Hord now stuck the sword Biorn's gift into the opening in the mound. They sleep through the night and come to it in the morning and then nothing had changed there. The fourth day they broke up all the long beams and the fifth day they took out the door. Hord then told men to beware of the blast and stench which was blowing out of the mound, and he himself stood behind the door while the stench was at its greatest. Then two men were struck dead by the foul air which blew out, but they had been curious about it and not followed Hord's advice. Then Hord said:

'Who wants to go into the mound? And it seems to me that he who made a vow to overcome Soti is the one who ought to.'

Hroar was silent then. And when Hord saw that no one was prepared to go into the mound, he drove into the ground two rope-pegs.

'Now shall I,' he says, 'go into the mound, if I may keep the three treasures that I choose from the mound.'

Hroar said he would say yes to this for his part, and all agreed to it. Then spoke Hord:

'What I want, Geir, is that you should hold the rope, because I trust you best to do it.'

Then Hord went into the mound, and Geir held the rope. Hord found no treasure in the mound and now says to Geir that he wishes him to come into the mound with him and to take with him fire and wax.

'For both are things of great power,' says he. 'Ask Hroar and Helgi to look after the rope.'

They did so, and Geir went down into the mound. Eventually Hord found a door and they broke it down. Then there was a great earthquake and the lights went out. A great stench blew out. There in the side mound was just a little gleam of light. Then they saw a ship and great treasure in it. Soti sat in the bow and was horrible to look at. Geir stood in the entrance to the mound, but Hord went up and was going to take the treasure. Soti uttered this:

> Why were you so keen, Hord, to break into
> the earth-dweller's house, even though Hroar asked?
> I have never to blood-serpent shaker [sword wielder, Hord]
> done harm in my life.

Hord said:

> This is why I came to find the fellow
> and to take ancient treasure from the ghost:
> it is widely known that there cannot be
> anywhere in all the world
> a worse man wielding weapons.

Then Soti leapt up and ran at Hord. There was a tough encounter in which Hord was greatly outmatched. Soti took hold of him so hard that Hord's flesh was bunched up into ridges. Hord told Geir to kindle the wax candle and see how Soti responded to that. And when the light spread over Soti, his strength diminished and he fell down. Hord then managed to get a gold ring off Soti's arm. It was such a fine treasure that it is said that no gold ring as good has reached Iceland. And when Soti lost the ring, he uttered this:

> Hord plundered me of the fine ring,
> twice as bad it seems to me to lose it
> than the whole of Grani's burden.
> It shall be the deadly destruction
> of you and all those who possess it.

Hord said:

> Though I was certain of this,
> that all the pronouncements of the destroyer of good deeds [Soti]
> would be fulfilled, yet should not the most ancient coward
> longer enjoy sea's fire [gold].

'You shall know this for certain,' says Soti, 'that this ring shall cause the death of you and of all who possess it, unless it is a woman who possesses it.'

Hord told Geir to bring the light up to him and see how friendly he was, and at that Soti plunged down into the ground and would not wait for the light. So they parted. Hord and Geir took all the chests and took them to the rope and all the treasure that they found. Hord took sword and helmet that Soti had possessed, and they were the greatest treasures. They now gave a pull on the rope and realised that the men had gone away from the mound. Hord pulled himself up the rope and got out of the mound. Geir tied the treasure on the rope and Hord pulled it out.

This is to be told about Hroar and Helgi and their companions, that when the earthquake happened, all the men panicked who were outside, except for Helgi and Hroar, and they had to hold those who were outside still. But when they met again, there was a joyful meeting. They felt they had recovered Geir and Hord from Hel. Hroar asked Hord what had happened, and he uttered a verse:

> I did not have to deal with a wealth-maple [man]
> either easy or cowardly.
> That devil was hard to overcome under the heathen regime.
> I know, when he began to see the light
> Soti's look was ugly. The cruel keeper of spells
> chose to plunge into the earth.

They now left with their booty. They could not find Biorn anywhere, and people assumed that it must have been Odin. Hord was thought to have achieved a famous deed in the mound-breaking. He then spoke with Hroar:

'Now I consider that I have a right to the three treasures that I choose.'

Hroar said that was true, 'and it is most fitting for you to have them.'

'Then shall I,' says Hord, 'choose sword, ring and helmet.'

Then they shared out all the other treasure and there was no dispute between them. The earl did not want any of the treasure when they offered it to him. He said it was fitting for Hord to have the largest share of it. They now sat in great honour and stayed there for that year.

16

In the spring Hord said that he wanted to go to Iceland, but the earl and Hroar said they were very keen for him not to leave, and felt that such a man had never been there before. Hord said:

'I shall propose an alternative to this for you: give me Helga, the earl's daughter, as wife.'

The earl said this would be given a good response. The match was fixed with the agreement of Helga and Hroar. Hord loved his wife Helga greatly. He then had a great deal of wealth. They set out raiding in the summer, all the foster-brothers, Hord, Hroar, Geir and Helgi, and they took four ships; each of them was in charge of one. They were well off for both wealth and fame and did well in their raiding.

17

Now the story is to be taken up where earlier it was left off, that Sigurd, Torfi's foster-brother, went abroad from Eyrar and reached Norway and was there the winter, and the following summer he got himself on a ship with merchants and went south to Denmark. At that time King Harald Gormsson was ruling there. Sigurd got on good terms with the king for he proved the most valiant man. He quickly increased both in wealth and reputation until he got into a band of *vikings* and proved the greatest hero, and so it went on for some summers right until Sigurd became leader of a *viking* band. He then was himself in charge of five ships.

There was one summer that he was sailing in the east past Balagards-sida, and when he got to the sounds that are called Svinasund, evening had come. They were there during the night. And in the morning the first thing they knew was that *vikings* were rowing towards them there on seven ships. They asked who was in charge of the ships. A man stood up on the poop on one ship, both great and swarthy. He says he is called Biorn Blasida (dark-side) and is son of Ulfhedin, son of Ulfham, son of Ulf, son of Ulfham the Shape-shifter, and asked who was their leader. Sigurd said who he was.

'Would you rather go ashore ungirded,[9] and give us ships and possessions, or do you want to fight us?'

'We would rather choose to defend our possessions and freedom and would rather fall honourably.'

Then both sides got ready. The most violent battle broke out there. Sigurd went forward bravely, and eventually all Sigurd's ships had been cleared of defenders, and three of Biorn's. Then Sigurd stood up alone and defended himself for a long time and right on until shields were borne down on him. He was then captured, and he had by then alone killed seven men. It had then become the evening of the day. He was then tied fast by the arms and his legs were fettered and six men were got to guard him during the night, and he was to be executed in the morning, but the *vikings* all slept ashore. Sigurd asked who was going to provide the entertainment. The guards said he had no need of entertainment 'when you are going to die tomorrow.'

'I am not afraid of my death, and I will recite you a poem, if you like.'

They said they would agree to that. He then recited so that they all fell asleep. He rolled himself over to where an axe was lying, managed to cut the rope off his arms and after that managed to kick off his fetters in such a way that it took off both his heel-bones. Then he killed all the guards. Then he dived into the water and swam ashore. Then he walked across the headland, for he did not want to risk playing about with the *vikings*. Then he saw four ships lying and *booths* on shore. He went boldly to the tents and it was then nearly morning. He asks who was in charge there. They said he was called Hord, who was their leader, Hroar and Geir and Helgi, and asked in return who he was. He told them. Then he went up to Hord and asked the latest news. Hord immediately realised who Sigurd was and invited him to join him. Sigurd said he would accept that and told him of his disastrous expedition and asked Hord to even things up with the *vikings* for him. He did not think this was likely to be possible, but yet said he would do as he asked. They set to straight away and cleared their ships of cargo and put rocks in its place, then rowed out past the headland. But when the *vikings* became aware of this, they got ready and thought they were lacking an expected friend in that Sigurd had gone. Now a battle broke out between them. The foster-brothers went forward

[9] I.e. without either weapons or other possessions concealed under their clothing.

strongly, and yet Sigurd acquitted himself blamelessly. But towards the end of the day, Hord attempted a boarding of the ship that Biorn Blasida was on, and Geir was right behind him. Each went along one side of the ship and slew absolutely every mother's child forward of the mast. Biorn Blasida then leaps against Hord. Hord was then come aft of the mast and Biorn strikes at Hord with a two-edged sword. Hord does not however get his shield in front of himself. He then jumped backwards over the mast-transom towards the bow, and the sword goes so hard into the transom that it sinks in over both edge-strips.[10] And when Hord sees this, that Biorn is bending forward after striking the blow, he strikes both hard and swiftly across his shoulders cutting the man in two below his ribs with the sword Sotanaut, and thus Biorn Blasida lost his life. And by the time this had been done, Geir had slain every mother's child on the ship, and Hroar had cleared one ship together with Helgi. Sigurd had cleared one ship and the *vikings* fled on the fourth. Hord and his men took there a great deal of booty. They now dressed their men's wounds. Sigurd healed so that it was no hindrance to him. He accompanied Hord all his life afterwards, as long as he lived, and was considered the most valiant man. They now sailed back to Gautland in the autumn and stayed the winter there with good entertainment.

18

Geir now became keen to go to Iceland and asked Hord to give him permission to leave. Hord told him to go as he wished, but still to maintain his friendship with him. Helgi remained behind with Hord, and Sigurd too. Geir went away. It took a long time to get favourable winds and they reached Oslofiord in the east and put up tents on shore. Gunnhild Mother of Kings found this out and sent her men to kill Geir. They came in the night and beat them up under the tents after letting down the tents upon them. Geir alone got away with his weapons and before that was the death of nine men. He travelled until he got to Bryniolf son of Thorbiorn and father and son got him on a ship and gave him some money. It was thought that Gunnhild had forced

[10] Viking swords sometimes had narrow strips of harder metal welded along the edges to improve their cutting-power.

him to come to Norway by her magic. She was now very annoyed that Geir got away. Now they set out to sea.

Geir came out to Eyrar during the summer. Then Geir's father Grim was dead, and also his grandfather Hogni in Hagavik, but Gudrid and Thorbiorg had kept the farm at Grimsstadir. Geir went there and stayed there the winter, but in the spring he bought land at Nedri-Botn and moved his dwelling there and it was very profitable. Gudrid and Thorbiorg moved there.

19

Indridi son of Thorvald and Thorgrima Smith-woman set up a farm in lower Skorradal where it is now called Indridastadir, but his mother Thorgrima had been living at that time at Hvamm, while his father Thorvald was dead.

That summer, the first that Geir lived at Botn, a man came out who was called Orm, at Vikarsskeid by Thiorsa. Their ship was wrecked and all the goods were lost. There were fifteen men on the ship and they found no lodging. Orm had been two winters earlier at Hvita and had had lodgings with Indridi, and now Indridi rode from the north in a party of three to see Orm and said he could not accept his being unprovided for. He invited him home with him and all his crew. Orm accepted this and thanked him for the offer.

They all rode from the south past Bakkarholt, over Grafning and Bildsfell and so past Ulfliotsvatn and from there to Olfusvatn and got there at dusk. Grimkel greeted them but did not invite them in. Then Indridi asked for the hand of Grimkel's daughter Thorbiorg.

'You, farmer, know of my origin and also of my circumstances. I would like to know your answer immediately.'

Grimkel said, 'We cannot do that on the spur of the moment, and this cannot be arranged so quickly.'

There were no invitations to them forthcoming from him. Indridi rode to Hagavik in the evening. And when they were ridden off, the lady Sigrid said to Grimkel:

'Your attitude is very strange, not to give your daughter in marriage to Indridi, who seems to us to be the most remarkable man, and send after them, and do not sit in the way of your honour and that of your daughter.'

Grimkel said, 'Let us do as you wish.'

Then men were sent after them to Hagavik. They rode back with the messengers. Grimkel now received them very well. They now discussed the affair and it was decided that Indridi shall marry Thorbiorg and shall get with her forty *hundreds*, and the wedding was to be straight away at Olfusvatn. Indridi himself was to be responsible for how pleased those who were not present might be.

Indridi left his companions behind there and went in a party of three and went to fetch Thorbiorg from her home in Botn. He went over Iorukleif and so to Grimsstadir and from there over Botnsheid and so to Botn. Geir was not at home. Many people said that Geir must have wanted to marry Thorbiorg, but still she did not say anything in opposition to these arrangements nor to going with Indridi. They now travel until they get to Olfusvatn. Preparations have then been made for the wedding.

Grimkel went to Thorgerd Horgabrud's temple and was going to make a pronouncement about Thorbiorg's marriage, but when he came into the temple the gods were all in a great commotion and were getting ready to leave their pedestals. Grimkel said:

'What's the meaning of this and where are you off to, and where will you now direct good fortune?'

Thorgerd said, 'We shall not direct good fortune to Hord, since he has plundered my brother Soti of that fine gold ring of his and done much other disgrace to him. I will though instead direct good fortune towards Thorbiorg, and such a great light shines above her that I am afraid that it will cause a separation between us. But you will have only a short time to live.'

He then went away and was very angry with the gods. He went home for fire and burned up the temple and all the gods and said they should never again tell him grievous tidings. And in the evening when people were sitting at table, Grimkel *Godi* suddenly dropped dead and he was buried south of the farmyard.

All the property came into the keeping of Indridi and Illugi, because Hord was not here in this country. Indridi wanted to have nothing to do with looking after Grimkel's property except for Thorbiorg's *dowry*. Illugi took over the management straight away that autumn, but in the spring the property was divided with Sigrid and she had land at Olfusvatn and was considered a good mistress.

20

A few winters later Hord son of Grimkel came out to Eyrar and his wife Helga and Sigurd Torfi's foster-brother, Helgi Sigmund's son and thirty people. Hord was now thirty years of age. He had then been abroad fifteen years together and become well off for both wealth and honour. Illugi the Red from Holm came to the ship and invited Hord to stay and all his men and went himself to meet them and treated them in the most honourable way. Hord received this well and thought it was a princely offer. Hord went to Illugi's with twenty-five men and they were served beer all winter with the greatest splendour, and Hord was very pleased. Illugi offered him all his own property which he had taken into his care. Hord said he preferred to claim his property from his kinsman Torfi and said he would go to see him.

Then he went in a party of twelve men and came to Breidabolstad and saw Torfi and claimed his property. Torfi said he was not sure about this claim, 'because I am not obliged to hand over the property to you if you turn out a worse man than your father.'

Hord said that had hardly been put to the test yet, but said he would pursue his claim on the property. Then Hord rode away and told Illugi, when he got back. Illugi told Hord to give way.

'And I feel sure that then things will be better between you, for Torfi is a clever and cruel-minded man.'

Hord said that was the last thing he would do.

'He has always treated us badly, and never well. I will go straight away and get men together.'

Hord rode and gathered men from round Akraness, and Illugi gathered them from below and from the west, round Heynes and Gardar to Fellsoxl, and round Klafastadir, and Hord west of Kuludalsa. They rode up over Midfell and so to Breidabolstad.

Torfi was outside and welcomed them. Illugi tried for a settlement and said it was essential for them to be reconciled, such closely-related people. Torfi said it was more than likely that Hord was in the right.

'He will surely become a man of consequence,' he says. 'He has responded much more quickly. I will grant him terms and make land available to him here. I will hand over to him here with the land thirty cows and thirty farm-hands. I will provide everything for the farm this year. I want to know what sort of man he will turn out to be. He shall be responsible for all the property he takes over, both land and stock.'

Illugi said this was a good offer, and Hord accepted it and they were reconciled on these terms. Hord moved there in the spring and Illugi handed over to him all his property. Hord's farm was profitable. He kept open house for travellers. No one tried anything on with Hord, and he did not interfere with others. He lived there two years.

21

There was a man called Aud. He lived at Audsstadir opposite Uppsalir or a little lower down, an odd man and wealthy, of an insignificant family and yet somewhat quarrelsome. His son was called Sigurd. He had mares, dark piebald in colour, two of them. He was proud of these horses. Illugi the Red had given Hord a stud of horses, five in all, when he left Holm, all of them black in colour. Aud's piebald mares began to consort with these and they ran away from their pastures. Hord said he thought it a pity that Aud had too little benefit from his horses. Hord did not have a very good relationship with Torfi. People did not contend much with Hord, and he was always on good terms with people. Torfi was then living at Uppsalir. He had a *godord* and was thought awkward and difficult to deal with. A second summer it went the same way, that Aud's horses went away from him and to Hord's horses. Hord ordered his horses to be taken over the mountain so that Aud's mares should not find them. This was done, yet still Aud's mares found the horses.

It happened during the mowing of the meadows that Sigurd son of Aud came back from the stud and had not been able to catch his horses. Then Hord sent Helgi son of Sigmund to give him help. Helgi went with Sigurd and was in a bad temper and said Aud was the entire cause of these troubles and difficulties. And when he gets to the horses, he sees that the boy had injured the stallion. Then he said:

'You have the makings of a wicked man, and you are not going to ruin many good animals from now on.'

Then he killed the boy. A little while later Hord came up and said:

'You are a wicked man, to have killed one who was only a young person, and moreover without cause. It would be fitting for me to kill you. I do not now feel like doing that, though it would be better for you not to live after such an evil deed. This will be the beginning of your ruin. It has now come about, what I had a feeling would happen, and it is very likely that it will somehow turn out to cause the death of both of us and of many others, along with the other things that will happen and that must be foreordained.'

Hord then threw a cloak over the body and after that first of all went home, and a little later Hord went to Audsstadir, and when Hord went from the western side into the enclosure, then Aud went from the northern side into the enclosure, and when they met, Hord said:

'This has turned out badly, and yet against my will, that your son was killed. I will now give you *self-judgement* and demonstrate that I believe this has happened most unfortunately and pay out all the money directly, and most people will reckon that you can hardly expect a better outcome to the case as it now stands.'

Aud replies, 'I have just been to see my friend Torfi and delegated the case to him, and he has promised me to pursue it to the fullest extent of the law, and indeed I could easily have foreseen that you people of Breidabol would suffer a harsh fall.'

Hord said, 'That was very wrong of you to cause trouble between me and Torfi, and you shall now pay for it.'

Then he drew the sword Sotanaut and cut Aud apart in two pieces and his workman. Hord had then become so angry that he burned the farm and all the farm buildings and two women who refused to leave. And when Torfi learned of this he said that no one before had dared to do such a thing, 'to carry out such unparalleled wickedness against my friends, and yet it is not easy to rid oneself of Hord.'

And when he heard that Hord was not at home he set out to Breidabolstad on a summons and referred the cases to the Althing. After that he went home. And when Hord learned this, he sent Helgi south to his brother-in-law Indridi and asked him to ride to the *assembly* and respond to his cases and to offer terms. He said he could not bring himself to offer any terms himself because of his enmity with Torfi. Helgi went and saw Indridi and told him what Hord had said. Indridi replies:

'I have promised Illugi the Red to go to the Kialarness *Assembly*, but I will invite Hord to stay here with me.'

Helgi replies, 'There is less need for you to go to the Kialarness

Assembly than to represent such a brave fellow as your brother-in-law, and you must be just a coward.'

Thorbiorg said, 'It would have been some help if a reliable man had come with the message, but now maybe nothing will come of it. This misfortune has also come about because of you.'

Helgi went back and did not tell Hord about Indridi's invitation, but said that he was not willing to give him any help. He was not very pleased with this and uttered a verse:

> My brother-in-law proved unreliable to me in lawsuits,
> and so is he to other wave-fire-junipers [men].
> The useless heir of Thorgrima decided instead to stay at home.
> Weapon-wielder [warrior, Indridi] is harsh to us,
> and will be worse later.

And when people came to the *assembly* and the courts went into session, then Torfi asked if anyone was willing to bring forward compensation on behalf of Hord.

'I shall,' says he, 'accept compensation if anyone is willing to offer it, but I am not inclined to let this case drop under my feet.'

There were no responses forthcoming and Hord was outlawed and Helgi too. And when Hord heard of his outlawry, he uttered a verse:

> Great gold-ring keeper [man, Torfi] also managed indeed
> at the Althing to make estuary-fire-cultivator [man, Hord]
> outlaw throughout sword-trees' households
> in heath-cod's solace and snake's sickness.[11]
> This occasions us no fear.

He and Torfi did not meet for the time being.

22

A little later Hord went with all his people to his foster-brother Geir's. Hord first burned all the buildings on the farm and also the hay; he

[11] heath-cod = snake, whose solace is summer and whose sickness is winter (because they hibernate in winter).

said Torfi should gain little wealth from them. Some people say that Hord had been living at Uppsalir at this time and Torfi at Breidabolstad. Hord was sixteen and twenty years old when he fell into outlawry and went to Botn. All his household went with him and his followers and set up a garrison there. There was one day that Torfi[12] uttered this verse:

> Certainly Torfi, scornful land-owner
> will believe he can ride up to Botn against men.
> Flingers of fire-red Nile sand [gold] will, I guess, offer resistance.
> I believe that thanes will give sustenance to the wolf[13]
> if an equal number of targe-trees [warriors]
> can be present here inside.

It was a drain on their resources that year, because supplies were less than they needed, and Geir did not look after the farm work as well as before. They then got through the livestock, so that the following summer the animals scarcely fed the people. The next autumn all the livestock were entirely slaughtered except for just a few cows.

And one morning during the winter before Yule, Geir touched Helgi on the legs. He got up straight away and they went over the ridge to Vatnshorn in Skorradal. The farmer was not at home. He was at a wedding at Lund in Reykiardal at Koll's. Geir said:

'Now we shall have to get supplies for the farm as best we can, and you must do one or the other: keep watch or go into the cowshed.'

Helgi chose to keep watch. Geir then went into the cowshed and untied the cattle. There were two men in a hay-store playing a board-game, and there was a light burning there. Then one of them said:

'Are the cattle loose in the cowshed?'

The other said it must be the women's fault and they had not tied the cattle up. Now one of them went out to the doorway, and when Geir saw this he leapt at him and killed him, and when the one who had gone first was a long time, the other went, and when he got to the doorway of the barn he met the same fate as the first. Geir killed this one too. Then they led off a seven-year-old ox.

[12] Presumably an error for Hord.

[13] I.e. fight a battle so that wolves may get carrion.

And when they got back to Botn, Hord was very displeased and said he would leave if they were going to steal.

'It seems to me,' he said, 'much better to go raiding if there is no other way to survive.'[14]

Geir told him not to part from him for this reason.

'You alone shall make all our decisions.'

And so it was, that Hord did not go away.

But when women came to the cowshed at Vatnshorn, they thought it strange that all the cattle were loose. They thought the herdsmen must be asleep. They tied up the cattle, but when they got to the entrance to the barn, they found them there dead. Then word was sent to the farmer. He came back home. There was a great deal of talk about this thing.

Hord would not let the ox be used until a man had been sent to Vatnshorn to tell the truth about Geir's expedition. Some people also say that Hord must have compensated the farmer at Vatnshorn for his men and ox, and so he would not have brought a charge for the case afterwards.

23

Kolgrim the Old, son of Hersir Alf of Trøndelag, was living at Ferstikla at this time. He was a settler. His son was Thorhall, father of Kolgrim, father of Stein, father of Kvist, father of Kali. Kolgrim sent word to the Botn-dwellers that they should hold ball-games and scraper-games[15] with each other on Sand. They accepted. Now the games were begun and they continued over Yule. The Botn-dwellers generally got the worst of it, for Kolgrim contrived it that the men of Strond were stronger in the games. The Botn-dwellers used up a lot of hide for their shoes, having to walk frequently; then the ox-hide was cut up for footwear. People thought that Kolgrim had wanted to find out about the disappearance of the ox and that was why he had set up the games. He thought he recognised the ox-hide on their feet. They were then called Ox-men. Again they were treated roughly in the game. They then talked about it, when they got home, that they thought they had been treated

[14] It may be that these words are supposed to be spoken by Geir rather than by Hord. Otherwise Hord is distinguishing open plunder from furtive theft.

[15] The nature of this game is unknown.

roughly, and said they would soon give up the games. Hord spoke harshly to them and said they were not half cowards if they didn't dare to avenge themselves.

'And you are,' he says, 'only ready for evil deeds.'

At this time there had come to Hord these two, Thord Cat and Thorgeir Gyrdilskeggi (belt-beard), an outlaw. Now Hord had horn-scrapers made for himself during the night. Then they were all ready to go to the game if Hord was going, though before they had been rather reluctant. Onund son of Thormod of Brekka was set against Hord, a popular man and of great strength. This game was very rough, and before evening came there lay dead of the Strond-dwellers six men, but none of the Botn-dwellers. Now both sides went home. Onund was accompanied by all those who lived further out than Strond. And when they got to a little way in from Brekka, then Onund told them to go on ahead.

'And I am going,' he says, 'to tie up my shoe.'

They did not want to leave him. He sat down, and rather heavily. Then he died and is buried there. It is now called Onund's hillock. These cases were not prosecuted against Hord or his men.

At this time Thorstein Gullknapp (gold-button) lived at Thyril, malicious and underhanded, crafty and well off, but Thorvald Blaskegg (dark-beard) lived at Sand, a worthy farmer and an important man.

24

There was a man called Ref, son of Thorstein, son of Solmund, son of Thorolf Smior (butter). He lived at Stykkisvoll in Bryniudal. He was a powerful *godords*-man and a strapping fellow. Later on he was known as Ref the Old. His mother was called Thorbiorg Katla. She lived at Hrisar. She had great skill in magic and was the greatest sorceress. Ref's brother was called Kiartan. He lived at Thorbrandsstadir, a big man and strong and with a nasty character, an unfair man in everything. As a result he was terribly unpopular with the generality of people. There was a man called Orm, son of Hvamm-Thorir, a popular man and a great smith. All these men were hostile to the Botn-dwellers.

Hord and his men got news from the *assembly* in the summer that there were men planning to gather together and kill them, and they realised that as the livestock had been slaughtered, they would now need to go raiding. Geir told them to build a fortification and said they would not easily be attacked. Hord said he thought they would have their food supplies cut off.

'And I would rather have us go to the holm which lies here offshore in Hvalfiord opposite Blaskeggsaros beyond Dogurdarnes. This holm has sheer cliffs down to the sea and is as wide as a great cattle-pen.'

There they went during the *assembly* with everything they had. They took a great ferry from Saurbæ from Thorstein Oxnabrodd to assist them, and a six-oared boat from Thormod of Brekka, and a four-oared seal-boat from Thorvald Blaskegg. They made themselves a great long-house, and one end faced north-east and the other south-west, and there were doors in the middle of the long-house walls on the western side. The long-house stood right on the southern cliff-edge, but one could pass to the north between the cliff and the doorway that was in the gable-wall. Only from the north was it approachable, but to the west of the long-house were concealed ditches. It was their law that everyone should be thrown over the cliff if they could not get up for more than three nights. All were bound to go wherever Hord decided, or Geir, if they themselves were with them. Tasks were shared out between them. All the buildings had their timbers taken down at Botn and were transported out to Holm. This holm is now called Geirsholm. It took its name from Geir son of Grim. A *hundred* and eighty people were on Holm when they were at their maximum and never fewer than in the seventies when they were at their minimum. These have been named: Hord and his wife Helga, the earl's daughter, their son Grimkel, and Biorn (he was two winters old), Geir and Sigurd Torfi's foster-brother, son of Gunnhild, Helgi son of Sigmund, Thord Cat and Thorgeir Gyrdilskeggi (he was one of the worst of all the Holm-dwellers for suggesting criminal deeds and kept urging all kinds of outrages). Nearly all the doubtful characters found their way there and swore oaths to Hord and Geir to be loyal and true to them and to each other. Thorgeir Gyrdilskeggi and Sigurd Torfi's foster-brother transported water from Blaskeggsa in a group of twelve men and filled the seal-boat with water and poured it into the pool that was out on Holm. So time passed for a while.

25

Thorbiorg Katla boasted of this, that she said the Holm-dwellers would never do her any harm, she had such great faith in her magic. And when they heard of this on Holm, Geir said he wanted to put it to the test and set out in a party of twelve men after the *assembly*. Thord Cat went with him. And when they got to the valley they saw that the animals had wandered north over the mountain that stands between Bryniudal and Botn. Geir had two men look after the ferry. Thord Cat stayed on the ridge and kept guard. And when Thorbiorg Katla came out, she became aware by her magic and second sight that a ship was come from Holm. She then fetched her head-scarf and waved it up over her head. Then a great darkness came over Geir and his men. She then sent word to her son Ref that he should gather men together. They came to be fifteen in all and they came upon Thord Cat unexpectedly in the darkness and captured him and killed him, and he is buried on the lower part of Cat's Head. Geir and his men got to the sea. Then the darkness lifted and they saw them clearly, and Ref and his men attacked and fought. All the men were killed who were with Geir, and three of Ref's party. Geir got onto the ship and so to Holm and was badly wounded. Hord mocked his expedition a great deal and said Katla had still not come to grips with them. Helga was a good healer and she made Geir completely better. The men on Holm were in great fear at all this.

And when Geir's wounds were dressed, Hord went aboard the ship in a party of twelve and went straight in to Bryniudal and said he wanted to put Katla to the test again. Two guarded the ship and ten went to find the animals. Katla again shook her scarf and sent word to Ref and said it would now be worth meeting the Holm-dwellers, 'when their leader is now the man with fine hair who thinks himself the greatest hero.'

Ref came in a party of six. Hord's sight was not obscured by Katla's magic and they carried on as they had planned and slaughtered animals onto their ship until they had fully loaded it, while Ref and his men looked on. Afterwards they transported it out to Holm, and thus they parted.

26

And when it was nearly the end of summer, Hord went in a party of twenty-four to Saurbæ, because Thorstein Oxnabrodd had boasted of this, that his nurse Skroppa, who was skilled in witchcraft, would be able to see to it by her magic that no harm should come to him from the Holm-dwellers. And when they came to land, seven guarded the ship in the water, and seventeen went ashore. They saw a great bull on the gravel bank above the boat-shed. They wanted to have a go at him, but Hord was against it. Two men from Hord's party went towards the bull and followed their own counsel. The bull brought its horns against each of them in turn; one of them aimed at its side, the other at its head. Each of their spears flew back and at their breast, and they were both killed. Hord said:

'Follow my advice, because not everything here is as it seems.'

Now they reached the farm. Skroppa was at home and the farmer's daughters, Helga and Sigrid, but Thorstein was in a *shieling* in Kuvallardal. This is in Svinadal. She opened all the buildings. She created an illusion, for where they sat on the *platform* there seemed to them to be three boxes. Hord's men talked about wanting to break open the boxes. Hord forbade it. Then they went north from the yard and were going to see if they could find some animals. Now they saw where a young sow was running with two piglets north out of the yard. They got in front of her. Then they seemed to see a great crowd of men coming against them with spears and full armour, and now the sow was to the north of them shaking its ears with its piglets. Geir said:

'Let's go to the ship. We shall be up against odds here.'

Hord said it would be better not to run so soon without having a go. Just then Hord took up a great stone and struck the sow to death, and when they went up they saw that it was Skroppa lying there dead, and the farmer's daughters were standing upright over her, where it had looked like piglets. Now they saw, as soon as Skroppa was dead, that it was a herd of cattle that was coming towards them, and not men. They drove these same animals to the ship and slaughtered them and loaded the ferry with meat. Geir forced Sigrid to go away with him and afterwards they went out to Holm. Skroppa was buried in from Saurbæ, between it and Ferstikla, in Skroppa's Gill.

Thorstein Gullknapp was left in peace by the Holm-dwellers, because they had come to terms secretly that he should transport all vagabonds to Holm and keep them informed of all the schemes of the people of the mainland. He had sworn them oaths to fulfil all this and not to betray them in anything, and they had promised him not to do any raiding there.

27

During the winter before Yule twelve of them in all went to Hvamm to Orm's at night-time. Orm was not at home. He was gone somewhere on business. He had a slave called Bolli who always looked after the farm when Orm was not at home. They broke into the storehouse and took out goods and food. They took Orm's chest that had his valuables in and went off with it all. Bolli felt it had gone badly for him when no watch had been kept over the storehouse. He declared he would get the chest off the Holm-dwellers or die in the attempt and told them to tell the farmer that he should be in a party of eighteen at the boat-shed the fourth night from then and should not let himself be heard.

Now Bolli got himself ready. He wore tattered shoes and a simple hooded cloak. He stayed the first night in Bryniudal, but not at any of the farms. He came to Thorstein Gullknapp's and said his name was Thorbiorn, said he was an outlaw and said he wanted to go out to Hord and join his band. Thorstein Gullknapp took him out to Holm, and when Hord and Geir saw the fellow, he did not strike them both in the same way. Geir thought it was a good idea to take him on, but Hord said he thought he was a spy. Geir prevailed, however, and he swore them oaths before they took him on. He told them a great deal about the mainland but said he was tired. He lay down and slept through the day. Geir and his men could not get the chest open and asked Thorbiorn how he suggested they should go about it. Thorbiorn said there was no problem.

'There is nothing in it,' he said, 'except the farmer's workshop tools.'

He said that Orm felt the only real loss he had suffered in the Holm-dwellers' raid was that his tool-chest had gone.

'And I was then,' he says, 'at Mosfell when the raid was reported. I shall take him his chest, if you like.'

Geir thought there was little advantage to be had from the chest, since there was nothing in it but only tools. Two nights Thorbiorn stayed there trying to persuade them to let the chest go. Hord was not keen to accept any advice of Thorbiorn's, saying it would turn out badly. Geir would have his way, however, and six of them in all went during the night to Orm's boat-shed. They carried the chest ashore and up into the boat-shed and placed it under the side of the hull of Orm's ship. Then Thorbiorn called out that they were to stand up and take the thieves. Then they leapt up, those that had been waiting there, and attacked them. Geir then took hold of the stub of an oar and struck out on both sides, and thus defended himself very bravely. Geir then reached his ship. Four of Geir's men were lost. Orm took a ferry and rowed after Geir. Back on Holm, Hord suddenly spoke:

'It is more than likely that Geir is in need of men, and I am not sure how this Thorbiorn has proved for him.'

Then he took a ship and rows in along the fiord. He comes upon the chase between Orm and Geir. Then Orm soon turned back and to the shore. Geir went out to Holm with Hord.

Afterwards Orm gave Bolli freedom and land at Bollastadir and all he needed to set up a farm. He lived there afterwards and became a wealthy man and fearless.

28

After the *assembly* in the summer Hord and Geir went in a party of twenty-four men on a ferry one evening and landed in Sialfkviar, in front of the entrance to Holm. They left six to guard the ship, and eighteen went ashore. They drove animals from Akrafell. Hord saw that a man was coming out at Holm in shirt and linen breeches. It was at dawn. Hord recognised this as Illugi, for he was the keenest-sighted of all men. Now Illugi noticed what they were doing and immediately sent men to Gard[ar] and to Heyness and also to Kuvallara to gather men. He did not move to attack them until he had thirty men. And when Hord sees the gathering of men, he told Geir to choose which he preferred, to slaughter the animals and cut them up and load the ship or to keep off Illugi and his men so that they couldn't get to them. Geir said he would rather cut up the animals than deal with Illugi. Hord said:

'Now you have made the choice that I much prefer. I am also more used to this. I will keep them off in a group of twelve men, and we must always stay the same number, but you will be the fewer cutting up the animals as any of us fall.'

Thus they were fourteen who were cutting up the animals.[16] Now began the attack between Hord and Illugi. It was extraordinary how bravely Hord defended the sheep-pens, for Illugi's party attacked hard. Men were continually coming to reinforce Illugi's party, so that in the end they became altogether forty men, but Hord's group were twelve in all. His men now had been badly wounded, for the difference in numbers was great. Sigurd Torfi's foster-brother put up a valiant show, as he always did. Helgi son of Sigmund also defended himself like a man. Thorgeir Gyrdilskeggi loaded the ferry. Geir was not backward in slaughtering the animals and then cutting them up. Nine fell of Hord's party before the ferry was loaded, and when they went aboard the ship, the others attacked hard, the men of the mainland, and then six of Hord's party fell before they could take cover behind the side of the ship. Hord was wounded by a double axe; everyone was wounded in some way.

Illugi then had ships got together, although Hord and his men had disabled all the large ships. A north-east wind was blowing against Hord's party. They bound their wounds and rowed along the northerly shore past Kataness and Kalmansarvik. They laid the cargo on a skerry, for the weather was pushing them back. Geir insisted upon staying there and one man with him, but Hord thought it foolishness to risk themselves there. Hord held the ferry in down the fiord. Then they rested, for they had worked hard even though they were tough. Illugi's party pursued Hord's hard, and they were coming round the ness. Then Hord gave the ness a name and called it Kataness, because he thought there were a lot of cats[17] going past it. As soon as Illugi's party came up with them, they immediately attacked them. Then Hord said:

'You are pursuing hard, brother-in-law, and I had a premonition of this long ago, which now has been fulfilled.'

Illugi said, 'You have also done much to deserve it.'

[16] There is a discrepancy in the numbers. It presumably ought to be twelve in both groups.

[17] *Kati,* in English 'cat', was a kind of small boat.

Then a hard attack took place. Hord defended one side of the ferry, and six the other side. A little later Holm-dwellers arrived on three ships and immediately leapt onto the ferry. Then Illugi retreats, and they chase him out along the fiord.

There was a man called Brand, son of Thorbiorn Koll (top) from under Midfell. He went at Geir on the skerry and fought with him and killed the one who was with him. Geir defended himself well, but Brand was in a party of seven. Then Hord came up at that moment and said Geir had fared not much differently from what he had expected. Then Brand fled. They made after him and killed him (it is now called Brand's Flats in from the skerry, that is east of Kalmansa) and five other men, but the sixth got away. But Hord and Geir took all the booty to Holm. Hord then uttered a verse:

> Flood-moon-trees [men] fifteen had Illugi the Red felled before.
> Homestead-Tyr [man, Illugi] was reluctant to make peace.
> Rather well did fierce-minded Geir repay that onslaught.
> Now have fallen of gold-giver [Illugi]
> just as many wolf-feeders [warriors].

Now the summer came to an end.

29

The next winter, after Yule, Hord and Geir and forty men went up Alptarskard and so into Svinadal and from there into Skorradal and lay hidden during the day, but went down to some sheep-sheds during the night and drove away from there in the morning eighty wethers that Indridi had up along Vatn. Then there came a heavy snowfall and a storm caused by witchcraft against them. Then the bell-wethers became exhausted, when they got close to the mountain, and Geir and the men wanted to leave the sheep behind, but Hord said that would be unmanly, just because there were a few flurries of snow or a bit of damp weather against them. Hord then took the bell-wethers, one with each hand, and so dragged them on over the mountain. This made a deep track. They drove along it the rest of the animals. Thus it has been called Geldingadragi (wether-drag) there since. And when they got into Svinadal, there was no snow there. They went then to their ship and slaughtered the animals there. This has since been called Gorvik (gore-bay) there. They now go out to Holm. Now the winter went by.

In the springtime Hord and Geir and Sigurd Torfi's foster-brother, Helgi and Thorgeir Gyrdilskeggi went with sixty fighting men. They went north over Alptarskard to Indridastadir and lay hid there in the woods until cattle were being driven to pasture. The one who was guiding the cattle was called Svart, and a small boy with him. Hord and his party went to the cattle and drove them west of Vatn. Svart also kept with them. They went over Geldingadragi into Svinadal. There they killed Svart. Then they went to sleep up there in the valley. The boy guided the cattle back while they slept. Hord woke up and watched from beneath his shield. He let the boy go on his way and said to him:

'Go now, boy, for I would rather my sister had it than the Holm-dwellers.'

The boy came home and told Thorbiorg what Hord had said and said it was a great shame about such a man.

'And he was kind to me, but his men killed Svart.'

She made no reply to the boy. So it is now called Kuhallardal (cow-turn-valley), because there the cattle turned from them. Geir awoke and wanted to go after the cattle, but Hord said they should not. Then they collected together the farmers' swine from Svinadal and drove them down onto the sand and slaughtered the swine there and put them on the ship. It is now called Svinasand there. Then they went out to Holm.

30

During the Althing in the summer the Holm-dwellers went in to Dogurdarness. They went along Sildamannagata to Hvamm in Skorradal and took Thorgrima Smith-woman's oxen by Skorradal lake to the south and drove them south onto the ridge. One was a dapple-grey ox. It sniffed around a lot. It ran back towards them, and then one after another did the same, and out into the lake and they swam across where it was narrowest and then walked back to Hvamm. Then Hord said:

'There is power in Thorgrima's magic when cattle cannot do what they want.'

Thorgrima had been asleep and awoke sooner than expected and looked out. She saw the wet oxen and then said:

'You've had a hard time, but those fellows did not hold on very tight.'

Hord now asked his friends whether they did not now want to change their way of life and activities.

'It seems to me,' he says, 'that our situation is rather poor as it is, when we have only what we get by raiding to live on.'

They said it was up to him.

'Then I would like,' he says, 'us to go to merchants in Hvita and give them two hard choices, that they give up the ship to us or otherwise we shall kill them.'

Geir said he was quite ready to do this.

'But first I want us to burn in their houses Torfi son of Valbrand and Koll at Lund, Kolgrim the Old, Indridi and Illugi.'

Hord said, 'Less than that of your great plans will be fulfilled, and it is more likely that we shall all be killed, because people are not going to put up with all the unfairness with which we are treating them.'

There were more who were against going to the ship, but were in favour of crimes, with the exception of Sigurd Torfi's foster-brother. Hord said:

' "That will have to come to pass which is fated", and the situation is that nothing can be done about it. But it is much more against my nature to be stuck in these crimes any longer.'

They went back to Holm the same night and stayed there three weeks. Then they went to the mainland, eighty men. Hord then said he was willing for them to burn Illugi or Indridi in their house.

'Since they have continually,' he says, 'been against me, and never on my side, such great troubles as I have been in.'

They went during the night into Svinadal and lay there in the woods during the day, and the second night they went into Skorradal and hid there.

31

The same night that Hord left Holm, Thorbiorg dreamed at Indridastadir that eighty wolves were running to the farm there and flames were burning from their mouths and one among them was a white bear, and it seemed rather sad, and they stayed a while at the farm and afterwards ran west from the yard to a little hill and lay down there. And Indridi said this represented the feelings of the Holm-dwellers towards him. Thorbiorg said she thought that it must be they themselves and that they were coming soon. She told Indridi to channel a well-stream to the house and to cover it over, for she claimed to dream true. This was now done. Thorbiorg had great chimneys built. She had valuables put up on the crossbeams because water was up to the middle of the walls. She had no small number of men there ready.

Soon after, Hord and his men came. He went up to the doorway and was ahead of his band. He knocked at the entrance. Thorbiorg went to the door and greeted Hord in friendly fashion and invited him to stay and his special friends. She tried to make him leave that band of hooligans and said that there were many who would then be on his side. Hord asked her to come out into the open to him and said she would be welcome to be with him if she separated from Indridi. She said that would be less right and declared she would not separate from him. Then they dragged a pile of wood to the doorway and set fire to the farm, but they fought it off with water, the people inside. The attack made little progress. Geir was surprised at this. Hord said:

'I expect it is my sister who has suggested this water supply.'

They went to look and found the stream and channelled it away, but yet there was enough water in the farm, so much had already run in. Hord saw a man standing up in one of the chimneys and holding a bow. Hord shot the man with a javelin and killed him. After this Hord saw a troop approaching the farm that Thorbiorg had sent for. Geir said they would now have to withdraw. Hord was not against it. They then turned away. None of the buildings there was destroyed. A large number of men came to Indridastadir. The Holm-dwellers went home and did nothing for a while.

32

Farmers held a meeting at Leidvoll near Laxa by Grunnafiord so as to put an end to the Holm-dwellers being allowed to continue all the crimes that they were committing. All the local leaders were sent word that they were to come to this meeting, and all the farmers and workers. And when Indridi was getting ready to go to the meeting, Thorbiorg asked where he was planning to go. He told her.

'Then I shall go with you,' she says, 'for you must know that I shall be true to you.'

He did not want her to go to the meeting, and said it would be no fun for her to hear what was said there. She said she was aware of that. Then Indridi rode to the meeting.

A little later Thorbiorg had a horse saddled for herself and went with one other person to the meeting. There was there a large crowd of people and a lot of shouting, but when she came they were as if struck dumb and they were all silent. Then she said:

'I think I know what you are up to and your intention, and I shall not hide from you what I have in mind, that I shall be the death or have it brought about of any man who kills my brother Hord.'

Then she rode away. At this *assembly* were Torfi son of Valbrand, Koll from Lund, Indridi, Illugi, Kolgrim, Ref and Thorstein Oxnabrodd and Orm of Hvamm and many other local leaders. Then Torfi said:

'It is obvious to the people who are present here, and everyone can be in agreement about it, that these criminals should be put to death, otherwise first those who are closest by will be robbed of everything, and then all the other local people. You can see that they will not spare others, when Hord has tried to burn his brother-in-law's family in their house. Let us quickly adopt some good plan so that no news of it reaches them. This is for everyone the most urgent thing to do.'

Illugi said they were the source of too many crimes for things to be allowed to stand, declared that there had joined the band the most evil people.

'I shall pay no regard to any relationships in this. We have found out about them, that they were planning the same thing for us as for Indridi.'

Kolgrim said that those who were closest were feeling the greatest cold from this, but there would not be long to wait before others had the same thing on their hands, though they were placed further off. Similar things were said by one after another. Ref said the only thing to do was for some one to be got out to Holm who would swear oaths to them that there would be no treachery used against them, and say that it was the wish of all the local people that they should go away from Holm, wherever they liked, and that they should then all be reconciled with each other. In this it was Torfi who was the greatest proponent of this plan, and in addition it was he who recommended that they should immediately that night ride in to the fiord so that the Holm-dwellers should not know about it.

'For it seems to me,' he said, 'that some people on Strond are to be suspected.'

They rode immediately that night. They ate breakfast the following morning on the ness there in the fiord which they afterwards called Dogurdarness (breakfast ness). That same morning Thorgeir Gyrdilskeggi and Sigurd Torfi's foster-brother went to fetch water in a party of twelve on a smack. The Holm-dwellers had no idea that people were gathering together or that there was any treachery being planned against them.

33

But when the people on the mainland found out about Sigurd and his companions' expedition, they sent Koll son of Kiallak in a party of twenty-four men, and when they met, Thorgeir Gyrdilskeggi ran off straight away with six men, but Sigurd Torfi's foster-brother made ready to defend himself with four men, and there was a very hard attack. Sigurd then again defended himself very bravely, for he was both strong and skilful with weapons. They went on fighting until all Sigurd's companions were fallen, but he was then still not wounded. Thorvald Blaskegg then attacked hard and many others. Then five of Koll's men were fallen. Sigurd then still defends himself superbly well. He then kills many more men; he then, however, suffers some wounds. Thorvald Blaskegg then went at Sigurd and thrusts through him with a spear. Sigurd had been fighting with an axe. He then threw the axe at Thorvald, and the axe hit his head, and both fell down dead. Sigurd had then been the death of nine men, and his companions had killed three. Altogether there fell there at the river-forks seventeen men from the two parties. They are now called Blaskegg's rivers.

Thorgeir Gyrdilskeggi stopped on Arnarvatn Heath and took refuge in a cave at Fitiar and gathered together a band of men and remained there until the men of Borgarfiord went for them. Then Thorgeir fled north to Strandir and was killed there, as is told in the Tale of Alfgeir.

34

Now the leading men looked around for someone who could be got to go out to the Holm, but most declined to do this. Torfi then urged that the person that went would gain a great deal of prestige from it, and would be thought a greater man than before, and said it was probable that those who were on the Holm would have forfeited their good luck because of their crimes. Ref's brother Kiartan son of Katla—a very great fighter and the fastest of men—he said he would have a go at going if they would give him the ring Sotanaut if Hord was caught.

'But I have in any case something to pay the Holm-dwellers back for.'

They agreed to this, and he seemed the most promising for it of those who were there then. Then Kiartan said:

'Isn't the most obvious thing to use Thorstein Gullknapp's boat? He has often done us a bad turn.'

They all thought this was a good idea, and said that this would give the Holm-dwellers the least ground for suspicion.

Kiartan son of Katla now rowed out on Thorstein Gullknapp's boat. He was wearing a mail-coat under his cloak, and when he got to Holm, he told Hord that the people on the mainland wanted to make peace. He said Illugi and his friends had played a major role in letting them go free. Geir believed this and thought it was probably true, since he was using Thorstein Gullknapp's boat, for he had sworn oaths that he would never behave treacherously towards them. Many were keen to get away and were tired of being there and urged going with Kiartan away from Holm. Then Hord said:

'Geir and I have very often not been of one mind, for frequently we have seen things differently. I think it is an evil man they have chosen for this, in the person of Kiartan, to be the bearer of such important matters, such great problems depending on it for both sides. There has also not been great friendship between us and Kiartan.'

Then he said: 'Let's not bring that up now, for that is not appropriate for those who are bringing proposals of peace, but it is nothing but the truth I am telling you, and I will swear to it if you find that more convincing.'

Hord said he looked to him as if his oaths would not be reliable, and then uttered a verse:

This weapon-storm-tree [warrior, Kiartan]
who anxiously urges departure seems to me
that he cannot fail to be spying.
This wave-burning-Baldr [man, Kiartan] would never
get away unharmed, who urged this,
if bow-destroyer [warrior, Hord] had his way.

Then nearly all were in favour of leaving. Some took passage for themselves with Kiartan straight away. Hord said he would not go at all.

'But I am quite happy for them to find out how true Kiartan will be to them. But I think,' he says, 'that you will be less cheerful by the latter part of the day.'

Kiartan was the better pleased the more he took away. Many boarded the ferry. Kiartan said they would come themselves to fetch their fellows on the next trip.

They now left Holm. The gathering of men could not be seen until the ship came round the point. But when they had beached the ship, the farmers penned them in with their great numbers. And when they came ashore, they were all taken and held and sticks were twisted in their hair and every one of them was beheaded. Then the men of the mainland rejoiced that they had had so little trouble with such criminals, and they thought the prospects were now good that they would all be defeated.

35

Kiartan went a second time out to Holm. The Holm-dwellers asked why their comrades had not come to meet them. Kiartan said they had been so happy at their release that they had run ashore in high spirits. Geir believed this and accompanied Kiartan aboard with many men. Hord was against this trip and said it would have dire consequences. He refused to go. Helgi son of Sigmund remained behind with him and Helga the earl's daughter and their two sons and six other men.

Geir and the others now went away from Holm, and Hord was not at all pleased that Geir wished to go with Kiartan. But when they rowed on round the ness, Geir saw the crowd of men on shore. He realised then that they must have been betrayed. Then he said:

'"Bad counsels turn out badly", and are often seen so too late, and Hord has often been closer to the mark than I. I think that once again it will be so, and it is now most likely that here there will be an end to all our activities, and it would be well if Hord got away, for he alone will be a greater loss than all of us together.'

They had now very nearly reached the shore. Geir then leapt overboard into the water and swam along by the rock. There was an *Easterner* called Orm who was with Indridi, a man of great strength. He could shoot better than anyone and was well equipped with all skills. He shot a javelin after Geir and it hit him between the shoulders and it caused his death. He was greatly praised for this deed. It is called Geir's point where the body drifted ashore.

36

Helga the earl's daughter was standing out on Holm and saw what happened. She told Hord and told him to look. It did not look the same to both of them. She said it would lead to dire consequences. The men of the mainland praised Kiartan highly and said he would prosper greatly from these trips. They said there were not many left now. Kiartan said he was now going to knock in the final nail by getting Hord and duping him into it also in the end. He used a six-oared boat and now goes out to Holm. Hord asked where Geir was and why he did not come to meet him. Kiartan said he had been kept on the mainland until he came.

'Thus peace can be made between everyone at once.'

Hord said, 'You are taking on a great deal, Kiartan, in transporting all of us Holm-dwellers to the mainland, and you must be getting a big reward from the people of the mainland. I shall not go anywhere. I have always mistrusted you, and one can never read anything from a man's appearance if you turn out well.'

Kiartan said, 'Surely you are not so much more cowardly than your men, that you dare not go ashore.'

Hord then leapt up and could not put up with his goading and said he thought he would have no reason to taunt him about his courage by the time their dealings came to an end. Hord said Helga should go with him. She said she would not go and not her sons either, and said it had now come about, as they say, that "you cannot save a doomed man". Helga then wept bitterly.

Hord went aboard the ship in great anger and they go now until they come to where Geir was floating dead by a skerry. Hord then leaped up and said to Kiartan:

'Most miserable of men, and a short time shall you have to enjoy this treachery.'

Hord then struck at him with the sword Sotanaut and clove him lengthwise down to where his belt was, his whole body with double mail-coat. Just then the ship ran ashore and they were all captured who were on the ship. Indridi was the first to lay hands on Hord and tied his arms rather tightly. Then Hord said:

'Rather hard are you tying now, brother-in-law.'

Indridi answers, 'You taught me how to do that when you tried to burn me in my house.'

Illugi said to Indridi, 'Yet Hord has not got good brothers-in-law, and indeed he has not deserved them.'

Indridi answers, 'He has long ago forfeited the right for any such relationships to be paid regard to.'

He then pointed his axe forward and gave a sign that someone should strike at Hord, but no one would do it. Hord then twisted himself round hard and got free. He grabbed the axe from Indridi's hand and leapt out over the circle of men three deep. Helgi son of Sigmund got free and leapt straight after him. Ref mounted a horse and rode after them and could not catch them. Then war-paralysis came over Hord;[18] he struck it off himself the first time and the second. A third time war-paralysis came over him and then they managed to pen him in and made a circle round him and he again jumped out over them, first killing three men. He took Helgi son of Sigmund on his back. Then he ran to the mountain. They chased hard after him. Ref was fastest, for he was on horseback, and he dared not attack Hord. Then came war-paralysis again over Hord. Then the main rout got to him. Then he threw Helgi off his back. Then he said:

'Powerful sorcerers are involved here, but you shall not have your will over anything I can do something about.'

Then he cut Helgi in two in the middle and declared they were not going to kill his foster-brother before his very eyes. It looked to people

[18] I.e. he was panic-stunned (literally, a war-fetter came over him).

as though Helgi was more or less dead already. Hord was then so furious and terrible to look at that none of them dared to approach him from the front. Torfi said that anyone who dared to strike at Hord should have the ring Sotanaut which Hord had on his arm. Then they made a circle round him. Then Thorstein Gullknapp arrived from his home at Thyril. They then attacked Hord hard. He even then caused six men's death. Then his axe came off its shaft. At that moment Thorstein Gullknapp struck at the nape of his neck with a long-shafted axe, for none of them dared to go for him from the front, even though he was without a weapon. From this wound Hord got his death. He had then killed of them thirteen men including the four he killed by the ship before he was captured. Everyone praised his valour, both his friends and enemies, and it is considered that there has been no one of his time who has been braver in every way and wiser than Hord, though he was not blessed with success. It was also his followers who were responsible for this, if he got involved in such crimes, and this also, that "there is no escaping fate".

37

The men of the mainland praised Thorstein Gullknapp for this deed and gave him the ring Sotanaut and said they were very pleased for him to have it. But when Thorstein heard of Thorbiorg's pronouncement, he heartily wished he had never done the deed. Nearly sixty men were killed of the Holm-dwellers besides the foster-brothers on Dogurdarness. Now the leading men talked about it being advisable to fetch Helga and kill her and Hord's sons. Then some thought it too late in the day. Then they made a compact about this that they should be granted no truce nor given any help, otherwise they would all take vengeance. Thus it was laid down with great emphasis. They planned to go out in the morning, but stayed there during the night.

38

Helga remains now on the island and feels certain now of all the tricks and treachery of the people of the mainland. She now considers her position. What she now decides to do is that she throws herself into the water and swims ashore from the Holm during the night and carried with her her four-year-old son Biorn to Blaskeggsa, and then went to meet her eight-year-old son Grimkel, for his swimming was then getting weak, and carried him ashore. This is now called Helga's sound. They went during the night up onto the mountain from Thyril and rested in the ravine which is now called Helga's ravine. She carried Biorn on her back, but Grimkel walked.

They go on until they and she come to Indridastadir. She then sat down out under the enclosure wall and sent Grimkel to the house to beg Thorbiorg for sanctuary. Thorbiorg was sitting on the *platform* when the boy came in. He asked her for sanctuary, and she stood up and took him by the hand and went out with him and asked who he was. He told her. She asked what had happened and where Helga was. Grimkel told what he knew and took her to Helga. Thorbiorg then could not speak, she was so overcome. She took them to an outhouse and locked them in there.

Late that day Indridi came and a lot of men in his party. There was no sign that anything was wrong with Thorbiorg, and she served food to the guests. But when they told her the news and that it was Thorstein Gullknapp who had killed Hord and attacked him from the rear while he had stood before him motionless, then Thorbiorg uttered a verse:

> There was in hard Unn's storm [battle]
> Hord felled to earth.
> He has beaten eight
> and five in battle.
> Magic of mighty spells was able to hold rather strongly.
> Brand of bitter brands [warrior, Hord]
> would otherwise still be standing.

And when they got into bed in the evening, Thorbiorg drew a knife and tried to stab her husband Indridi, but he held it off and was wounded deeply in the hand. Then he said:

'There are now two things, Thorbiorg, that we have a serious problem, and you want to take serious steps about it; so what must be done to bring about a reconciliation between us?'

'Nothing but this, that you bring me Thorstein Gullknapp's head.'

Indridi agreed to do this.

He set out in the morning on his own and rode straight to Thyril. He then dismounted and walked down Indridastig (Indridi's path) past Thyril and waited there until Thorstein went to his sacrificial temple as was his custom. And when Thorstein came, he went into the temple and prostrated himself before the stone where he sacrificed which stood there in the temple, and prayed. Indridi was standing outside near the temple. He heard this uttered from inside the stone:

You have here
for the last time
with doomed feet
trodden the earth.
On you shall rightly
before the sun shines
harsh Indridi
repay hatred.

Then Thorstein went out and towards his house. Indridi easily saw him going. Indridi told him not to run so hard. He then got round in front of him and immediately struck him with the sword Sotanaut under the throat so that it took off his head. He announced this killing as his deed back at Thyril. He said Thorstein had long been disloyal. He rode home and gave Thorbiorg the head. She said she was not bothered about it, now it was off the body.

'Now you will,' says Indridi, 'be reconciled with me.'

She said that would not happen until he took Helga and her sons in, if they chanced to come there, and gave them all the support they needed.

'Then I shall,' she said, 'give you all my love from then on.'

Indridi said he thought they must have jumped into the sea and drowned, as they were not found on the Holm.

'And I will promise you this, since I know that there will be no need to take it up.'

Then Thorbiorg fetched Helga and the boys and brought them in. Then Indridi spoke and was not pleased:

'I have opened my mouth quite wide enough, and yet the only thing to do now is keep one's word.'

And he did fulfil all his promises and no one blamed him for this. Everyone thought Thorbiorg had behaved magnificently.

39

There was a man called Thorolf and he was known as Starri (stiff), skilled with his hands and quite wealthy, uncaring and irreverent, bold and aggressive and tough in everything. He came the same autumn to Indridastadir and offered the farmer his services. Thorbiorg said he should certainly take him on, and he did so. He stayed there for a while doing smith's work. Helga the earl's daughter was pleasant with him, and Thorbiorg was too. He believed he was having an affair with the earl's daughter, and she was not unresponsive. Thorolf had been with Ref that summer and had not liked it there. He now asked Thorbiorg if he could stay the winter. She replies:

'I will let you stay the winter and give you the ring Sotanaut, Helga the earl's daughter and much other wealth if you kill Ref in Bryniudal.'

He replies, 'That is not a bad job for me. I believe I am just the man to be able to get that done if I have the sword Sotanaut. And it is not to be expected that I would do a small service and take a great reward.'

They made it a bargain. It was not easy to get the sword, for Indridi had it always on him wherever he went. One day Thorbiorg took the sword Sotanaut and made gaps here and there [in the scabbard] so that the sword could fall down of itself. And when Indridi went to gird on the sword it fell down out of the sheath. He found this strange, but Thorbiorg said that was the nature of the sword if it knew something was going to happen. He told her to mend the sheath. She said she would do it when she had time.

Indridi had to go west to Myrar to settle a dispute between his friends. He did not take the sword with him. And when he had gone, Thorbiorg gave Thorolf the sword Sotanaut and told him to use it like a man if he wanted to be married to Helga.

Thorolf went to Ref's and got there late in the day. He hid in a pile of turf and heaped peat round him so that nothing showed except just his nostrils. Ref was wary, so that he bolted the doors every evening and had torches taken round all the buildings twice, first before the evening meal and again before people went to bed, and this was done now as well. Thorolf was still not discovered. Thorolf could imitate anyone's voice. He stood up, as soon as they had gone to bed. He woke up Ref's servant-woman and said he was a shepherd. He told her to ask Ref for some shoe-leather, because he said he had to go up on the mountain in the morning. She said he did not stint his work, said he should not by any means have less than others.

'And there is none of the workers who is more useful than you.'

He said that should be so by the time he was finished. Ref slept in a *bed-closet* and he would not allow anyone to go to him there at night. Nevertheless she went and told Ref of the shepherd's request for shoe-leather. She said it wasn't right for him to be without shoes or anything else that he needed to have 'when he is concerned all the time for your property, both night and day.'

Ref was cross with her for coming with such a matter to him at night.

'But there is a bit of poor shagreen out in the peat-shed, and he can take some shoe-leather for himself from that.'

And when she had gone, Thorolf pushed a piece of wood in the shutter so that it did not close. He had been standing up over Ref while they had been talking, and he was afraid to do anything. Ref fell asleep, but Thorolf daredn't attack him. Ref's mother, Thorbiorg Katla, called out:

'Wake up, my son, the devil is standing over you and is going to kill you.'

Then Ref went to stand up, and at that moment Thorolf struck off both his feet from under him, one where the calf was narrowest, the other at the ankle. Then Thorolf leapt out into the room from the *bed-closet*. Then Thorbiorg Katla went up to him and grabbed him and forced him under her and bit his windpipe in two and so left him dead. Ref took the sword Sotanaut, but the ring disappeared from Thorolf, the one that Thorbiorg and Helga had given him, and which Hord had taken from Soti. Ref was healed and carried on a chair ever after, for he never managed to walk, and yet he lived on a long time after this, so that he came to be called Ref the Old, and was always considered the most worthy man.

40

A little later Indridi came home and heard what had happened. He felt sure that Thorbiorg must have been involved in the plot. But he did not want to lose the sword. Afterwards he went to see Ref and asked him to hand over the sword.

'For I have had nothing to do with this plot,' he says.

Ref gave him the sword.

'I do not want to lose your friendship,' says Ref.

Indridi then took his sword and rode home afterwards. It can be remarked by this what a leader Indridi has been, that such a warrior as Ref was dared do nothing other than hand over the sword to Indridi when he asked, such a great mutilation as he had suffered from it.

A little later there was a meeting between Thorgrima Smith-woman and Ref's mother, Thorbiorg Katla, and afterwards they were both found dead on Mulafell. They were all torn and cut asunder in pieces, and it has been thought to be haunted there afterwards near their grave-mounds. People assumed that Indridi's mother Thorgrima must have wanted to get the ring Sotanaut for Indridi, but Katla wanted to keep it from her and would not let it go and so they killed each other off. The ring was never found afterwards.

41

A few winters later a ship came to Breidavik. On it was Tind son of Hallkel and Thord son of Kolgrim from Ferstikla. They rode from the ship, Tind to Hallkelsstadir and Thord over Hvita and was making for home. And when Helga the earl's daughter found out this, she said to her son Grimkel that his father's death was slow to come into his mind. She told him then to lie in wait for Thord son of Kolgrim.

'For his father was your father Hord's greatest opponent.'

Grimkel was then twelve years old.

'I would like you, kinsman,' she says, 'to kill Thord, for valid vengeance is in him.'

Grimkel was in a party of three. They met near Bakkavad on the eastern side of Hvita below some stacks of turf. A little later they were all found dead from both parties. There was a man called Skeif who lived at Hvitarvellir, a man of small means. Some supposed that he must have killed wounded men and then taken fine possessions that Thord had had with him and were never heard of again. Skeif went abroad and never came out again and got to be rolling in money.

Indridi did not want to risk Helga here in this country and her son Biorn. They went abroad from Eyrar to Norway and then on to

Gautland, and Hroar was still alive then. He was glad to see his sister Helga, but thought Hord was a great loss. Helga did not marry again as far as is told. Biorn became a great man and came back to Iceland and killed many men in vengeance for his father and became the most valiant man. Twenty-four men were killed in vengeance for Hord. Compensation was paid for none of them. Some were killed by Hord's sons and kinsmen and relatives by marriage, and some by Hroar. Thorbiorg daughter of Grimkel was involved in the killing of nearly all of them; she is thought to have been a most remarkable woman. She and Indridi lived at Indridastadir until old age and were considered very great people, and there are many people descended from them.

Hord was nineteen and twenty winters old when he was killed, and most of these years had brought him honour and esteem, except for the three winters that he was in outlawry. The priest Styrmir the Wise also says that he thinks he was in the first rank of outlawed men because of his wisdom and skill with weapons and all kinds of abilities; and because of this also, that he was so highly esteemed abroad that the earl in Gautland gave him his daughter in marriage; and thirdly because for no single man in Iceland have so many men been killed in vengeance, and they were all uncompensated for. Now here we end the saga of the Holm-dwellers. God give us all good days without end. Amen.

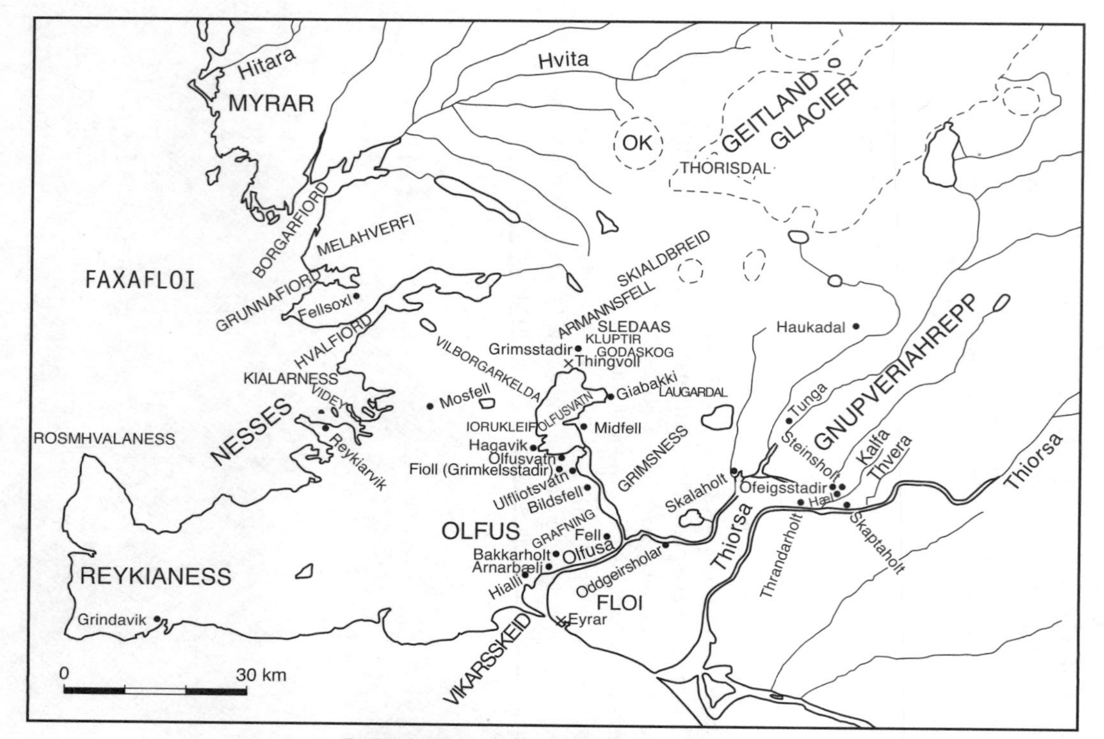

SOUTH-WEST ICELAND

TEXT SUMMARIES

THE SAGA OF GISLI

1. Thorkel Skerauki and his family in Norway. His son Gisli kills a berserk to defend his family's honour and is killed when he refuses to return the sword Greyflank.
2. Thorbiorn Sur becomes head of the family. His son Gisli kills Bard and defeats Skeggi to defend his sister Thordis's honour.
3. Skeggi's people try to burn Thorbiorn's family in their house and they are saved by using whey to put out the fire. Gisli and his brother Thorkel kill their attackers.
4. The family emigrate to Iceland. Thorbiorn Whey and his wife die and Gisli and Thorkel become heads of the family.
5. Gisli, Thorkel and Thordis marry.
6. Gest the Wise prophesies quarrels. Gisli tries to avert these by arranging oaths of brotherhood between himself, his brother and their brothers-in-law Thorgrim and Vestein, but the plan fails.
7. Thorgrim kills two Norwegians to avenge his son. He goes abroad with Thorkel, and Gisli goes abroad with Vestein.
8. Gisli returns to Iceland, leaving Vestein to conduct business in England, after making a token for each of them to use to give warning of danger.
9. Thorgrim and Thorkel return to Iceland. Thorkel overhears his and Gisli's wife gossiping and becomes jealous of Vestein.
10. Thorkel decides to go and live with his brother-in-law Thorgrim. Gisli prepares a winter feast.
11. Thorgrim and Thorkel get the magician Thorgrim Neb to make a spear out of the fragments of Greyflank. Gisli is told of Vestein's return to Iceland. He sends his token to warn him, but the messengers fail to meet him.
12. The messengers try again to intercept Vestein, but are too late; repeated warnings fail to prevent him from turning up at Gisli's feast. Vestein has brought gifts for Gisli and Thorkel, but Thorkel refuses them.

13. Gisli has bad dreams for two nights. On the third there is a great storm. He and his men go out in the night to save the hay. An unknown attacker comes to the house and kills Vestein. Gisli takes charge of the weapon. Thorgrim and Thorkel are informed.
14. Vestein is buried. Thorgrim ties on his Hel-shoes. Gisli and Thorkel affirm friendship.
15. Games are held and Thorgrim is worsted by Gisli. Thorgrim holds an autumn feast in honour of Frey. He sends for the tapestries that Vestein had offered Thorkel as a gift. Gisli agrees to let them have them, and arranges with the messenger for the doors at Thorgrim's farm to be left unlocked.
16. During the night Gisli goes out secretly and kills Thorgrim without being discovered.
17. Thorkel and his friends go to Gisli's farm to make the killing known; Thorkel conceals Gisli's snow-caked shoes. Thorgrim is buried and Gisli puts a large stone in the burial boat as an anchor. He and Thorkel affirm friendship.
18. Thorgrim's brother Bork pays Thorgrim Neb to work a spell preventing the killer from getting any help or shelter. He marries Thordis, his brother's widow. Thorgrim's posthumous son, Snorri Godi, is born. At the games Gisli and his partner Thorstein worst Bork and Thorkel. Gisli recites a verse in which there is a concealed confession of his killing of Thorgrim. Afterwards Thorstein quarrels with Berg Short-leg and gets his mother, Thorgrim Neb's sister, to cast a spell causing an avalanche to fall on Berg's farm.
19. Gisli gets Thorstein out of danger, and Bork has Thorstein's mother killed. Gisli has Thorgrim Neb killed. Gisli's sister Thordis, who has worked out the meaning of Gisli's verse confession, informs her husband Bork. Thorkel persuades him not to take instant vengeance. He lets Gisli know about all this. He afterwards meets him to tell him that Bork is going to summons him to the Assembly at Thorsness.
20. Thorkel agrees to keep Gisli informed. Gisli changes places with his slave to escape Bork's pursuit, and the slave is killed in mistake for him. They fail to find Gisli, and go to his house to summons him. He sells his land and takes refuge in Geirthiofsfiord.
21. Gisli tries to get his friends to negotiate a settlement, but nothing comes of it. He is outlawed at the Assembly. He lives in various

places with friends or with his wife Aud in Geirthiofsfiord, but no one will give him lasting help.

22. Bork arranges for Eyiolf the Grey to hunt Gisli down. Spying-Helgi is sent to find out where he is. He thinks he has found out and tells Eyiolf, but they fail to find him. Gisli starts to have dreams of the future.
23. Spying-Helgi is again sent to try to find out where Gisli is, and tells Eyiolf he has seen him near Aud's dwelling. Eyiolf fails to find him and offers Aud money to give him away but she refuses. Gisli goes to see his brother Thorkel and gets money from him. He goes to stay the winter with Gest the Wise's mother Thorgerd.
24. In the spring he goes back to be with Aud in Geirthiofsfiord. He has more dreams. He stays another winter with Thorgerd, and then goes back to Geirthiofsfiord for the summer. He goes to see his brother Thorkel again, but gets no help. He prophesies Thorkel's death. Gisli goes out to Hergilsey and stays with Ingiald.
25. News of his whereabouts leaks out and Spying-Helgi is sent to find him. Helgi discovers where he is hiding and tells Bork.
26. Bork mounts an expedition to Hergilsey. Gisli escapes them by impersonating an idiot out fishing.
27. Bork fails to find Gisli; Gisli takes refuge with Ref, whose wife helps to distract Bork's men from the search.
28. Bork, Gest and Thorkel go to the Assembly in Thorskafiord. Vestein's sons Berg and Helgi turn up in disguise and kill Thorkel to avenge their father.
29. The boys go to take refuge in Geirthiofsfiord. Aud prevents Gisli from finding out about what they have done.
30. She tells Gisli when it is too late for him to punish them for his brother's death. He has more dreams.
31. Spying-Helgi is again sent to find out where Gisli is. Havard, kinsman of Gest the Wise, makes sure that Helgi is not able to find the place again, though Eyiolf goes with a party of men to hunt Gisli out. Eyiolf and his men go to Aud's dwelling and offer her money.
32. Aud throws the money in Eyiolf's face. Havard prevents him from harming Aud.
33. Gisli has more dreams.
34. He goes to his hide-out to sleep. Eyiolf arrives with his men and

tracks him down. They attack Gisli for a long time without harming him, and Aud helps his defence.

35. Gisli kills several of Eyiolf's men and runs up onto a bluff.
36. Gisli kills more men but is severely wounded. He dies killing another of his enemies.
37. Eyiolf goes to announce his success to Bork. Bork's wife Thordis, Gisli's sister, lunges at Eyiolf with Gisli's sword but only wounds him slightly. Eyiolf is offered compensation and Thordis declares herself divorced from Bork.
38. Vestein's sons and Gisli's wife Aud and other survivors of Gisli's household go to Norway. Gisli and Thorkel's brother Ari turns up and kills Vestein's son Berg. Helgi goes to Greenland and prospers. Gisli's widow Aud and Vestein's widow Gunnhild go to Denmark and become Christian and go on pilgrimage to Rome; they do not return. Ari goes to Iceland and prospers.

THE SAGA OF GRETTIR

1. Onund's viking raids.
2. Onund loses his leg in the Battle of Hafrsfiord against Harald Harfagri and goes to the British Isles.
3. Ofeig Grettir and his family. Onund is betrothed to Ofeig's daughter.
4. Onund fights vikings.
5. Onund goes to the Hebrides.
6. Ofeig emigrates to Iceland. Onund returns to Norway.
7. Onund in hostilities with King Harald's men.
8. Onund emigrates to Iceland.
9. He settles in north-west Iceland.
10. Ofeig is killed in a feud and Onund is involved in the settlement.
11. Onund dies. His sons become farmers. There are disputes over land ownership. Thorgeir is attacked and gets his nickname Bottle-back.
12. Dispute over a stranded whale. Onund's son Ofeig Grettir is killed. Settlement is achieved.
13. Onund's sons Thorgrim and Thorgeir divide their property and Thorgrim goes to live at Biarg in Midfiord. His son Asmund goes

abroad as a merchant. He marries in Norway and has a son, Thorstein Dromund. His wife dies and Asmund returns to Iceland. He marries Asdis and settles at Biarg after his father's death.

14. Asgrim's family. Grettir's childhood: he is given three tasks by his father and because of his impatience fails at them all.
15. Grettir fights Audun at the games on Midfiord lake.
16. Grettir has a fight with Skeggi about a lost knapsack on the way to the Althing and kills him. He is condemned to outlawry for three years.
17. He sets out for Norway. He is unco-operative on board ship but eventually demonstrates his strength and endurance at baling. The ship is wrecked and the crew take refuge on an island with Thorfinn.
18. Grettir breaks into Kar the Old's grave-mound and takes much treasure including an ancient cutlass. He gives it all to his host.
19. Thorfinn goes away to the mainland for a Christmas feast. His farm is attacked by berserks. Grettir manages to trick them into trusting him and kills them all and thus saves Thorfinn's wife and daughter from them.
20. Thorfinn returns and rewards Grettir with his friendship and gives him the cutlass. Grettir goes to the north of Norway and stays with Thorkel.
21. He quarrels with a fellow guest called Biorn, and outdoes him in killing a dangerous bear.
22. Biorn sails to England and on his return he and Grettir meet near Trondheim. They fight and Biorn is killed. Earl Svein fails to achieve a reconciliation with Biorn's brother Hiarrandi.
23. Hiarrandi attacks Grettir and he and several of his men are killed. The earl will not decide on the case against Grettir until a third brother, Gunnar, can be present.
24. Gunnar attacks Grettir and he and several of his men are killed. Several people intercede for Grettir's life with the enraged earl, including his half-brother Thorstein Dromund. Grettir is allowed to go free as long as he leaves Norway. He sets out for Iceland.
25. A kinsman of Asmund Hærulang is killed in a dispute over a stranded whale.
26. The suit for the killing is taken to the Althing.
27. The killer is outlawed.

28. Grettir arrives back at Biarg. He goes to seek out a quarrel with Audun (cf. ch. 15). They fight and are covered with *skyr* until they are separated by Bardi Gudmundarson. Grettir offers Bardi help on his expedition to Borgarfiord to avenge his brother.
29. Grettir has a scrap at a horse-fight.
30. Thorbiorn Oxen-might and Thorodd Poem-bit introduced. Grettir waylays his enemies from the horse-fight. They are separated by Thorbiorn Oxen-might.
31. Bardi goes to Borgarfiord without asking for Grettir's help and returns after the Battle of the Heath. Grettir waylays him but is prevented from fighting him.
32. Thorhall hires Glam as a shepherd. He is killed by a supernatural creature and is buried away from the farm. He begins to haunt the valley.
33. Thorhall takes on Thorgaut as a shepherd. He is killed by Glam. Glam also kills all the farm animals in the valley.
34. Grettir decides to go and tackle Glam.
35. Grettir stays two nights at the farm without meeting Glam. The third night they fight inside the farm and Grettir is dragged outside. Glam curses him with fear of the dark and is then finally laid.
36. Thorbiorn Oxen-might holds an autumn feast. Thorbiorn Ferdalang scoffs about Grettir.
37. Thorbiorn Ferdalang and Grettir prepare to go abroad on the same ship. They quarrel and Thorbiorn is killed. Grettir goes to Norway.
38. Grettir is shipwrecked off the coast of Norway and swims across a sound to fetch fire for his companions. This accidentally results in the deaths of Thorir of Gard's sons.
39. Grettir goes to King Olaf and offers to submit to ordeal to prove his innocence. He is mocked by a strange boy in the church and strikes his mocker. He is prevented from undertaking the ordeal.
40. Grettir kills a berserk to save a Norwegian farmer and his family from disgrace.
41. Grettir stays with Thorstein Dromund. They compare each other's physique and Thorstein declares he will avenge Grettir's death.
42. Grettir's father Asmund dies of sickness.
43. Thorbiorn Oxen-might ambushes Grettir's brother Atli to avenge Thorbiorn Ferdalang. Atli survives but kills several of his attackers.
44. A settlement is reached at the Hunavatn assembly.

45. Atli takes on a workman who has run away from Thorbiorn Oxen-might. Thorbiorn goes and kills Atli.
46. Grettir is made full outlaw at the Althing for the deaths of Thorir of Gard's sons.
47. Grettir arrives back in Iceland and learns of the deaths of his father and his brother and of his own outlawry. He borrows a farmer's horse without permission and the Sodulkolla verses are composed. He returns to Biarg.
48. He goes and kills Thorbiorn Oxen-might and his son.
49. Thorodd Poem-bit tries to take vengeance for his brother, but Grettir has left Biarg.
50. He goes to Reykiaholar and is there at the same time as the foster-brothers Thorgeir and Thormod. They compete at demonstrating their strength but do not openly quarrel.
51. An attempt is made to free Grettir from outlawry but it fails. A price is put on his head.
52. Grettir lives as an outlaw by plundering farms in the Western Fiords. He is captured by some farmers and freed by Thorbiorg, wife of Vermund.
53. Grettir stays the winter with Thorstein Kuggason.
54. Grettir spends the summer in central Iceland. His encounter with Lopt (Hallmund).
55. Grettir lives on Arnarvatn Heath. The outlaw Grim is sent to him to gain his confidence and kill him, but Grettir finds him out and kills him.
56. Thorir of Gard sends Thorir Red-beard to try to kill Grettir. He attacks Grettir when he comes out of the water after rescuing their nets and is killed.
57. Thorir of Gard goes with men across the heaths to attack Grettir. Grettir fights them off, and eighteen of Thorir's men are killed; he finds that he has been assisted by Lopt (Hallmund).
58. Grettir goes and stays in a cave in western Iceland.
59. Gisli Thorsteinsson goes out to try to win the price that has been put on Grettir's head. Grettir humiliates him.
60. Farmers organise an expedition against Grettir but they are repelled.
61. Grettir goes up to the glaciers and stays in Thorisdal.
62. Another outlaw called Grim goes up onto Arnarvatn Heath. His fish are stolen by Hallmund, who is killed by Grim.

63. Thorir of Gard goes against Grettir on Reykiaheid and fails to find him.
64. Grettir goes to Sandhaugar which is being troubled by trolls. He carries the farmer's widow over the river to the Christmas service.
65. Grettir fights in the farm with a troll-wife. She drags him outside the farmhouse and he severs her right arm and she disappears into a waterfall. Later Grettir plans to explore her retreat.
66. He dives under the waterfall and finds a giant in a cave. He kills the giant and brings back bones of the trolls' victims.
67. The valley is now cleansed. Gudmund the Great advises Grettir to go to Drangey. A child is born to the widow at Sandhaugar which is believed to be Grettir's.
68. Snorri Godi's son Thorodd goes to kill Grettir but fails.
69. Grettir goes to Biarg. His young brother Illugi decides to go with him to Drangey. They take Thorbiorn Glaum as a servant. A farmer takes them out to the island.
70. Thorbiorn Ongul and the other owners of Drangey are introduced.
71. The farmers discover that Grettir is on the island. He refuses to leave.
72. Grettir goes to Hegraness to take part in the games. He is given formal safe-conduct under an assumed name. He returns safely to the island. The farmers get Thorbiorn Ongul to undertake to get Grettir off it.
73. Thorbiorn Ongul goes out to try to persuade Grettir to leave Drangey, but he refuses.
74. Grettir and Illugi are on Drangey for two winters. One night their fire goes out.
75. Grettir swims to Reykianess. His encounter with a servant girl. He is ferried back to the island with fire.
76. Thorbiorn Ongul takes Hæring to Drangey to try to ambush Grettir. He is killed.
77. A further attempt is made to release Grettir from outlawry, but it is put off until the following summer.
78. Thorbiorn Ongul takes his old nurse to the island to see if she can help to get rid of Grettir. Grettir throws a stone which injures her.
79. The old woman casts a spell on a piece of driftwood. It comes ashore on Drangey and Grettir injures his leg trying to chop it.
80. Grettir's leg festers. He is nursed by Illugi.

81. Thorbiorn Ongul is persuaded by the old woman to go out to Drangey with his men in a storm.
82. Grettir is incapacitated by his injured leg. Ongul's party arrive at the island and surprise Thorbiorn Glaum with the ladder unguarded. They attack Grettir and Illugi in their hut. Grettir is killed and Thorbiorn Ongul takes his head and cutlass. He has Illugi and Thorbiorn Glaum killed.
83. Thorbiorn Ongul fails to get praise for killing Grettir and Illugi. He visits Grettir's mother and taunts her.
84. Thorbiorn Ongul fails to get a reward and is outlawed at the Althing.
85. In Norway Thorstein Dromund hears of Grettir's death. He follows Thorbiorn Ongul to Constantinople.
86. They both join the Varangian guard. Thorbiorn Ongul boasts of killing Grettir and is killed by Thorstein Dromund, who is imprisoned for the deed.
87. He is heard singing from a street outside the prison by Spes, a wealthy married woman. She obtains his release and takes him into her home.
88. They fall in love and her husband becomes suspicious. Three times he surprises them together, but Thorstein always escapes. Spes's husband challenges her to prove her innocence.
89. Spes is carried over a ditch by Thorstein disguised as a beggar. She swears an oath that she has not been touched by anyone except her husband and the beggar. Her husband is disgraced and she obtains a divorce.
90. Thorstein and Spes marry. After two years living in Constantinople they go to Norway.
91. Thorstein and Spes repent and go to Rome for absolution.
92. They both become hermits and die in purity of life.
93. The saga ends. Sturla's judgment on Grettir.

THE SAGA OF HORD

1. Biorn Gullberi settles in Iceland
2. Grimkel Godi, Torfi, Sigurd Torfi's foster-brother, Grim the Small introduced.
3. Indridi introduced. Grimkel betrothed to Signy.
4. Grimkel's wedding.
5. Grim the Small marries Gudrid.
6. Signy's dream.
7. Hord is born and is cursed by his mother; he is fostered by Grim the Small. Geir is born.
8. Signy dies in childbirth. The child, Thorbiorg, is saved by her half-brother Grim.
9. Torfi gives Thorbiorg to the vagrant Sigmund, who passes her on to Grim the Small.
10. Grimkel Godi summonses Torfi. A settlement is arranged at the Althing.
11. Illugi the Red introduced. His wedding to Grimkel's daughter Thurid.
12. Hord, Geir and Helgi go to Norway.
13. Geir kills a Norwegian courtier and the Icelanders take refuge in Oslofiord.
14. The Icelanders go to Gautland and vow to break into Soti's grave-mound.
15. Hord breaks into the mound and wins Soti's sword, ring and helmet. The ring is cursed.
16. Hord marries Helga, the earl's daughter.
17. Sigurd Torfi's foster-brother goes to Scandinavia and is captured by vikings in the Baltic. He escapes and joins Hord and Geir's band of raiders.
18. Geir returns to Iceland and goes to live in Hvalfiord.
19. Indridi marries Thorbiorg. Grimkel Godi dies.
20. Hord and his wife Helga, Sigurd Torfi's foster-brother and Helgi Sigmund's son return to Iceland. Hord claims his inheritance from Torfi and begins to live at Breidabolstad.
21. Quarrel with Aud. Helgi Sigmund's son kills Aud's son and Hord kills Aud. Hord and Helgi are outlawed.
22. Hord goes to live with Geir. They run short of food and Geir and Helgi go raiding.

23. Games at Sand, which end with Hord killing Onund.
24. Hord, Geir and their friends go out to live on Geirsholm.
25. Raids on Thorbiorg Katla.
26. Raid on Thorstein Oxnabrodd's farm. Skroppa is killed.
27. Raid on Orm's farm. Orm's treasure chest rescued by Bolli.
28. Raid on Illugi's farm.
29. Raids on Indridi's livestock.
30. Raid on Thorgima Smith-woman's cattle. The outlaws plan to burn Indridi in his house.
31. Attempt to burn Indridi's house which fails.
32. Meeting of farmers to plan to get rid of the outlaws.
33. Sigurd and eleven others killed while fetching water to the island.
34. Kiartan son of Katla goes to the island and tricks a number of the outlaws into going with him to the mainland, where they are killed.
35. Kiartan goes to the island again and persuades Geir and many others to leave with him. Geir is killed.
36. Hord and the remainder of the outlaws are persuaded to leave the island, leaving Helga and their two sons behind. He escapes for a while but is eventually killed by Thorstein Gullknapp, after himself killing Helgi to prevent his enemies from doing so.
37. Thorstein is rewarded with the ring Sotanaut. The farmers plan to fetch Helga and her and Hord's sons from the island.
38. Helga swims to the mainland with her two sons and goes to Thorbiorg to ask for sanctuary. Thorbiorg persuades Indridi to go and kill Thorstein Gullknapp and to spare Helga and her sons.
39. Thorbiorg persuades Thorolf Starri to go and try to kill Ref, one of the leaders at the killing of Hord, and gives him Hord's sword Sotanaut which Indridi had acquired as well as the accursed ring. Ref is wounded but Thorolf is killed.
40. Indridi goes to recover Hord's sword. Thorgrima Smith-woman and Thorbiorg Katla kill each other while fighting for possession of the ring Sotanaut.
41. Helga persuades her son Grimkel to try to kill Thord son of Kolgrim in vengeance for his father. Both Grimkel and Thord are killed. Helga goes to Gautland with her son Biorn, who later returns to Iceland and leads a successful life there, killing many men in vengeance for his father.

THE SAGA OF GISLI

Thorkel Skerauki = Isgerd
Raud
Biartmar
Thorstein Cod-biter
Ari = (1) Ingibiorg (2) = Gisli
Thorbiorn Sur = Thora
Styrkar
Vestein = Hild
Helgi
Sigurd
Vestgeir
Thordis
Bork = (2)
Thorgrim = (1)
Thordis
Thorkel = Asgerd
Ari
Gisli = Aud
Vestein = Gunnhild
Saka-Stein
Thorodd
Snorri Godi
Berg
Helgi

THE SAGA OF GRETTIR

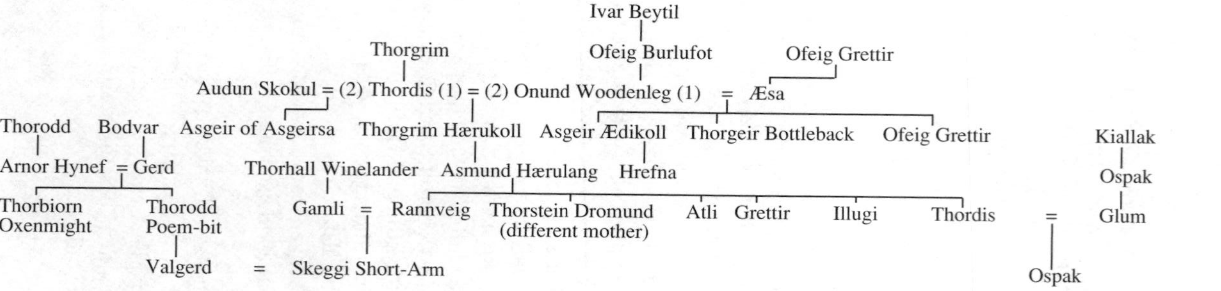

THE SAGA OF HORD

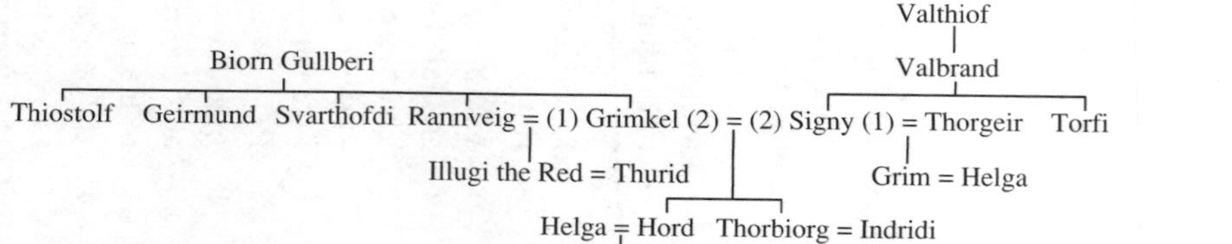

BIBLIOGRAPHY

This list includes all the books referred to in the Introduction and Notes that do not there have complete references. Unless otherwise stated, translations of the Icelandic sagas listed here are in *The Complete Sagas of Icelanders*, 5 volumes. Reykjavík: Leifur Eiríksson (1997).

Bandamanna saga = the Saga of the Confederates

Beowulf, edited and translated by Michael Swanton. Manchester: Manchester University Press (1978).

Bergbúa þáttr = the Tale of the Mountain-Dweller

Bjarnar saga Hítdælakappa = the Saga of Bjorn, Champion of the Hitardal People

The Book of the Icelanders: in G. Jones, *The Norse Atlantic Saga*. London: Oxford University Press (1964, 1986).

The Book of Settlements, translated by Hermann Pálsson and P. Edwards. Winnipeg: University of Manitoba Press (1972).

R. B. Dobson and J. Taylor, *Rymes of Robyn Hood*. Stroud: Sutton (1997).

Droplaugarsona saga = the Saga of Droplaug's sons; also in *The Fljotsdale Saga and The Droplaugarsons*, translated by Jean Young. Everyman's Library (1990).

Eyrbyggia saga = The Saga of the People of Eyri

Fagrskinna, a Catalogue of the kings of Norway, translated by Alison Finlay. Leiden: Brill (2004).

Fóstbræðra saga = the Saga of the Sworn Brothers

Grágás = *Laws of Early Iceland* I, translated by Andrew Dennis, Peter Foote, Richard Perkins. Winnipeg: University of Manitoba Press (1980).

Gunnlaugs saga = the Saga of Gunnlaug Serpent-Tongue

Heiðarvíga saga = the Saga of the Slayings on the Heath

Hrólfs saga kraka = *The Saga of King Hrolf Kraki*, translated by Jesse L. Byock. Penguin Books (1998).

Hrómundar þáttr halta = the Tale of Hromund the Lame

Íslenzk fornrit I ff. Reykjavík (1933 ff.; in progress).

Kormaks saga = Kormak's saga

Kristni saga (The Saga of Christianity): in Gudbrand Vigfusson and

F. York Powell, *Origines Islandicae*. Oxford: Clarendon Press (1905), I 376–406.

Laxdæla saga = the Saga of the People of Laxardal

Ljósvetninga saga = the Saga of the People of Ljosavatn

Medieval Scandinavia. An Encyclopedia, edited by Phillip Pulsiano. New York: Garland (1993).

Morkinskinna. The Earliest Icelandic Chronicle of the Norwegian Kings (1030–1157), translated by Theodore M. Andersson and Kari Ellen Gade. Ithaca: Cornell University Press (2000). Islandica LI.

Njáls saga = Njal's saga

Orms þáttr Stórólfssonar = Orm Storolfsson's Tale

Örnólfur Thorsson (ed.). *Grettis saga*. Reykjavík: Mál og Menning (1994). Sígildar sögur 4.

Örvar-Odd's Saga, in *Seven Viking Romances*, translated by Hermann Pálsson and Paul Edwards. Penguin Books (1985).

The Poetic Edda, translated by Carolyne Larrington. The World's Classics (1996).

Saxo Grammaticus, *The History of the Danes*, translated by Peter Fisher, edited by Hilda Ellis Davidson. Cambridge: Brewer (1979).

H. Shetelig and H. Falk, *Scandinavian Archaeology*, translated by E. V. Gordon. Oxford: Clarendon Press (1937).

Snorri Sturluson, *Edda*, translated by Anthony Faulkes. Everyman (1987).

Snorri Sturluson, *Heimskringla*, translated by Samuel Laing. Part One, *The Olaf Sagas*. Part Two, *Sagas of the Norse Kings*. Everyman's Library (1964, 1961).

Snorri Sturluson, *King Harald's saga. Harald Hardradi of Norway.* From Snorri Sturluson's *Heimskringla*, translated by Magnus Magnusson and Hermann Pálsson. Penguin Books (1966).

Þorvalds þáttr víðförla = the Tale of Thorvald the Far-Travelled

Vatnsdæla saga = the Saga of the People of Vatnsdal

Völsunga saga = *Vǫlsunga saga. The Saga of the Volsungs*, edited and translated by R. G. Finch. London: Nelson (1965).

THE VERSES

The *dróttkvætt*, or court metre, in which the majority of the verses in the sagas were composed, makes use of a rigid pattern of alliteration, half rhyme and full rhyme. Its rhythmic unit is developed from the Germanic half line, with three instead of two stressed syllables, and having the third foot always of the falling or trochaic type. There are four pairs of these half lines in a stanza, joined by the alliteration; the first stave of the second half line is the head stave of the pair, and it always carries the alliteration. There is half rhyme in the first half line of each pair, with the last stressed syllable making one of the rhyming couple (always in the Icelandic, often in the English); full rhyme is similarly placed in the second half line. Each half line normally contains six syllables. The following translated stanza will serve as illustration; the alliteration is marked by bold, the half and full rhymes by italic:

> I **f***ought* a lone **f***ate*ful
> **F***ight*, this was my n*ight*mare;
> **S***in*gle, not **s***oon* I was
> **S**l*ain* by their m*ain* power.
> **G**ood fl*esh* by my **g***ash*ing
> **G***ave* I mouths of r*av*ens,
> **B***ut* in your wh*ite* **b**osom
> **B**right bl*ood* drops fell r*udd*y.

The second verse in ch. 24 of *The Saga of Gisli* differs in having the alliteration but full end-rhyme instead of internal rhyme.

The majority of the verses in *The Saga of Grettir* and *The Saga of Hord*, like those in *The Saga of Gisli*, are spoken by the respective heroes, and in the same *dróttkvætt* form as most of the verses in *The Saga of Gisli*. Some verses in all three sagas are in the simpler form of some Eddic verse, with shorter lines (containing only two stressed syllables) and less internal rhyme, though alliteration is always present (e.g. *The Saga of Gisli*, ch. 21, the first two verses; *The Saga of Hord*, ch. 11, the second verse, and ch. 15, verses 1–4). These include verses spoken by supernatural characters and some by women, and the autobiographical series of Grettir (*The Saga of Grettir*, chs 24 and 52) and Hallmund (*The Saga of Grettir*, ch. 62). The kennings (poetical periphrases) in the verses are obscure to modern readers, though they are highly conventional and mostly fall into a few traditional patterns. (The translations of the verse in *The Saga of Gisli* do not always reproduce the meanings of the original kennings precisely, but nevertheless the kennings used there are included in the following explanations.) The majority refer to persons, either the speaker or the one addressed, sometimes to one of the other characters, and usually replace their names. Male persons are referred to in terms of their conventional heroic roles as warriors and seafarers or other attributes, particularly the universal ideal quality of generosity, with base-words that may be words for a kind of tree or names of gods or other supernatural beings. Female persons are referred to in terms of their adornment or conventional feminine roles, again with base-words that may be words for tree or feminine mythological names. The following kennings for **man** or **men** are used in *The Saga of Grettir*:

Distributor of wealth, battle-axe destroyer (ch. 4), shaft-sharpener (ch. 9), metal-Gauts (ch. 12), flinger of neck-rings, scatterer of rings (i.e. generous man; ch. 14), ship-fir, winners of gold, embellisher of battle, ship-Tveggi (ch. 17), gold-reducer, battle-Ull, gold-harmer (ch. 18), sword-trees (ch. 19), battle-Niord (ch. 21), ring-Baldr (ch. 22), Thund's people (whose companion is Thorfinn; ch. 24), sea-horse-rider (ch. 27), gold-Gaut (ch. 28), experiencer of battle, harm-doers (ch. 31), bow-slinger, shield-wielder (a four-element kenning, see below; ch. 37), war-urger (ch. 40), battle-tree, sword-breaker, battle-demander, helm-pine, shield-Frey, bow-pine, gold-keeper, battle-pusher (ch. 47), wealth-breakers (ch. 60), battle-tending trees, shield-wielders, ship adorner (ch. 63), sword- (or spear-) empowerer (ch. 66), neck-ring bush, shield-bushes, shield-raisers, battle-Niords, serpent's lair robbers (i.e. generous men; ch. 72), battle-desiring bushes, battle-trunks (ch. 75), Hrist's defender, spear-man, shield-tree, oar-maple, point-tree, scatterer of gold, spear-wielders, sword-tree (ch. 80), gold-Niords, war-trees, weapon-Frey (ch. 83), battle-makers, sword-belt fasteners, ship-urger (ch. 87).

In *The Saga of Gisli*: ship-tree (ch. 17, here Thorgrim), god of war-blade gleaming, wearer of grim war-mask (Thorgrim; ch. 18), gold spenders (ch. 21), glad or brave spender, storm tamer, treader of sword weather (the Icelandic has a kenning here which goes: ruler of the wind of the Skioldungs—an early Danish dynasty, great in legend—i.e. ruler of battle), waster of wave fire, ring-speeder (ch. 22), trees of the spear's greeting, seekers of sark's hatred, strife-gods (literally wakers of strife of weapons; ch. 24), lords of masted fiord-elks (ch. 32), crow feeder (the Icelandic has a kenning for 'the rest' in line 2 of the sixth verse in ch. 33: comforters of the early flyer, i.e. the raven, on which the one in the English is based), gods of slain net (the Icelandic has 'corpse-net', which is taken to mean shield), corpse-stream eagle's eye-delight providers (warriors, who give delight to the eye of the eagle of blood, the carrion bird; the Icelandic has here the simpler kenning: nourishers of carrion fowl), shield troll-woman wielders (men who wield the troll-woman, the malevolent enemy, of the shield, i.e. the axe or sword; ch. 33), tree of hard edge hatred (the Icelandic here has: tree of the sword-voice; ch. 34).

In *The Saga of Hord*: demander of battle (Valbrand; ch. 3), gold-desirer, wealth-seeker, gold demander (the young Hord; ch. 7), sword-harmer, sword-snatcher (ch. 9), weapon-reddener, ring-breaker or -spender (Illugi; ch. 11), destroyer of swords (ch. 12), sword-shaker, wealth-maple (ch. 15), gold-juniper, weapon-wielder, gold-ring keeper, gold cultivator, sword-trees (ch. 21), land-owner, flingers of gold, targe-trees (ch. 22), gold-trees, homestead-Tyr, gold-giver, wolf-feeders (ch. 28), battle-tree, gold-Baldr, bow-destroyer (ch. 34), brand of bitter brands (i.e. Hord; an unusual type of kenning: bitter brands are swords, their brand is presumably a piece of wood on the pattern of kennings with trees as base-word; ch. 38). Indridi is called Thorgrima's heir in ch. 21. A dead man is called earth-dweller in ch. 15 (his house is the grave-mound).

It will be seen that nearly all these kennings are conventionally complimentary, whoever is being referred to. But the evil ghost Soti is called destroyer of good deeds and keeper of spells in ch. 15 of *The Saga of Hord*, and a bad man is called lame-harmer in ch. 22 of *The Saga of Gisli*.

The following kennings for **woman** are used in *The Saga of Grettir*:

Ground of hoards, linen-Gerd, ring-Hlin (ch. 14), wealth-*norn*, linen-Nauma (ch. 17), gold-willow (ch. 19), gold-dame (ch. 47), ale-keeping

Saga (ch. 60), gold-Sol (ch. 63), seam-prop, penis-Hrist, jewel-Freyia (ch. 75; these three refer to a servant-girl), (precious) stone-land (ch. 80), brooch-Nauma, gold-Frid (ch. 83), rings' Grund (ch. 87).

Again, these kennings are mostly generalised kennings for **woman** without any specific features reflecting individual characteristics.

The verses in *The Saga of Gisli* contain an unusual number of kennings for **woman** that use the names of heathen goddesses, some of which are rarely found elsewhere. Such names are not retained in the translation, but they are these in the original Icelandic:

Bil, Eir, Freyia, Fulla, Gefn, Gerd, Gna, Hild, Hlin, Hlokk, Lofn, Nanna, Nauma (also the name of a troll-wife), Niorun, Saga, Siofn, Sol, Syn, Thrud, Var, Vor; also used are the valkyrie-names Gondul and Thogn.

In the translation, the following kennings for **woman** are found: oak of herbs, snake-plot goddess (ch. 14), land of the wave fire (ch. 22), band goddess (chs 22, 33), thread-work goddess (ch. 24 and 33), ale goddess, wealth goddess (ch. 24), tree of the sea's fire (ch. 26), goddess of threads, sea-flame goddess, linen goddess (ch. 30), bowl goddess, goddess of hawk-track fire (fire of the hand = gold), doom goddess (referring to the worser dream-woman as a valkyrie), necklet goddess (the Icelandic, after emendation, has 'gold-wearing goddess'), ring goddess, thread-goddess, belt goddess, sea-fire goddess (ch. 33), linen goddess (ch. 34), goddess of shower of spear-shaft's hall (i.e. of gold; ch. 36).

In *The Saga of Hord*: brooch-prop, jewel-Niorun (ch. 3), wealth-slope (ch. 7), thread and embroidery prop, silver bowl Gna (ch. 9), gold-Aud (ch. 11).

The **weapons**, **ships**, **battle**, **ale**, **jewels** and **gold** that often appear as parts of the above kennings are also sometimes referred to in subsidiary kennings, giving circumlocutions of three or more elements. **Weapons** are referred to as follows (Gi = *The Saga of Gisli*, Gr = *The Saga of Grettir*, H = *The Saga of Hord*; figures refer to chapters):

Axes: troll of storm-clashing (Gr 3), troll of battle (Gr 4), wound-harmer (Gr 11), hammer-troll, battle giantess (the name Grid is used; Gr 16), troll-woman of the shield (probably meaning axe rather than sword; Gi 33).

Arrows: bow's dew (Gi 34).

Swords (or cutlass): shield-fire, shield's fire (Gr 3 and 24), shield-fish (Gr 11), wound-harmer (Gr 17; cf. under **axes**), fire of battle, harmer of helmets (the last might be any weapon; Gr 18), war-fire (Gr 19), wound-snake (Gr 37), battle-adder (Gr 57), battle-pole (perhaps for spear; Gr 66), battle-fire (Gr 80), arm brands (H 12), blood-serpent (H 15), war-blade (Gi 18), sark's hatred (sark = coat of mail; Gi 24), battle-ice (Gi 30), fires of Odin, troll-woman of the shield (this kenning usually means a battle-axe; Gi 33). The name Warflame in *The Saga of Gisli* is a kenning for sword.

Shields: sword-wall (Gr 37), battle-bowl (Gr 40), wall of arrows' passage (Gr 40), Thund-cloud (Gr 47), Vidrir's wall (Gr 63), fray-house, Hlokk's hangings (shields were sometimes hung on the walls of buildings), Hild's wall (Gr 72), Mimir's wall (Gr 80), wooden bastion wide-hard, slain net (Gi 33).

Ships: shore-steed (Gr 8; shore = one of the props used to support a beached ship), rib-steed (Gr 9), wind-cloth (i.e. sail) horse, ness-grasp (i.e. sea) reindeer (Gr 17), sea-horse (Gr 27, 63), wave-horse (Gr 87), fiord-elks (Gi 32).

Battle: sword-clash, storm-clashing (Gr 3), storm-weather of Hrotti, spear-storm destruction (Gr 8), spears' doom (Gr 17), Hrotti-storm, weapon-din (Gr 18), storm of swords (Gr 27), Mist's moot, Hild's storm, Gungnir's greed (Gr 31), Hedin's maid's (Hild's) meeting (cf. Snorri Sturluson's *Edda*, pp. 122–3), shield-storm, sword-wind (Gr 47), Thrott's storm (Gr 48), weapon-shower (Gr 54), weapon-storm (Gr 57), point-play (Gr 62), shield's threat (Gr 63), sword-storm (Gr 66), shield-storm (Gr 72), arrow-wind, spear-storm (Gr 75), spears' tumult, weapons' quarrel, storms of wounds (Gr 80), edge-moot (Gr 87), wound-storm (mail-coat-strap storm would also mean battle, and the kenning seems to have too many elements; H 3), Hild's rain (H 11), weapon-storm (H 34), Unn's storm (H 38), spear's greeting, strife of weapons (in Icelandic; Gi 24), storm of weapons (Gi 33), hard edge hatred (sword-voice in Icelandic; Gi 34). Giving sustenance to the wolf (H 22) means fighting a battle and providing carrion, cf. wolf-feeders as a kenning for warriors (H 28). Cf. *The Saga of Gisli*, ch. 33, verses 4, 6 and 8, lines 5–6, where the Icelandic means literally 'nourishers of carrion fowl'.

Ale: horn-flood (Gr 60).

Jewel: island-bone (Gr 75).

Gold: serpent's path, Fafnir's bog, serpent's seat or lair, snake-slope, snake-plot, adder's earth (referring to the idea that serpents commonly sleep on hoards of gold; Gr 17, 18, 63, 72, 80, H 11, Gi 14, 30), wave-light, wave-fire, sea's fire or sea-fire, sea's flame or sea-flame, estuary-fire, flood-moon, wave-burning (Gr 18, 47, 83, H 7, 15, 21, 28, 34, Gi 22, 26, 30, 33; these kennings, the equivalent of 'fire of the sea' are explained by Snorri Sturluson in his *Edda*, p. 95), Syr's tears (Gr 83; see Snorri Sturluson's *Edda*, p. 30); Sirnir's voice (H 7; see Snorri Sturluson's *Edda*, p. 61), Grani's burden (H 15; see *Völsunga saga*, ch. 20), Nile sand (presumably referring to the finding of gold dust in rivers; H 22), fire of hawk-track, i.e. of the hand (Gi 33), shower of spear-shaft's hall (i.e. of the hand; Gi 36).

In a number of cases, personal and place-names are indicated by kennings using a kind of riddling word-play (which Snorri Sturluson in his *Edda*, p. 155, ironically calls *ofljóst*, 'too clear'). It usually involves using a kenning for the synonym of a homonym:

The great ship of the Red Sea is Dromund, rock-god's (giant's) slayer is Thor, Regin's house is *stein* 'stone'. This gives the name Thorstein Dromund (Gr 24).

A word for 'bear' (*hlébarðr*) is used as a substitute for the personal name Bersi, which is also a word for 'bear' (Gr 24).

Audun, whose name is also one of Odin's names, is replaced by Ialfad, another of Odin's names (Gr 28).

Grettir's name, which is also a name for a serpent, is replaced by various other terms for serpent: mountain-band (Gr 28), dale-eel (Gr 47), Thund's darling's (Odin's wife's, Iord's, i.e. earth's) thong (Gr 52), ground-salmon (Gr 54).

For Thorbiorn, Hafli's opponent is substituted (Gr 48). Hafli is a giant, whose opponent is Thor. Biorn is also a name for Thor. Similarly, in Gi 18, Giant-bane Grim (literally: troll-friend's destroyer-grim; the friend of the troll-woman is the giant, whose destroyer is the god Thor) is Thorgrim. Might of ox and bull is Thorbiorn Oxen-might (Gr 48).

Wetherfiord is for Hrutafiord (*hrut* means 'wether') (Gr 48, 57).

For Isafiord, we have sea-thatch (ice) fiord; the rowan tree is Thorbiorg (*Thors biorg*, 'Thor's saving', or the help of Sif's husband, was, according to Snorri Sturluson's *Edda*, p. 82, a rowan; Gr 52).

Bragi's wife, whose name is Idunn, is used as a substitute for *idunnar* 'of the turbulent water' (Gr 66).

Hallmund is little stone (*hall*) fist-land (*mund*, 'hand'; Gr 54).

The following expressions are similar to these: the woman shut and locked in the refuge of the dead (Hel) is also called Hel. She is also Byleist's niece, and stands for death (Gr 24).

Sometimes half-kennings are found, where a base-word is used without a determinant, e.g. 'support' (*skorð*) in *The Saga of Grettir* ch. 17, verse 4 is a half-kenning for woman, i.e. a word such as 'jewel' is understood. Cf. *The Saga of Gisli*, ch. 30, where in 'golden one, of seagull's ground', seagull's ground, i.e. the sea, is probably a half-kenning for gold, stemming from a full kenning for gold of the type fire of the sea; the Icelandic phrase here means literally 'support (*skorða*) of sea-gull's gound'. A shield is also called 'thane' without any qualification in *The Saga of Hord*, ch. 11. In *The Saga of Gisli*, chs 24, 33, 'goddess' is used as a half-kenning in the translation where the Icelandic has in each case a determinant relating to female attributes (embroidery, wealth). The expressions 'wife' and 'my lady' in *The Saga of Gisli*, chs 22, 32 also correspond to proper kennings in the Icelandic.

Kennings are used for a few other concepts too, sometimes with deliberate comic effect:

arm: tree of hands (Gr 80), shoulder-leg (Gr 87), sleeve-plain (H 12).

bear: hibernator (literally 'winter-passer'), wool-otter (Gr 21), greedy-tooth, harsh-minded one (Gr 22).

blood: wound-sea (Gr 11; its house is the wound); wound flood (Gi 24 and 33), slaughter's gilt (Gi 24; there is no kenning in the Icelandic here), froth of fires of Odin, sword-loosed tides (no kenning here in original), wound rain, sword rain, corpse-stream (Gi 33).

breast or **heart**: fortress of stratagems (Gr 24).

cave: storm-resounding pot (Gr 54), mountain hall (Gr 57), Nauma's hall (Gr 66).

death: bane-speech (from the sword's mouth; Gi 17), pain's ending (Gi 18). Blood-vengeance perceived as repayment is called bitter coin in Gi 21.

eye: sleep's cistern (Gi 14); **eyelashes**: twigs of hazel, sight twigs (Gi 14), eye fringe (Gi 33).

fiord: ness-grasp (Gr 17); cf. **sea** below.

foot: ankle's thorn-tree (Gr 40).

giants: crag-dwellers (Gr 62), troll-wife's friend (Gr 66). Gang (Gr 66) is a proper name for a giant used as a common noun.

glaciers: tumbling great-freezes (Gr 54).

hand: hawk-track (Gi 33), spear-shaft's hall (Gi 36).

jaw: tooth-yard's dwelling (Gr 40).

mind: Hlokk's storm (H 12; see Snorri Sturluson's *Edda*, p. 154).

mouth: snack-port (Gr 40).

penis: balls-branch (Gr 75); also called *faxi* 'maned-horse'; thigh-forest is pubic hair.

poet: verse-teller (Gr 47), Ygg's drink-server (Gr 47), linker of strong letters (literally payer-out of poetry; Gi 24), praise-rune maker (literally praise-adorner), ode-contriver (Gi 30); poetry is dwarfs' liquor twice in *The Saga of Gisli* (ch. 26, 34), pouring which is reciting or making; for the story behind these kennings see Snorri Sturluson's *Edda*, pp. 61–4).

raven: early flyer (Gi 33, see under kennings for man above), corpse-stream hawk or eagle (Gi 33).

sea: prow-land (Gr 63), seagull's ground (Gi 30); cf. **fiord** above

snake: gold-dweller (Gr 63), land-thong (H 11), heath-cod (H 21); compare the kennings for Grettir's name above, e.g. mountain band (Gr 28), earth's thong (Gr 52).

stone (a precious one, i.e. a jewel): island bone (Gr 75).

summer: snake's solace (H 21).

tears: storm of cheek, grief's nut-fruits, pity's fruit (Gi 14).

winter: snake's sickness (H 21).

wound: head-scratch (Gr 60), edge-track (Gr 62), house of blood (Gr 11).

GLOSSARY OF ICELANDIC TERMS

Assembly, thing: It is thought that in the first century or so of the settlement in Iceland each *godi*, or chieftain, would arrange local assemblies, 'things', for dispute resolution and discussion of public affairs. Later it became established practice that spring assemblies, each under the supervision of three *godis*, were held on thirteen fixed sites in the country. Every householder was legally bound to be the *assembly-man* of some chieftain, not necessarily of the *godi* who lived closest; and if he had means above a certain minimum, he was bound to attend assemblies in support of his chieftain or to contribute to the expenses of those who did attend. Certain lawsuits could be brought to a spring assembly and if not settled there would go to the General Assembly, the Althing, which met for a fortnight around mid-summer each year; other more serious cases could only he prosecuted before a court at this main gathering. In the developed system there were four courts at the Althing, one for each Quarter of the country (see *The Saga of Gisli*, ch. 19, *The Saga of Grettir*, ch. 25). The Althing is often referred to as 'the assembly' (e.g. *The Saga of Grettir*, chs 16, 37, 46, 51). Brief local autumn meetings were also held, often on the same site as the spring assembly; they were chiefly intended to publicise the decisions of the General Assembly, held shortly before. Judicial assemblies were also held by Norwegian rulers in various localities in Norway.

Assembly-men, thing-men: householders who belonged to the following of a *godi*.

bed-closet: Most members of the household in a medieval Icelandic dwelling would sleep on the raised plank flooring that ran most of the length of the hall-walls on each side, which was also the place to sit by day (see *platform, living-room*). Part of this might be partitioned off with a door fastening on the inside for the principal members of the household.

berserk: a warrior who fights in a frenzy, as if possessed. Berserks cultivated this battle-fury and were subject to fits of rage. They are sometimes called *úlfheðnar* ('wolf-skins') and may have sometimes identified themselves in some way with fierce animals and worn animal pelts. They are represented as typical bullying villains in many sagas.

blue translates *blár*, which means a very dark colour, blue-black, and is said to be the colour of Hel (cf. *The Saga of Grettir*, ch. 32; in the same chapter, however, *blár* of eyes is translated 'dark', though some mansucripts have *grár* 'grey' here). Note also *kolblár* 'black as coal', ch. 80.

booth: at the assemblies, which were held in the open air, men lived in huts called 'booths' which had permanent walls of stone and turf and were roofed for the occasion with awnings of cloth. The term is also used for temporary dwellings used by seafarers alongside their ships at landing places (cf. *The Saga of Grettir*, chs 22, 37).

cutlass: the nearest English equivalent to *sax*, which was a short, rather heavy, single-edged sword.

Double-month (tvímánuðr or *corn-harvest month)* ran from late August to late September in the traditional Icelandic calendar.

dowry: The price and dowry (*mundr* and *heimanfylgja*) were respectively the sum (in cash, land or chattels) paid or promised by the bridegroom at the time of the marriage contract (it became the property of the wife, but was administered by the husband, though any income derived from it also went to the wife); and the wife's dowry, administered by the husband to his own profit, but repayable on divorce. The second was a customary payment, the first an obligatory one.

duels (hólmgöngur) are often described as fought according to prescribed rules, and traditionally on islands *(hólmar)*. According to *The Saga of Grettir*, ch. 19, they were banned by Earl Eirik; according to *Gunnlaugs saga*, ch. 12, he banned Gunnlaug and Hrafn from fighting duels in Norway.

Easterner = Norwegian. See Index.

foster-brothers: in most contexts these are sworn brothers (e.g. *The Saga of Grettir*, ch. 25), like Thormod and Thorgeir, the heroes of *Fóstbræðra saga*.

godi (goði, pl. *goðar):* an Icelandic chieftain who in pre-Christian times had both religious and secular authority; they acted as priests in the heathen religion and would have had the responsibility of conducting religious sacrifices as well as judicial assemblies. From about

930 they numbered 36; they were augmented to 39 in the 960s and to 48 about 1005. Together they formed the Law Council at the Althing, the ultimate source of law in the country.

godord: the authority of a *godi* and treated as if it were property; it was heritable but could also be sold or lent. A woman could own a *godord* but could not act as a *godi*: the authority had to be transferred to a man (who would usually be a kinsman) in any affairs that chieftains were required to conduct.

hersir: a high rank in early Norway; loosely equivalent to 'Lord' in English.

hneftafl: A board game in which two players with an unequal number of pieces were engaged, one attempting to capture a king, the other to escape the attack. A number of Viking-Age boards and playing pieces have come to light, but so far it has not proved possible to reconstruct the precise rules of the game. The pegs mentioned in *The Saga of Grettir*, ch. 70 would have been to stick into holes in the board.

homespun: this cloth (*vaðmál*) was one of Iceland's chief products in the early period and soon became used as a form of currency, with its value related to that of silver. It became a staple export and Icelanders going abroad usually took marketable homespun with them (they would also have to pay for their passage and provide their own food, often paying with part of their wares; cf. *The Saga of Grettir*, ch. 17). Dyed or patterned cloth (cf. *The Saga of Hord*, ch. 12) would have been much more valuable in foreign markets than standard undyed homespun.

hundred: normally means the long hundred, 120. As a currency value, it could be used of ounces of silver but more commonly of ells of *homespun* (an ell was about half a metre). There was little coinage in use at the time of these sagas. As a form of currency homespun was counted in 'ounce-units', and the early Icelandic laws reckon on 6 ells of cloth as constituting one such unit, though three- and four-ell units ('triple, quadruple units') were also known. Fines and compensation were usually calculated in terms of such units. As time went on the value of homespun generally depreciated against the value of silver by weight. It is estimated that circa 1000, 18 ells of cloth would change hands for one ounce of silver, by circa 1100 the figure was 48 ells to the ounce. The standard value of a cow of stipulated quality was then the homespun hundred, 120 ells of cloth, the equivalent of 2·5 ounces of silver weighed. Opinions differ on the value of the 'hundred of silver', regularly cited as the *wergild* sum. The most recent calculation, depending on a distinction made between 'ounces counted' and 'ounces weighed', gives an answer of 40 ounces of silver weighed, most probably thought of as the price of 20 cows. See *wergild.*

kenning: a poetical periphrasis, in the form of a compound word with two elements or a noun with one or more dependent genitives, such as 'tree of weapons' for 'warrior'. See Note on the Text, pp. xxvi–xxviii, and The Verses, pp. 343–50.

landed man: lendr maðr was usually of a family prominent in his district, held land in fief from the king of Norway and acted as his local lieutenant, military leader and counsellor. It is not known how many landed men existed at any given time in early Norway, probably at least fifty.

Lawspeaker (after about 1272 *Lawman*)*:* the president of the Icelandic parliament, elected by the *godi*s for a three-year term, a span which could be extended by re-election. He had no executive function, but had the duty of reciting the laws at the General Assembly in the course of his three years of office and could be consulted as authority on points of law.

league, sea-league: vika is an Icelandic sea-mile, equivalent to about 4 English nautical miles.

living-room: medieval Icelandic farms normally had one main room (*stofa*, *The Saga of Grettir*, ch. 20; *skáli*, *The Saga of Grettir*, ch. 28; *skáli,* 'room' *The Saga of Gisli*, ch. 16) with raised *platforms* down each side which were used for sitting on during the day and for sleeping on at night (cf. *bed-closet*). In some farmhouses one end of a *platform* might be panelled off from the rest of the room to give privacy to the farmer and his wife (see *bed-closet*). Trestle-tables were put up on the ground in front of the *platforms* at meal times (cf. *The Saga of Grettir*, ch. 18). Otherwise there was little in the way of furniture. Cf. *The Saga of Grettir*, ch. 28.

mark: a weight of eight ounces; or eight 'ounce-units', 48 ells of standard *homespun*.

moving-days: the time when people might legally change their residence and when they often took up new employment. These were four days in the seventh week of summer, beginning on the Thursday which fell between 21st and 27th May each year.

norn: one of the three sisters who control men's fates in Norse mythology; they appear, like names of goddesses and valkyries, in *kennings* for woman.

platform: medieval Icelandic farm-houses had platforms along the side walls of the main room that were used for seats and beds. The floor between them was unboarded. Sometimes there was also another kind of platform or dais called *pallr*, which was usually a raised wooden platform across one end of the building which could be used for the women of the household to sit on.

Quarter: Iceland was divided into four Quarters in about 962, and thereafter a court was established for each Quarter at the annual Althing.

skald: poet.

self-judgement (sjálfdœmi): this was when the injured party was allowed to assess the amount of compensation himself.

shieling (sel): a building used by the women and the shepherd who in summer lived on higher pastureland, usually at some distance from the main farm, grazing flocks and processing their milk into butter, cheese and *skyr* for later transportation to the farm.

skyr: a kind of cultured skimmed milk, something like yoghurt, which when thickened keeps well and has been a staple of Icelandic diet.

summoning-days: a summons to answer a case to be brought at the *Assembly* was an essential legal preliminary. It was normally made in the presence of witnesses at the home of the man to be prosecuted and should take place as a rule a fortnight before the Spring *Assembly*.

thing: see *assembly.*

trolls: supernatural creatures in Norse mythology, more or less identical with the giants.

valkyrie, valkyr: 'chooser of the slain', one of the female supernatural creatures sent to battle to bring the slain to Odin's hall Valhöll; their names are used, like those of goddesses, in kennings for woman.

viking: a member of a Scandinavian band of raiders; but the word *viking* in many sagas has come to be a pejorative term, more or less the equivalent of 'pirate'.

wergild (manngjöld): The normal wergild (for a death; sometimes for an injury if the result of attempted murder, cf. *The Saga of Gisli*, ch. 37; *The Saga of Grettir*, ch. 21) was theoretically the same for all free men. See *hundred*.

West, the: this nearly always means the British Isles from a Norwegian standpoint.

Winter Nights: the first days of the first month of winter (the native calendar counted only two seasons, summer and winter), which began on the Saturday falling in the week 11th–17th October each year. Workmen were sometimes taken on for a year at the beginning of winter, though according to *Grágás* I 126, 'A man is to enter a household as he agrees with the householder, either in the *moving days* or at midsummer.' This was a time for one of the biggest pagan festivals (it coincided with the autumn slaughtering of cattle), enacted however more in private cult celebrations (house-parties) than in public temple-worship. The celebrations and sacrifices made up a fertility rite, at the centre of which stood the god Frey.

INDEX OF NAMES

When place-names are given in Old Norse form, the modern forms are normally added in brackets, and vice versa; when names are translated, the original forms are given in brackets. Names of fiords are often also used for the valleys leading into them. References are to chapter numbers. Gi = The Saga of Gisli, Gr = The Saga of Grettir, H = The Saga of Hord.

Adaldal, northern Iceland Gr 38
Æsa, daughter of Ofeig Grettir, first wife of Onund Wooden-leg Gr 3, 10, 11
Æsundir (Asen, island off Nordmøre, Norway) Gi 3
Agder, district in southern Norway Gr 3, 7
Akrafell (Akrafiall), mountain on Akraness H 28
Akraness, south-western Iceland H 11, 20
Akrar, farm on Myrar Gr 60, 61
Aldis, daughter of Ofeig Grettir Gr 3, 13
Alf of the Dales, son of Eystein Gr 27
Alf, hersir, of Trøndelag H 23
Alfdis of Barra, daughter of Konal Gr 3, 10
Alfdis, wife of Ref at Haug Gi 27
Alfgeir, unkown hero of the lost *Álfgeirs þáttr* ('Tale of Alfgeir') H 33
Ali, Thorbiorn Oxen-might's workman Gr 45
Almenningar (Eastern Almenningar), towards the northern end of Strandir, north-west Iceland Gr 25, 27
Alof, daughter of Ingolf Gr 11
Alptarskard (now Brekkuskarð), a pass north of Hvalfiord H 29
Althing, the general assembly of Iceland, held each summer at Thingvoll; sometimes referred to as 'the asssembly' (e.g. Gr 16, 37, 46, 51) Gr 10, 12, 25–27, 32, 34, 51, 57, 77, 82–84; H 10, 21, 30
Alvidra, farm on the north side of Dyrafiord Gi 4
Ambattara, river on Vatnsness Gr 44
Andakil, area in Borgarfiord, western Iceland H 9
Annmarkastadir, farm in Haukadal (modern Sel?) Gi 18, 19
Ar, in Gautland Gr 3
Ari Masson, son of Atli the Red Gr 27
Ari, son of Thorbiorn Sur (Súrsson) Gi 2, 38
Ari, son of Thorkel Skerauki Gi 1
Armannsfell, mountain north of Thingvoll Gr 32
Arnarbæli, farm in Olfus H 10
Arnarfiord, Western Fiords, Iceland Gi 4, 15, 20, 22
Arnarholt, farm in Borgarfiord, western Iceland H 1

Arnarvatn, lake in western central Iceland Gr 62
Arnarvatn Heath, western central Iceland Gr 54–56, 62; H 33; 'the heath' Gr 56, 57
Arnbiorn, kinsman of Thorfinn son of Kar the Old Gr 22, 23
Arness, farm in Trekyllisvik Gr 9, 11
Arngeir, son of Bersi Godless Gr 58
Arni, son of Skeggi of Saxa Gi 3
Arnkelsbrekka, in Biarnardal Gi 12
Arnor Hynef (downy-nose), son of Thorodd Gr 30
Arnor, a talkative fellow Gi 6
Arnor, son of Thorbiorn Oxen-might Gr 48
Arnor Thordarson, known as Earls' poet Gr 60
Arnora, daughter of Thord Gellir Gr 77
Arnthor, Norwegian queen's treasurer H 13
As, farm in Borgarfiord Gr 62
As, farm in Vatnsdal Gr 16, 25, 35
Asbiarnarness, farm at the end of Vididal Gr 28, 31
Asbiorn, son of Ofeig Grettir Gr 3
Asbrand Thorbrandsson Gr 44
Asdis, daughter of Bard Iokulsson and mother of Grettir Gr 13, 14–17, 37, 45, 47, 48, 69, 83, 84
Asdis, daughter of Gamli Skeggiason Gr 84
Asgeir Ædikoll (madcap) Gr 15, 26, 28 (here it should be Asgeir of Asgeirsa)
Asgeir of Asgeirsa, son of Audun Skokul Gr 11, (28); Asgeir of Asgeirsa and Asgeir Ædikoll are evidently muddled up in *The Saga of Grettir*, and it is uncertain which is meant in Gr 25, 44, 51, 84
Asgeir, son of Audun, son of Asgeir Gr 28
Asgeirsa, river and farm in Vididal, northern Iceland Gr 11, 15
Asgerd, daughter of Thorbiorn Selagnup, wife of Gisli's brother Thorkel Gi 5, 9
Asgrim, son of Ellida-Grim Gr 8, 53
Asgrim, son of Ondott Kraka and Signy Gr 7, 8
Aslaugarhlid ('Aslaug's slope'), western Iceland (Kaldárbakkahlíð) Gr 59
Asmund under Asmundargnup Gr 13
Asmund Beardless, son of Ofeig Grettir Gr 3
Asmund, son of Ondott Kraka and Signy Gr 7, 8, 37
Asmund son of Thorgrim Hoary-top, known as Hærulang (with long grey hair) Gr 13, 14, 16, 17, 25–28, 30, 31, 34, 35, 37, 42, 47, 48, 54, 59, 65, 68, 72, 75, 90, 93
Asmundargnup (Gnúpr, 'peak'), farm in Vididal Gr 13
Asny, daughter of Vestar Gr 3
Asta, daughter of Gudbrand Kula Gr 1
Asvor, daughter of Ofeig Grettir Gr 3
Athelstan, king of Wessex 925–39 Gi 1
Atli, son of Asmund Hærulang Gr 14–16, 28–30, 36, 42–45, 47–49, 51, 54

Atli the Red, son of Ulf the Boss-eyed Gr 27
Aud of Audsstadir H 21
Aud (or Unn) the Deep-minded, Icelandic settler Gr 10, 26 (see *Laxdæla saga*)
Aud, used as the name of a goddess in kennings for woman H 11
Aud, daughter of Vestein, Gisli's wife Gi 4, 5, 9, 10, 12–16, 20, 21, 24, 30, 31–36, 38; Aud's steading in Geirthiofsfiord Gi 22, 29, farmhouse Gi 23
Audbiorg at Annmarkastadir, sister of Thorgrim Nef Gi 18, 19
Audsstadir, farm in the northerly Reykiardal H 21
Audun son of Asgeir Ædikoll Gr 28 (mistake for son of Asgeir at Asgeirsa son of Audun Skokul)
Audun, son of Asgeir of Asgeirsa, at Audunarstadir Gr 15, 16, 28, 34; see also Ialfad
Audun, earl in Norway, called Geit (nanny-goat) Gr 7
Audun Skokul Gr 11, (28)
Audun in Vindheim Gr 18
Audunarstadir, farm in Vididal Gr 15, 28, 34
Augastadir, farm in the northerly Reykiardal H 10
Austra ('east river'), river in Dalir Gr 68
Bæ, farm in Borgarfiord, western Iceland Gr 47; H 8
Bakkarholt, farm in Olfus H 19
Bakkavad, ford over Hvita H 41
Bakki, farm in Borgarfiord (Hvítárbakki) Gr 47
Bakki, farm in Hrutafiord (Prestsbakki) Gr 30
Balagardssida, south-west coast of Finland H 17
Baldr, name of a god in Norse mythology, used in kennings for man Gr 22 (Biorn); H 34 (Kiartan)
Balkastadir, farms in Hrutafiord 5
Balki Blæingsson Gr 1, 2, 5, 58
Ball-glacier, Balliokul, glacier in central Iceland (Baldjökull, the north-western part of Langjökull) Gr 54, 57, 62
Bandvettir, horses (the name means a pair of mittens attached to each other by a string) Gi 11
Bard Iokulsson, father of Asdis Gr 13, 34
Bard, sea-captain Gr 17
Bard of Surnadal Gi 2
Bardardal, northern Iceland Gr 64, 65, 67; people of Gr 65
Bardastrond, part of the south coast of the Western Fiords Gi 19, 23, 28, 32 (Strond Gi 23, 32)
Bardi Gudmundarson (Viga-Bardi) Gr 28, 31, 34 (see *Heiðarvíga saga*)
Barra, island in the Hebrides Gr 1, 3, 4, 10 (pl. Barreyiar = Barra Isles)
Battle of the Heath Gr 31 (Heiðarvíg, western Iceland, 1014; see *Heiðarvíga saga*)
Battle of the Nesses Gr 37 (Nesia orrosta, on the western side of Oslofiord, *c.*1015; see Snorri Sturluson, *Heimskringla* I 151–2)

Bear, i.e. Bersi son of Poet-Torfa, whose name is a hypocoristic word for the animal Gr 24
Beard-Bialfi (Skegg-Bialfi), a merchant Gi 8
Berg Skammfot (short-leg) Gi 18, 19
Berg, son of Vestein Vesteinsson Gi 4, 28, 38
Bergen, Norway (Björgvin) H 12
Bersastadir, farm on the north side of Dyrafiord Gi 11
Bersi of Bersastadir Gi 11
Bersi Godless, son of Balki Gr 58
Bersi, son of Poet-Torfa Gr 15, 23, 24
Bialfi see Beard-Bialfi
Biarg, farm in Midfiord Gr 13, 14, 16, 25, 28, 29–31, 34, 35, 37, 42, 43, 45, 47, 48, 49, 67, 69, 83, 84; men of, people of Gr 29, 30, 43
Biargaos, river-mouth on the eastern side of Vatnsness, northern Iceland Gr 44
Biarnardal, off Onundarfiord Gi 12
Biarnarfiord (southerly), on the southerly Strandir Gr 12
Biarnar saga see under Saga of
Biarni at Iorvi Gr 60
Biarni, son of Skuf, shepherd in Hundadal Gr 27
Biarni the Wise (inn spaki), son of Thorstein *Godi* Gr 6
Biartmar of Arnarfiord, father of Aud's and Vestein's uncles Gi 4; sons of (Helgi, Sigurd, Vestgeir) Gi 10, 21, 29
Bildsfell, south of Olfusvatn H 19
Biorg, a range of mountains in Vestrhop, northern Iceland Gr 44
Biorn Blasida (dark-side), son of Ulfhedin, a viking H 17
Biorn Gullberi (gold-bearer), Icelandic settler H 1
Biorn on Haganess Gr 70, 81, 82
Biorn, brother of Hiarrandi and Gunnar Gr 21, 22, 80
Biorn Hitdælakappi (hero of the people of Hitardal) Arngeirsson Gr 58, 59, 61; called Biorn of Hitardal Gr 59 (see *Biarnar saga Hítdælakappa*)
Biorn, son of Hord and Helga H 24, 38, 41
Biorn, son of Hrolf of Ar and father of Thrand and Eyvind Gr 2, 3, 5, 6
Biorn, Odin in disguise H 15; Biorn's gift (Biarnarnaut), a sword H 15
Biorn, son of Ofeig Thunnskegg Gr 70
Biorn the Pale (inn blakki) Gi 1
Biorn, settler on Strandir (Biarnarfiord), northern Iceland Gr 9 (see *The Book of Settlements*, ch. 162, and *Laxdæla saga*)
Bitra, a fiord on the southerly Strandir (Inn-Strandir) Gr 43, 51
Blaskeggsa, river in Hvalfiord H 24, 38; called Blaskeggsar, Blaskegg's rivers H 33
Blaskeggsaros, river-mouth in Hvalfiord H 24
Bleikala (= a (dun) horse with a dark stripe down its back), name given to the mare Kengala Gr 14
Bodmod son of Grimolf Gr 12; see under Saga of

Bodolf father of Skeggi of Kelduhverfi, brother of Bodmod Gr 38
Bodvar of Bodvarsholar Gr 30
Bodvarsholar, farm in Vestrhop Gr 30
Boggul-Torfi at Marskelda Gr 27
Bollastadir, farm south of Hvalfiord H 27
Bolli, Orm's slave H 27 (cf. Thorbiorn)
Bordeyr, farm in Hrutafiord Gr 30
Borgarfiord, western Iceland Gi 19; Gr 27, 28, 31, 44, 47, 53, 54, 57, 61; men of, Borgfirders Gr 54; H 33
Borgarhraun, western Iceland (Eldborgarhraun) Gr 59
Bork the Stout, son of Thorstein Thorskabit, brother of Thorgrim; Thordis's second husband Gi 5, 15, 16, 18–23, 25–29, 37; Gr 68
Bothild, Ingiald's bondwoman Gi 25, 26
Botn (Nedri-Botn, now Litli-Botn), farm in Hvalfiord H 19, 22, 24, 25
Botn-Dwellers (Hord and Geir and their men) H 23, 24
Botnsheid, heath in from Hvalfiord H 9, 19
Bragi, a god; his wife is Idunn, whose name is used for *iðunnar*, Icelandic for 'of turbulent water' Gr 66
Brand, workman of Halldor at Hof Gr 81
Brand, son of Thorbiorn Koll H 28; Brand's Flats (Brandsflesiar, Brandsfles), on the north side of Hvalfiord H 28
Brand, Thorgeir Bottle-back's man Gr 11
Brattabrekka (= steep slope), between Borgarfiord and Dalir Gr 67
Breakfast Dale (Dogurdardal), above Skutilsfiord, Western Fiords Gi 7
Breida, farm in Skagafiord (Bræðrá) Gr 70
Breidabol, men of (i.e. of Breidabolstad) H 21
Breidabolstad, farm in the northerly Reykiardal H 2, 8, 9, 10, 20, 21, 22
Breidabolstad, farm in Sokkolfsdal Gr 68
Breidafiardardalir, district in western Iceland (= Dalir) Gr 57, 67
Breidafiord, western Iceland Gi 24, 25
Breidavik, bay on Snæfellsness H 41
Brekka, farm on Hvalfiardarstrond H 11, 23, 24
British Isles (*vestan haf*) Gr 5, 10, 59; see also the West
Bruin (Bessi or Bersi, Biorn), a bear killed by Grettir Gr 21
Bryniolf, son of Thorbiorn H 12, 13, 18
Bryniudal, in from Hvalfiord H 24, 25, 27, 39
Burfell, a mountain and a farm in Midfiord Gr 30
Bute, Isle of (Bót), Firth of Clyde, Scotland Gr 4
Byleist, brother of the god Loki, whose daughter is Hel, i.e. death Gr 24
Byrgisvik, bay on Strandir, northern Iceland Gr 9, 12
Cat's head (Kattarhöfði), on the inner part of Hvalfiord H 25
Christ Gr 82
Confederates, see under Saga of
Constantinople (Miklagard) Gr 85, 86, 88, 90, 91, 93

Dales, Dalir, district in western Iceland (= Breidafiardardalir) Gr 27, 68
Dalla Thorvaldsdóttir, wife of Bishop Isleif Gr 25
Deildartunga, farm in Borgarfiord Gr 47
Denmark Gi 8, 10, 38; H 17
Dogurdardal see Breakfast Dale
Dogurdarness, in Hvalfiord (now Þyrilsnes) H 24, 30, 32, 37
Drangar, farm on the northern part of Strandir, north-west Iceland Gr 9, 11, 12
Drangey, island in Skagafiord Gr 67, 69–76, 78, 79, 81, 84, 85
Dromund (in verse) see Thorstein Dromund
Dufunefsskeid, part of Kiol Gr 54
Dyrafiord, Western Fiords Gi 4, 7, 8, 9, 12
Dyrholmar, farm in Myrdal, on the south coast of Iceland (now Dyrhólar) Gr 80
Dyri, settler in Dyrafiord Gi 4
Easterners, i.e. Norwegians Gr 12; Easterner, Norwegian, i.e. Eyvind Gr 3–5; Hæring Gr 76; Orm H 35
Eastern Fiords Gr 61, 63
Eastmen's Fall (Austmannafall, above Skutilsfiord, Western Fiords; Austmenn = Norwegians, cf. Easterners) Gi 7
Egil, son of Audun Gr 34
Eid of As, son of Midfiord-Skeggi Gr 62
Eilif, son of Ketil the One-handed Gr 3
Einar of Giogur Gr 12
Einar, farmer in Iadar in Norway Gr 40
Einar, son of Magnus and Gudrun H 11
Einar son of Olvir Barnakarl Gr 3
Einar, son of Skeggi of Saxa Gi 3
Einhamar, bluff in Geirthiofsfiord Gi 35
Eirik of Guddalir, son of Hroald Geirmundarson Gr 70
Eirik Hakonarson, earl in Norway; went to England 1015 (1012 according to Icelandic sources), Earl of Northumbria from 1016, died *c.*1023; Gr 19
Eirik, son of Holmgongu-Starri Gr 70, 81
Eirik Olfus (tippler) Gr 7
Eirik Snara (snare) Gr 9, 11
Ellida-Grim, son of Asgrim Gr 8
England Gi 8; Gr 19, 22, 38
Eyiafiord, northern Iceland Gr 8, 37
Eyiardalsa, farm in Bardardal Gr 64–67
Eyiolf of Borg in Vididal, brother-in-law of Bardi Gudmundarson Gr 31
Eyiolf Egilsson Gr 34 (see *Laxdæla saga*, ch. 40)
Eyiolf from Fagraskogar Gr 60
Eyiolf the Grey, son of Thord (Gellir), Bork's cousin Gi 15–17, 22, 23, 25, 27, 31–37 (see *Eyrbyggja saga*)
Eyiolf Gudmundarson Gr 34
Eyr (Óspakseyri), farm on Bitra Gr 43, 51

Eyr, farm in Isafiord Gr 52
Eyr, farm in Skutilsfiord Gi 7
Eyr, headland or ness on Snæfellsness, western Iceland Gi 37
Eyrar, landing place on the south coast of Iceland (now Eyrarbakki) Gr 6; H 8, 12, 17, 18, 20, 41
Eyrarhvalsoddi (Valseyr, Dyrafiord) Gi 6
Eyvind the Easterner (i.e. from Norway), son of Biorn Gr 3–5
Eyvind of Eyvindarfiord Gr 11
Eyvindarfiord, on Strandir, northern Iceland Gr 11
Fafnir, a serpent, in a kenning for gold (that on which serpents lie) Gr 18
Fagrabrekka, farm in Hrutafiord Gr 30. On the battle there see *Hrómundar þáttr halta* and *The Book of Settlements*, ch. 168.
Fagraskogafiall, mountain in western Iceland Gr 58, 60
Fagraskogar, farm in western Iceland Gr 60
Fell, farm below Ingólfsfell (-fjall), south-western Iceland H 1, 12
Fellsoxl, farm inland from Akraness H 20
Ferdalang see Thorbiorn Ferdalang
Ferstikla, farm on Hvalfiardarstrond H 23, 26, 41
Fibuli (Årvågsfjord), in Nordmøre, Norway Gi 1
Finn the Wealthy, son of Halldor H 2
Finnbogi, son of Thorgeir Thorhaddsson Gr 60
Fioll, farm in south-western Iceland, south of Olfusvatn; later called Grimkelsstadir Hó2
Fiskilæk, stream and farm in Eyiafiord Gr 38
Fiskivotn, lakes on Arnarvatn Heath Gr 54
Fitiar, area near Arnarvatn Heath (Hellisfitjar, now Fugleyrar) H 33
Flatey, island in Breidafiord Gi 25
Fliot, district to the east of Skagafiord Gr 70, 72, 81
Fliotstunga, area inland from Borgarfiord Gr 16
Floi, area in southern Iceland H 10
Flokadal, Borgarfiord, western Iceland H 4
Flokadalsa, river in Borgarfiord, western Iceland Gr 47; H 1
Flosi, son of Eirik Gr 11, 12
Flydruness, north of Trøndelag, Norway (unidentified) Gi 3
Flysiuhverfi, district in western Iceland Gr 59, 60
Forsa, farm on Hiardarness Gi 27
Forsæludal, off Vatnsdal Gr 32
Frey, a Norse god Gi 15, 18; in kenning for warrior (Grettir) Gr 47, (Thorbiorn Ongul) Gr 83
Freyia, a goddess, in kenning for woman (servant-girl at Reykir) Gr 75; see also Syr
Frid, name of a goddess, in kenning for woman (Asdis) Gr 83
Fridarey (Frei, island in Nordmøre, Norway) Gi 2, 3
Fridgerd, daughter of Thord of Hofdi Gr 26

Fridmund, Icelandic settler Gr 32
Fridrek, German missionary bishop (in Iceland 981–6) Gr 13 (*Kristni saga, Þorvalds þáttr víðförla*)
Frodi, legendary king in Denmark Gr 3 (see *The Book of Settlements*, ch. 217)
Gamli, son of Skeggi Short-Arm Gr 84
Gamli, father of Thorhall the Winelander Gr 30
Gamli, son of Thorhall the Winelander Gr 14, 30, 42, 43, 48, 49, 51, 83, 84
Gang, name of a giant, used as a common noun Gr 66
Gard, farm in Adaldal Gr 38, 63, 77, 82
Gardar, farm on Akraness H 20; called Gard H 28
Garten, an island in the mouth of Trondheimsfiord (Gartar) Gr 22
Gaseyr or Gasir in Eyiafiord Gr 37, 46, 85
Gaut, a name for Odin, in kennings for warriors Gr 12, 28 (here for Bardi)
Gaut, son of Sleita Gr 27 (see *Fóstbræðra saga*)
Gautland (earldom in southern Sweden, Götaland) Gr 3; H 13, 14, 17, 41; Gautlander Gr 6
Geir, son of Grim the Small and Gudrid H 7, 11–19, 22, 24–31, 34–36; Geir's point (Geirstangi) H 35
Geirlaug, widow at Breidabolstad Gr 68
Geirmund, son of Biorn Gullberi H 1
Geirmund Heliarskin (dark-skin) Gr 2, 3
Geirmund Hvikatimbr (swaying timber) Gr 12
Geirmund, son of Ingiald, foster-son of Gisli and Thorkel Gi 10, 12, 15, 16, 38
Geirmund Ordigskeggi (rough-beard) Gr 70
Geirsholm = the Holm H 24
Geirthiofsfiord, in from Arnarfiord Gi 20, 21–25, 27, 29–31
Geitir, son of Lyting H 1
Geitland, inland from Borgarfiord Gr 61; H 11; Geitlander H 11; Geitland Glacier (Geitlandsjökull, part of Langjökull) Gr 61
Geldingadragi ('wether-drag or -trail'), trail between Skorradal and Svinadal or Hvalfiord H 29
Gemlufall, Dyrafiord Gi 12
Gemlufallsheid, heath between Dyrafiord and Onundarfiord Gi 12
Gerd, daughter of Bodvar of Bodvarsholar Gr 30
Gerd, a goddess (originally a giantess), in a kenning for woman Gr 14
Gerpir (probably a mistake for the nickname of Bodmod or Grimolf Gerpir, 'champion') Gr 12; see under Saga of Bodmod
Gervidal, valley and farm in Isafiord, Western Fiords Gr 52
Gest the Wise (inn spaki), son of Oddleif Gi 5, 23, 28, 29, 31, 32, 38 (see *Laxdæla saga, Njáls saga*); see also Guest
Giabakki, farm by Olfusvatn H 10
Gilsbakki, farm in Borgarfiord Gr 44, 47
Giogr, farm in Reykiarfiord on Strandir Gr 12

Gisli, son of Thorbiorn Sur (Súrsson) Gi 2–27, 29–38
Gisli, son of Thorkel Skerauki Gi 1
Gisli Thorsteinsson Gr 59
Giuki, legendary hero, father of Gudrun Gi 19 (see *The Poetic Edda*)
Gizur the White, son of Teit H 11
Glam, Swedish shepherd Gr 32–35, 82
Glaum (Merryman), see Thorbiorn Glaum
Glaumbæ, farm in Skagafiord Gr 69
Glera, the more southerly and the more northerly, farms in Eyiafiord, northern Iceland Gr 8
Glerarskogar, farm in Hvammsfiord, western Iceland (Breidafiardardalir) Gi 37
Glum, son of Ospak Kiallaksson Gr 14, 43, 51, 83
Gna, name of a goddess, used in kennings for woman H 9 (Thorbiorg)
Gnup, farm in Midfiord Gr 11
Gnupveriahrepp, district in the south of Iceland Gr 6
God Gr 19, 35, 51, 72, 92, 93
Godaskog, woods near Thingvoll Gr 32
Gonguskardsos or Gonguskardsaros, estuary in Skagafiord Gr 76
Gorvik, a small bay on the north side of Hvalfiord H 29
Grafning, area south of Olfusvatn H 19
Grani, the name of Sigurd the dragon-killer's horse, used in kennings for gold; its burden was the hoard Sigurd won from the dragon Fafnir in *Völsunga saga* and *The Poetic Edda*; H 15
Grannaskeid, farm in Surnadal (Skei) Gi 2
Greenland Gi 38
Grenitresness, at the entrance to Thorskafiord Gi 28
Grettir, son of Asmund Hærulang and Asdis Gi 22; Gr 14–25, 28–31, 34–43, 45–85, 87, 90, 93; see also Guest; called Grettir the Strong (inn sterki) Gr 39, 54, 56, 86, 90, 93; Grettir's Lift (Grettishaf), near Sledaas Gr 16; on Hrutafiord ridge Gr 30; below Fagraskogafiall Gr 59; Grettir's mound (Grettisthufa), on Sand Gr 84; Grettir's store (Grettisbur), storehouse at Vidvik Gr 82; the name is indicated in some kennings by word-play with *grettir* = snake, see Gr 28, 47, 52, 54. See also Ofeig Grettir
Grettir's Point (Grettisoddi, by Hitara) Gr 60
Grettisfærsla see *The Passing Round of Grettir*
Grettisgeil, a narrow place near Hæl in Gnupveriahrepp (now Hælsgróf) Gr 10
Grettisnaut, the cutlass that had been Grettir's (see Karsnaut) Gr 86
Grey-belly (Hösmagi), name given to a ram on Drangey Gr 82 (cf. Gr 74)
Greyflank (Grásíða), a sword Gi 1, 11; a spear 16; bits of (Grásíðubrot) Gi 11
Grid, giantess, in kenning for battle-axe; translated 'giantess' Gr 16
Grim, son of Gamli Thorhallsson Gr 14
Grim (giant-bane Grim) = Thorgrim *Godi* Gi 18
Grim the Halogalander, son of Thorir H 11
Grim, *hersir*, son of Kolbiorn Sneypir Gr 3, 6, 7

Grim, an outlaw Gr 55
Grim, an outlaw, son of Helga at Kropp Gr 62, 67
Grim the Small (inn litli), foster-son (or -brother?—*fóstri Signýjar*) of Signy H 2, 4, 5, 7, 9–11, 18, 24
Grim, son of Thorgeir and Signy (farmer Grim of Signyiarstadir) H 2, 8
Grim, son of Thorhall, son of Fridmund Gr 32
Grim, son of Thorhall Grimsson Gr 32
Grim, son of Thorhall the Winelander Gr 30, 42, 43, 44, 47, 53, 54, 57, 61
Grimkel *Godi*, son of Biorn Gullberi H 1–12, 19, 20, 41
Grimkel son of Hord and Helga H 24, 38, 41
Grimkelsstadir, farm in south-western Iceland (= Fioll), south of Olfusvatn H 2
Grimolf (father of Bodmod; see under Saga of) Gr 12
Grimsa, river in Borgarfiord, western Iceland H 1
Grimsness, south-west Iceland H 9, 10
Grimsstadir, farm north of Olfusvatn H 5, 9, 11, 18, 19
Grindavik, farm in south-west Iceland H 9
Griotgard, father of Thorbiorn H 12
Grund, a goddess, personification of the earth (or perhaps a common noun, 'resting place'), in kenning for woman (Spes) Gr 87
Grunnafiord, between Hvalfiord and Borgarfiord H 32
Gudbiorg daughter of Ofeig Burlufot Gr 1
Gudbrand Kula (ball) Gr 1
Guddalir, valleys and farm in from Skagafiord Gr 70, 81
Gudmund Eyiolfsson the Great (or the Mighty; *inn ríki*) Gr 67, 69 (see *Ljósvetninga saga, Njáls saga,* Snorri Sturluson, *Heimskringla* I)
Gudmund Solmundarson of Asbiarnarness, father of Bardi Gr 28, 31
Gudrid, daughter of Hogni of Hagavik, wife of Grim the Small H 2, 5, 7, 18
Gudrid, daughter of Ingiald, Aud's foster-daughter Gi 10, 12, 13, 20, 31, 34, 35, 38
Gudrun daughter of Giuki Gi 19 (see *The Poetic Edda*, *Völsunga saga)*
Gudrun, daughter of Iorunn H 11
Gudrun, wife of Thorhall Grimsson Gr 32
Guest (Gestr), assumed name of Grettir Asmundarson Gr 64, 65, 72
Gullberastadir, farm in the southerly Reykiardal H 1
Gungnir, Odin's spear, in kenning for battle (greed of Gungnir, that which Odin's spear is greedy for) Gr 31
Gunnar, brother of Biorn and Hiarrandi Gr 23, 24, 80
Gunnar, son of Thorir at Skard Gr 30, 43; see Thorir at Skard, sons of
Gunnhild, daughter of Ozur, queen of Erik Bloodaxe, 'Mother of Kings' H 13, 18
Gunnhild, mother of Sigurd Torfi's foster-brother H 2, 24
Gunnhild, wife of Vestein Vesteinsson Gi 4, 38
Gyda, wife of Ingiald Tryggvi Gr 7
Gyrid, daughter of Einar, Norwegian farmer Gr 40
Hæl, farm in Gnupveriahrepp Gr 10

Hæng (= Ketill Hæng son of Thorkel, earl in Naumudal (Namdalen), northern Norway) Gr 3
Hæring, a Norwegian sailor Gr 76, 78; Hæring's leap (Hæringshlaup), a cliff on the southern point of Drangey Gr 76
Haffiardara, river at the beginning of Snæfellsness in western Iceland Gr 59
Hafli, a giant, opponent of Thor; in pun on name Thorbiorn (Biorn is also a name for Thor) Gr 48
Haflidi at Reydarfell Gr 17
Hafr, son of Thorarinn Gr 72
Hafr, son of Thord Knapp Gr 72
Hafraklett, rocks between Olaf's Islands and Reykiaholar, Breidafiord Gr 50 (now Latur)
Hafrsfiord, a fiord in south-west Norway (Hafsfjord) Gr 2
Haganess, farm in Fliot, Skagafiord Gr 70, 81
Hagavik, farm by Olfusvatn, south-western Iceland H 2, 5, 11, 18, 19
Hakon Adalsteinsfostri (foster-son of Athelstan), son of Harald Finehair; king of Norway *c.*946–64 Gi 1
Hakon Eiriksson, earl in Norway (d. 1029) Gr 19
Halfdan the Black, ninth-century king in Norway Gr 2
Hall Gudmundarson Gr 28
Hallbiorn, a tramp Gi 28, 29
Halldor, son of Hogni H 2
Halldor, son of Thorgeir at Hof Gr 70, 72, 81, 82, 84
Halldora, daughter of Hrolf H 11
Halldora, daughter of Steinmod Gr 3
Halli at Kropp Gr 47
Hallkel (son of Hrosskel), father of Tind H 13, 41
Hallkelsstadir, farm on Hvitarsida H 41
Hallmund Gr 54, 57, 61, 62, 67; see also Lopt
Hallmund's Poem (Hallmundarkviða) Gr 62
Hallstein Hest (horse, stallion) Gr 7
Hallsteinsness, on Thorskafiord Gi 28
Hallvard, houseman of Gisli Gi 11, 12
Hallvard Sugandi (sucker), ninth-century viking Gr 1, 2, 5, 8
Halogaland, an area of northern Norway (Hålogaland) Gr 19, 20; Halogalanders (Thorir Thomb and his men) Gr 19; H 11
Hamar, in Borgarfiord, western Iceland Gi 38
Hamund, workman of Thorgeir Bottle-back Gr 11
Harald, unhistorical earl in Gautland H 13, 14
Harald Gormsson, king of Denmark (died *c.*986) H 17
Harald Greycloak (gráfeldr), son of Eirik Bloodaxe; king of Norway *c.*959–74 Gi 7; H 13
Harald Harfagri (fine-haired) or Lufa (unkempt), son of Halfdan the Black, king in Norway (*c.*885–935) Gr 2, 3, 7; H 1. He is said to have vowed not to

have his hair dressed until he had become king of all Norway. See Snorri Sturluson, *Heimskringla* II 53.
Harald Ring, Icelandic settler Gr 44
Harald Sigurdarson, Hardradi (harsh-ruler; king in Norway 1046–66; half-brother of St Olaf) Gr 88, 90, 91 (he escaped from the Battle of Stiklarstadir in 1030, and joined the Varangian Guard in Constantinople (1034–42); reigned in Norway at first with his nephew Magnus the Good, then alone; killed at the Battle of Stamford Bridge in 1066; see Snorri Sturluson, *King Harald's saga*)
Haramarsey, island off Sunnmær, western Norway (Haramsøy) Gr 17, 19
Harek, King Harald's steward Gr 7
Haug, farm on Hiardarness Gi 27
Haukadal, Dalir, western Iceland Gr 30
Haukadal, Dyrafiord Gi 4, 5, 11, 12, 19; men of (Haukdalers, Haukadal men) Gi 6, 9
Haukadal, farm in southern Iceland Gr 54
Haukadalsa, river flowing into Dyrafiord Gi 11
Haukadalsos, Haukadalsaros, the mouth of Haukadalsa Gi 4, 9
Haukadalsskard, a pass in western Iceland Gr 42
Havard, kinsman of Gest Oddleifsson Gi 31, 32
Havard, houseman of Gisli Gi 11, 12
Head (Hofdi), farm on Skagafiord, northern Iceland Gr 26, 70
Hebrides (Sudreyiar) Gr 1, 3–6
Hedeby (Heiðabær), Denmark (near the modern town of Schleswig, now in Germany) Gi 38
Hedin Hiarrandason, legendary king, father of Hild, whose meeting is battle (see Snorri Sturluson's *Edda*, pp. 122–3) Gr 47
Hedin, foster-father of Signy Gr 7
Hegraness, assembly-place in Skagafiord; Hegraness Assembly Gr 72
Hel, the name of the abode of the dead in Norse mythology and also of the woman who presides there, daughter of the god Loki (Snorri Sturluson, in his *Edda*, p. 27, describes her as half *blue* and half flesh-coloured; cf. Gr 32); Gr 24; Gi 14, 17 (Hel-shoes were presumably for the journey there); H 15. Translated 'the dead' Gr 3, 'death' Gr 35
Helga, wife of Grim son of Thorgeir H 8
Helga, daughter of Harald, earl in Gautland H 14, 16, 20, 24–26, 35–39, 41; Helga's sound (Helgusund) H 38; Helga's ravine (Helguskard) H 38
Helga, daughter of Ondott Kraka (crow) Gr 3
Helga, daughter of Thorgeir of Fiskilæk Gr 38
Helga, daughter of Thorir Thorkelsson Gr 30
Helga, daughter of Thorstein Oxnabrodd H 26
Helgafell, farm on Snæfellsness, western Iceland Gi 37
Helgi, son of Biartmar Gi 4, 21

Helgi, son of Ingiald (Ingiald's fool) Gi 25, 27
Helgi of Laugabol Gr 52
Helgi the Lean, son of Eyvind the Easterner Gr 3, 8
Helgi, son of Sigmund H 9, 12, 13, 14, 15, 16, 17, 18, 20, 21, 22, 24, 28, 29, 35, 36
Helgi (Spying-Helgi, Njósnar-Helgi) Gi 22, 23, 25, 31, 34
Helgi, son of Vestein Vesteinsson Gi 4, 28, 29, 38
Helguskard, Helgusund see under Helga
Hella, farm in Surnadal (perhaps Mjølkill in Øksendal or Helle in Vistdal, Romsdal, Norway) Gi 2
Hellisholar, hillocks near Reykiaholar, Breidafiord Gr 50
Hergilsey, island in Breidafiord Gi 24, 25
Hest, farm in Onundarfiord Gi 4, 11, 12
Heyness, farm on Akraness H 20, 28
Hialli, farm in Olfus Gr 6, 53, 54; H 10
Hialtadal, in from Skagafiord, northern Iceland Gr 70
Hialti, son of Thord Hialtason, at Hof in Hialtadal, brother of Thorbiorn Ongul Gr 70, 72, 81, 82, 85; see also Thord Hialtason, sons of
Hialti, son of Thord Skalp, Icelandic settler Gr 70
Hiardarness, on the northern side of Breidafiord Gi 27
Hiarrandi, brother of Biorn Gr 22, 23, 80
Hild, daughter of Biartmar Gi 4
Hild, name of a valkyrie, used in kennings for battle Gr 31; H 11; in kenning for shield Gr 72; cf. Hedin Hiarrandason
Hitara, river in Myrar Gr 58–60
Hitardal, western Iceland, Gr 59, 60
Hitarness, farm in western Iceland Gr 58, 60
Hlif, daughter of Hrolf and wife of Bjorn Gr 3
Hlin, a goddess, in a kenning for woman Gr 14
Hlokk, name of a valkyrie, whose hangings are shields Gr 72; used instead of the name of a troll-wife in a kenning for thought (see Snorri Sturluson's *Edda*, p. 154, *Skáldskaparmál* ch. 70) H 12
Hof in Guddalir Gr 70
Hof in Hialtadal Gr 70
Hof on Hofdastrond Gr 70
Hofdastrond, the eastern side of Skagafiord Gr 70, 81, 82
Hofdi (Head), farm on Skagafiord, northern Iceland Gr 26, 70
Hogni of Hagavik H 2, 5, 18
Hogni, father of Halldor H 2
Hol, farm in Biarnarfiord on Strandir (now Svanshóll) Gr 12
Hol, farm in Haukadal Gi 5, 12, 13, 17, 19
Holm (Innrihólmur), farm on Akraness H 11, 20, 21, 28
Holm, farm in Hitardal Gr 58

Holm, the Holm (Geirsholm), islet in Hvalfiord H 24–32, 34–36, 38
Holm-dwellers (Hólmverjar), those who lived on the Holm (Hord and Geir and their men), H 25–32, 34–37, 41
Holmgongu-Skeggi (duel-Skeggi) Gi 2
Holmgongu-Starri, son of Eirik of Goddalir Gr 70
Holt, farm in Onundarfiord Gi 12
Holtavarda Heath, western Iceland Gr 67
Hord, son of Grimkel and Signy H 7, 10, 11, 13–32, 34–39, 41
Hordland (Hordaland), district of western Norway Gi 7; Gr 1–3, 37
Horn, headland on Hornstrandir, north-west Iceland Gr 45
Hrafn of Ketilsey, son of Dyri Gi 4
Hraun, under, farm on Myrar (Staðarhraun) Gr 59
Hraundal, farm on Myrar Gr 60, 61; Hraundalers, men of Hraundal Gr 61
Hrefna, daughter of Asgeir Ædikoll, sister-in-law of Thorbiorg the Stout Gr 52
Hrisar, farm in Bryniudal H 24
Hrisey, island in Eyiafiord Gr 8
Hrist, a valkyrie, in kenning for woman (servant-girl at Reykir) Gr 75; in kenning for warrior (Hiarrandi) Gr 80
Hroald Geirmundarson Gr 70
Hroar, son of Harald, earl in Gautland H 14, 15, 16, 17, 41
Hrolf of Ar Gr 3
Hrolf the Geitlander, son of Ulf H 11
Hrolf, son of Ingiald Gr 3
Hrossholt, farm in western Iceland Gr 59
Hrotti, a sword-name in kennings for battle Gr 8, 18
Hrut Heriolfsson of Kambsness Gr 61
Hrutafiord, northern Iceland Gr 5, 14, 15, 29, 30, 36, 42, 48, 57, 58; men of, people of Gr 49, 51, 53, 55, 83; Hrutafiord ridge (Hrutafiardarhals; 'the ridges', Gr 48), east of Hrutafiord Gr 30, 37, 43, 44; see Wetherfiord
Hunavatn, lake in northern Iceland Gr 13, 33; Hunavatn Assembly Gr 44, 51
Hundadal, farm in Dalir Gr 27
Husaness, in Dyrafiord Gi 20
Hvalfiardarstrond, the northern side of Hvalfiord H 11; see Strond
Hvalfiord, south-western Iceland H 24
Hvalseyr Thing (probably at Valseyr, Dyrafiord) Gi 5
Hvalshausholm, landing place near Reykiaholar, Breidafiord Gr 50
Hvamm, farm on Bardastrond Gi 19, 23
Hvamm, farm in Dalir in western Iceland Gr 10, 26; district of (Hvammssveit) Gr 26
Hvamm, farm on the south side of Hvalfiord H 27, 32
Hvamm, farm in Skorradal H 3, 19, 30
Hvamm-Thorir, father of Orm H 24
Hvinir see Kvinesdal
Hvinisfiord (Kvinesfjord, now Fedafjord) in Agder, southern Norway Gr 3

Hvita, river in south-western Iceland (Borgarfiord) Gi 38; Gr 17, 47, 59; H 19, 30, 41
Hvitarsida, district in western Iceland Gr 17; H 10
Hvitarvellir, farm in Borgarfiord H 41; see also Vellir
Iadar, district in south-west Norway (Jæren) Gr 39
Ialfad, a name for Odin, word-play on the name Audun Gr 28
Iceland Gi 4, 8, 9, 11, 21, 24, 31, 38; Gr 5–8, 11–13, 24, 25, 38, 39, 41, 82, 84, 86, 90, 92; H 1, 15, 16, 18, 41; Icelander (= Grettir) Gr 20; Icelandic person Gr 93; Icelanders Gr 38; H 13
Idunn, see under Bragi
Illugi, son of Asmund and Asdis, brother of Grettir Gr 37, 42, 54, 67, 69, 72, 74–76, 78, 79, 80–84
Illugi the Black (inn svarti), son of Hallkel H 13 (see *Gunnlaugs saga*)
Illugi the Red (inn rauði), at Holm, son of Hrolf H 11, 19, 20, 21, 28, 30, 32, 34, 36
Indridastadir, farm in Skorradal H 19, 29, 31, 38, 39, 41
Indridastig, path near Thyril H 38
Indridi, son of Thorvald and Thorgrima Smith-woman H 3, 19, 21, 29–32, 35, 36, 38–41
Ingiald, son of Frodi, king in Denmark Gr 3
Ingiald, father of Geirmund and Gudrid (perhaps the same as Ingiald of Hergilsey) Gi 38
Ingiald of Hergilsey Gi 24, 25, 26, 27; Ingiald's fool (Ingjaldsfífl) see Helgi
Ingiald Tryggvi (trusty) Gr 7
Ingibiorg, daughter of Isi Gi 1
Ingigerd, wife of Isi Gi 1
Ingimund the Old, son of Thorstein (see *Vatnsdæla saga*) Gr 13, 31
Ingolf Arnarson, settler in Reykiarvik Gr 12
Ingolf of Ingolfsfiord Gr 11
Ingolfsfiord, Strandir Gr 9, 11, 12
Inn-Strandir, the southerly part of Strandir (= Sudurstrandir) Gr 9
Iokul Bardarson Gr 34
Iokul, son of Ingimund the Old Gr 13, 17, 43; Iokulsnaut, a sword ('that which had belonged to Iokul'; see Gr 17) Gr 18, 21
Iorukleif, on the western side of Olfusvatn H 11, 19
Iorun, daughter of (Hialti and) Vilborg H 11
Iorvi, farm in Flysiuhverfi Gr 60
Ireland Gr 1, 3, 4, 5; the Irish Gr 3
Isafiord, Western Fiords Gr 52
Isfirdingers, men of Isafiord Gr 52
Isgerd, wife of Thorkel Skerauki Gi 1
Isi of Fibuli Gi 1
Isleif Gizurarson (bishop in Skalaholt 1056–80) Gr 25, 84
Ivar Beytil Gr 1

Ivar, son of Kolbein Gr 12; see also Kolbein's sons
Kaldardal, western Iceland Gr 59
Kaldbak, a mountain and farm on Strandir, northern Iceland Gr 9, 11, 12; people of Gr 11, 12
Kaldbakskleif ('-cliff'), on Strandir, northern Iceland Gr 9
Kaldbaksvik, a bay on Strandir, northern Iceland Gr 9
Kalf, son of Asgeir Ædikoll Gr 15; cf. Asgeir of Asgeirsa
Kalf, river in the south of Iceland (Kálfá) Gr 6
Kalfaness, in Borgarfiord Gr 47
Kali, son of Kvist H 23
Kalmansa, river on Hvalfiardarstrond H 28
Kalmansarvik, a small bay on Hvalfiardarstrond H 28
Kamb, on Strandir, between Reykiarfiord and Veidileysa, north-west Iceland Gr 112
Kambsness, farm by Hvammsfiord, western Iceland Gr 61
Kar the Old Gr 18, 19
Kar, workman of Halldor at Hof Gr 81, 82
Karsnaut, the cutlass that had been Kar's; later called Grettisnaut Gr 82
Kataness, on Hvalfiardarstrond H 28
Katla, i.e. Thorbiorg Katla H 25, 34, 40
Kattarhöfði see Cat's head
Keldudal, off Dyrafiord Gi 4
Kelduhverfi, district in northern Iceland Gr 38, 62; men of Gr 57
Kelduness, in Kelduhverfi, northern Iceland Gr 38
Kengala (= with a crooked stripe down its back), Asmund's mare Gr 14, 29
Ketil the One-handed Gr 3
Ketil Raum Gr 13 (see *The Book of Settlements*, ch. 179)
Ketilseyr, farm in Dyrafiord Gi 4
Kialarness, assembly-place in south-west Iceland H 11; Kialarness Assembly Gr 10; H 21
Kiallak, son of Hrolf H 2, 33
Kiartan, son of Stein of Eyiardalsa Gr 64, 67
Kiartan, son of Thorstein and Thorbiorg Katla H 24, 34, 35, 36
Kiarval, ninth-century Irish king in Ossory, southern Ireland (Cearbhall; d. 887/888) Gr 1, 3, 5 (many Icelandic settlers are said to be descended from him; see *Laxdæla saga*)
Kiol, a route (Kjalvegur) through central Iceland Gr 54, 57
Kiotvi the Wealthy Gr 2
Klafastadir, farm on the northern side of Hvalfiord H 20
Kluptir (now Sandkluftir), a gully in western Iceland H 5, 10
Knappsstadir, farm in Fliot Gr 72
Knut the Great (Canute), son of Svein, king of England from 1014 and of Denmark from 1018 (d. 1035) Gr 19, 59
Kol, a slave Gi 1

Kolbein, friend of Onund Wooden-leg Gr 7, 9, 12; Kolbein's sons (Ivar and Leif) Gr 12
Kolbeinsstadir, farm in western Iceland Gr 59
Kolbeinsvik, farm on Strandir, northern Iceland Gr 9
Kolbiorn of Hella in Surnadal Gi 2, 3
Kolbiorn Sneypir Gr 3
Kolgrim the Old, Icelandic settler, son of Alf H 23, 30, 32, 41
Kolgrim, son of Thorhall H 23
Koll, son of Kiallak H 2, 4, 22, 30, 32, 33
Konal, son of Steinmod Gr 3
Kormak at Mel, brother of Thorgils Gr 15, 29, 30, 36
Kræklingahlid, in Eyiafiord, northern Iceland Gr 8
Kraku-Hreidar (son of Ofeig) Gr 70
Kropp, farm in Borgarfiord (Stóri-Kroppur) Gr 47, 62
Krossavik, farm in Vopnafiord, north-eastern Iceland H 1
Kuggi see Thorkel Kuggi
Kuhallardal ('cow-swerve-dale') = Kuvallardal H 29
Kuludalsa, farm on Akraness H 20; called Kuvallara H 28
Kuvallardal ('cow-plain-dale'), off Svinadal, north of Hvalfiord H 26
Kvigandafell (Talknafiord) Gi 5
Kvinesdal (Hvinir), in Agder, southern Norway Gr 7
Kvist, son of Stein H 23
Lækiamot, farm in Vididal Gr 25
Lækiarbug, farm on Myrar Gr 60
Lækiaros, stream-mouth and farm on the northern side of Dyrafiord Gi 11
Langadal, Western Fiords Gr 52
Langafit, meadowland below Reykir in Midfiord Gr 29
Langaness, north-east Iceland Gr 8
Langholt, in Skagafiord Gr 69
Lapp (Finn), inhabitant of the far north of Scandinavia Gr 72
Laugabol, farm on Isafiord Gr 52
Laugardal, south-western Iceland H 9, 10
Laxa, river in Grunnafiord H 32
Laxardal Heath, between Laxardal (Hvammsfiord) and Hrutafiord Gr 48
Laxdæla saga, Saga of the People of Laxardal, western Iceland Gr 10
Leidvoll, in Grunnafiord (unidentified) H 32
Leif, son of Kolbein Gr 12; see also Kolbein's sons
Liarskogar, farm in Hvammssveit, Dalir Gr 26, 27, 48, 49, 53
Lopt, assumed name of Hallmund Gr 54
Lower heaths, north of Thingvoll, western Iceland (less far inland than the higher route) Gr 53, 57
Lund, farm in the southerly Reykiardal H 2, 4, 22, 30, 32
Luta, kinswoman of Vestein Gi 12
Lyting (son of Arnbiorn), father of Geitir H 1

Magnus the Good (inn góði), son of St Olaf (king in Norway 1035–47) Gr 90 (see Snorri Sturluson, *Heimskringla* II 127–59)
Magnus, bishop in Skalaholt 1134–48, son of Einar H 11
Magnus, priest, son of Thord, H 11
Mak, father of Thorgils Gr 25–27
Mar, son of Atli the Red Gr 27
Marskelda, farm in the Dales, western Iceland Gr 27
Marsstadir, farm in Vatnsdal Gr 13
Medaldal, off Dyrafiord Gi 7, 11, 12, 19
Mel, farm in Midfiord (now Melstaður) Gr 15, 29; men of Gr 37
Melahverfi (now Melasveit), western Iceland H 9
Melar, farm in Hrutafiord Gr 14, 30, 42, 48, 49, 51, 83
Michael Catalactus, Greek emperor in Constantinople 1034–41 Gr 86
Midfell, farm and hill on the northern side of Hvalfiord H 2, 20, 28
Midfell, farm by Olfusvatn H 10
Midfiardarvatn, lake above Midfiord Gr 15, 28
Midfiord, northern Iceland Gr 11, 13, 15, 16, 25, 45, 47, 83; men of Gr 15, 16 (here Vatnsdal in manuscript)
Midfiord-Skeggi Gr 11, 12, 62
Midfitiar, Hrutafiord (the name is not recorded elsewhere) Gr 49
Miklagard see Constantinople
Mimir, a giant, in kenning for shield Gr 80
Mist, a valkyrie, in kenning for battle Gr 31
Modrudal Heath, eastern Iceland Gr 63
Modruvellir, farm in Eyiafiord Gr 67
Mokolla ('brownhead'), a ewe in Thorisdal Gr 61 (described as *mókollótt*, 'fawn-coloured and hornless')
Møre = Sunnmøre Gr 22
Mosdal, Arnarfiord Gi 29
Mosfell, mountain and farm in south-western Iceland H 11, 27
Mosvellir, Biarnardal Gi 11, 12
Mulafell (Múlafjall), mountain in from Hvalfiord H 40
Myrar, district north of Borgarfiord in western Iceland Gi 38; Gr 57–60; H 39; men, people of Gr 60, 61
Narfi, kinsman of Kormak at Mel Gr 30
Nauma, probably the name of a goddess, in a kenning for a woman (Haflidi's wife) Gr 17, (Asdis) Gr 83; apparently the name of a giantess, in a kenning for cave Gr 66
Nedri-Botn (now Litli-Botn), farm in Hvalfiord H 18; cf. Botn
Nefsstadir, farm in Haukadal Gi 11, 19
Ness, the, i.e. Snæfellsness Gr 42, 43
Nesses, the, Faxaflói, western Iceland H 9
Nesses, the, on the western side of Oslofiord (Nesjar) Gr 37
Nesses, the, on the south coast of the Western Fiords Gi 24

Nile, name of a river in Egypt, used in kenning for gold H 22
Niord, name of a god, in kennings for warrior(s) (Biorn) Gr 21, (men of Skagafiord) Gr 72
Niorun, name of a goddess used in kennings for woman H 3 (Signy)
Nordmøre (Nordmærr), Norway Gi 1
Nordrardal (Northriver valley), Borgarfiord Gr 30, 67
North (of Iceland), men of Gr 13, (55)
Northriver (Nordra), in Borgarfiord Gr 27
Norway Gi 1, 7, 8, 38; Gr 1–3, 6, 9, 12, 13, 17, 19, 20, 24, 37, 38, 40, 85, 86, 90, 91; H 13, 17, 18, 41
Norwegians (Austmaðr, pl. Austmenn; *maðr norrœnn* Gi 8) Gi 4, 7, 8, 12, 19, 20; (Norðmenn, Norrænir menn; cf. Easterners) Gr 5, 85; (men from Norway) Gr 86
Odd, son of Ofeig Gr 14
Odd, son of Orlyg Gi 7
Odd Pauper-poet (ómagaskáld) Gr 15, 29, 30
Odd Snorrason, late twelfth-century historian and monk at Thingeyrar in northern Iceland Gr 84
Oddgeirsholar, farm in Floi H 10
Oddleif, father of Gest the Wise Gi 6
Odin, a god in Norse mythology H 15 (cf. Biorn); in kenning for swords, his fires Gi 33; see also Gaut, Ialfad, Thrott, Thund, Tveggi, Unn, Vidrir, Ygg
Ofæra, part of the coast of Veidileysa on Strandir Gr 9
Ofeig Burlufot (clubfoot), son of Ivar Beytil Gr 1
Ofeig Grettir (grimacer), son of Einar Gr 3, 6, 10, 13
Ofeig Grettir the younger, son of Onund Wooden-leg Gr 11, 12
Ofeig of Ofeigsfiord Gr 11
Ofeig Skidason Gr 14
Ofeig Thunnskegg (thin-beard), son of Kraku-Hreidar Gr 70
Ofeigsfiord, on Strandir Gr 12
Ofeigsstadir, farm in southern Iceland Gr 6
Ogmund the Bad (illi), a berserk Gr 19, 20
Ok, mountain in from Borgarfiord H 10
Olaf, son of Eyvind Gr 11, 12
Olaf Feilan, son of Thorstein the Red Gi 5; Gr 10, 26
Olaf Haraldsson, the Saint, son of Asta, king of Norway (1015–30) Gr 1, 37–39 (the genealogy in ch. 1 is based on *The Book of Settlements*, ch. 161)
Olaf Peacock (pái) Hoskuldsson Gr 52 (see *Laxdæla saga*)
Olaf's Islands (Óláfseyjar), Breidafiord, western Iceland Gr 50
Olduhrygg, on Snæfellsness Gr 59
Oleif Breid (broad) Gr 3
Olfus, southern Iceland H 9, 10
Olfusvatn, lake in south-western Iceland (now Þingvallavatn) H 2; farm in south-western Iceland, south of the lake H 2, 3, 4, 5, 7, 9, 10, 11, 19

Olvir Barnakarl (children's friend) Gr 3. *The Book of Settlements*, ch. 379, gives the supposed origin of the nickname ('He wouldn't have children tossed by spear-points as was the custom of vikings at the time'), but it is perhaps more likely that it arose from his having a large number of children.
Ondott Kraka (crow) Gr 3, 6, 7; Ondott's sons (Asgrim and Asmund) Gr 7
Ongul, see Thorbiorn Ongul Thordarson
Onund of Medaldal, friend of Gisli Gi 7, 11, 19
Onund, son of Thormod of Brekka H 23; Onund's hillock (Önundarhóll), by Hvalfiord H 23
Onund Wooden-leg (tréfótr), son of Ofeig Burlufot Gr 1–12
Onundarfiord, Western Fiords Gi 4, 11
Orkadal (Orkdalen), south of Trondheim, Norway H 1
Orlyg, father of Odd Gi 7
Orm, son of Eyiolf Egilsson Gr 34 (see *The Book of Settlements*, ch. 177)
Orm, son of Hvamm-Thorir H 24, 27, 32
Orm, Norwegian trader H 19; maybe the same person H 35
Orm Storolfsson Gr 58 (see *Orms þáttr Stórólfssonar*)
Orm the Wealthy Gr 1
Orrastadir (Heath-cock's steading), in Haukadal (modern Koltur?) Gi 18
Osland, farm by Skagafiord Gr 82
Oslofiord (the Vik; the Skagerrak), Norway Gr 13, 91; H 12, 13, 18; men from (Víkverskir menn) Gi 7; H 12
Ospak, son of Glum, nephew of Grettir Gr 14, 51, 83
Ospak Kiallaksson Gr 14
Otradal, farm in Arnarfiord Gi 22, 31, 32, 36
Oxarfiord, northern Iceland Gr 12
Oxen-might = Thorbiorn Oxen-might Gr 48
Ox-men, nickname given to the Botn-dwellers (*yxnismenn*) H 23
Passing Round of Grettir, The, a poem (*Grettisfærsla*) Gr 52
Poet-Torfa, poetess (Skáld-Torfa) Gr 15, 23, 24
Pope's palace (Páfagarðr), Rome, the Vatican Gr 91
Rafarta, daughter of King Kiarval Gr 3
Rannveig, daughter of Asmund Hærulang, wife of Gamli Thorhallsson Gr 14, 30
Rannveig, first wife of Asmund Hærulang, mother of Thorstein Dromund Gr 13
Rannveig at Sæbol Gi 12
Rannveig, daughter of Thorbiorn of Arnarholt H 1
Raud of Fridarey Gi 2
Raudasand, on the south side of the Western Fiords Gi 28
Red Sea (Rauðahaf) Gr 24
Red-beard, see Thorir Red-beard
Ref, farmer at Haug Gi 27
Ref, workman of Holmgongu-Skeggi Gi 2
Ref the Old, son of Thorstein H 24, 25, 32, 34, 36, 39, 40
Regin, a dwarf, whose house is a stone (part of the name Thorstein) Gr 24

Reydarfell, farm on Hvitarsida Gr 17
Reykiaheid, heath in northern Iceland Gr 63
Reykiaholar, farm on Reykianess, Breidafiord, western Iceland Gr 27, 49, 50
Reykiaholt (Reykholt), farm in the northerly Reykiardal H 11
Reykianess, Breidafiord, western Iceland Gr 27, 49, 50
Reykianess (Reykjadiskur), on the western side of Skagafiord Gr 75
Reykianess, south-west Iceland Gr 17
Reykianess, on Strandir, northern Iceland Gr 9, 12
Reykiardal, northerly (now Reykholtsdalur), western Iceland H 2, 8
Reykiardal, southerly (now Lundarreykjadalur), western Iceland H 1, 2, 4, 22
Reykiardalsa, river in the northerly Reykiardal H 8
Reykiarfiord, on Strandir, northern Iceland Gr 9, 11, 12
Reykiarvik (Reykjavík), farm in south-western Iceland H 10
Reykiaskard, pass above Skagafiord Gr 69
Reykiastrond, the western side of Skagafiord Gr 84
Reykir, farm in Hrutafiord Gr 48, 49
Reykir, farm in Midfiord, northern Iceland Gr 29
Reykir, farm on the western side of Skagafiord Gr 69, 75, 84
Reyniness, farm in Skagafiord (now Reynistaður) Gr 69
Rifsker, on Strandir Gr 12
Rogaland, district of south-west Norway Gr 1, 2, 7; South Rogaland (men of) Gr 2
Rome Gr 91 (journey to, *Rómferð*), 92 (city of, *Rómaborg*); pilgrimage to (*suðr*) Gi 38
Rosmhvalaness, south-west Iceland Gr 12
Sæbol, farm in Haukadal Gi 4, 5, 7, 12–17
Sæmund the Hebridean (Suðreyski) Gr 31
Sæmundarhlid, Skagafiord Gr 69
Saga, a goddess, in kenning for woman (farmer's daughter) Gr 60
Saga of Biorn, i.e. *Bjarnar saga Hítdælakappa* Gr 58
Saga of Bodmod and Grimolf and Gerpir, an unknown saga (according to *The Book of Settlements* ch. 160, the saga of Bodmod Gerpir ('hero') and Grimolf) Gr 12
Saga of the Confederates (i.e. *Bandamanna saga*) Gr 14
Saga of Earl Eirik Gr 19 (see note)
Saga of the People of Laxardal, see Laxdæla saga
Saka-Stein, nephew of Bork (son of Thordis daughter of Thorstein Thorskabit) Gi 5, 7, 19, 20, 21, 27
Salten (Sálpti) in Halogaland Gr 20
Saltness, Dyrafiord Gi 19
Sam, son of Bork the Stout Gr 68
Samsstadir, farm in Laxardal, Dalir Gr 49
Sand (Miðsandur), on the northern side of Hvalfiord H 23
Sand (Stórisandur), central Iceland Gr 84

Sandaos (Sanda estuary, Dyrafiord) Gi 7, 12, 19
Sandhaugar, farm in Bardardal Gr 64–67
Saurar, farm in Keldudal Gi 4
Saurbæ, farm on Hvalfiardarstrond H 11, 24, 26
Saxa Island (Saxa ey, unidentified) Gi 2, 3
Scandinavia (Norðrlönd) Gr 85, 91
Scotland Gr 1, 3; Scottish firths Gr 4
Short-Arm see Skeggi Short-Arm Gamlason
Sialfkviar (= natural animal pens), on the north side of the entrance to Hvalfiord H 28
Sif, wife of the god Thor, whose help (*biorg*) was a rowan tree (Snorri Sturluson's *Edda*, p. 82); in a pun on the name Thorbiorg Gr 52
Sigar, legendary king who hanged Hagbard Gr 52 (see note 50)
Sigfast, father-in-law of King Solvi Gr 3
Sighvat, father of Signy Gr 7
Sigmund, a wandering beggar H 9, 12, 20, 21, 24, 28, 35, 36
Signy, daughter of Sighvat, wife of Ondott Kraka Gr 7
Signy, daughter of Valbrand H 2, 3, 4, 5, 6, 7, 8, 9, 10
Signyiarstadir, farm in western Iceland, south of Hvita H 2, 8
Sigrhadd of Viborg Gi 8, 14 (first verse)
Sigrid, daughter of Thorbiorn of Skalmarness, wife of Grimkel H 10, 12, 19
Sigrid, daughter of Thorstein Oxnabrodd H 26
Sigurd, son of Aud H 21
Sigurd, son of Biartmar Gi 4, 21
Sigurd, bishop in Norway Gr 38 (see Sagas of Olaf the Saint and Olaf Tryggvason in Snorri Sturluson's *Heimskringla* I)
Sigurd Muli (snout), of Fell H 1, 12
Sigurd, Norwegian Gi 8
Sigurd, husband of Spes Gr 87, 88, 89
Sigurd, Torfi's foster-brother (Torfafóstri), son of Gunnhild H 2, 8, 17, 18, 20, 24, 28, 29, 30, 32, 33
Sildamannagata, a route from the bottom of Hvalfiord H 30
Sirnir, name of a giant used in a kenning for gold H 7
Skagafiord, northern Iceland Gr 28, 67, 69, 70, 84; men of, people of Gr 72, 73, 75, 77
Skagi, a promontory in northern Iceland Gr 9
Skalaholt (Skálholt), south-west Iceland, one of two bishoprics in medieval Iceland (the second, founded in 1106, was at Hólar in the north). Ísleif was the first bishop there 1055–80 Gr 25, 84
Skalamyr, inland from Skagafiord, in Tunga (unidentified) Gr 70
Skalavik, a small bay in north-west Iceland Gr 5
Skald-Torfa see Poet-Torfa
Skalmarness, on the northern side of Breidafiord, western Iceland H 10
Skammfotarmyr (Short-leg's marshland), in Haukadal Gi 18

Skaptaholt, southern Iceland Gr 6
Skapti, son of Thorodd Eyvindarson, lawman or lawspeaker 1004–30 (d. 1030) Gr 27, 32, 46, 51, 53, 54, 76
Skard, farm in Haukadal, Dalir, western Iceland Gr 30, 43
Skarfsstadir, farm in Dalir, across the bay from Liarskogar Gr 53, 84
Skeggi from As Gr 16, 82
Skeggi, son of Gamli Skeggiason Gr 84
Skeggi see Holmgongu-Skeggi Gi 2, 3
Skeggi of Kelduhverfi, son of Bodolf Gr 38
Skeggi see Midfiord-Skeggi
Skeggi Short-Arm (skammhöndungr), son of Gamli Thorhallsson Gr 51, 83, 84
Skeggi, son of Steinvor at Sandhaugar Gr 67
Skeggi, son of Thorarin Fylsenni Gr 26
Skeggi, son of Thorir of Gard Gr 38; see Thorir of Gard, sons of
Skeif, farmer at Hvitarvellir H 41
Skeliavik, inlet in Steingrimsfiord Gi 7
Skialdbreid, mountain north-east of Thingvoll Gr 61
Skorradal, Borgarfiord, western Iceland H 3, 22, 29, 30; lower Skorradal H 19; Skorradal lake (Skorradalsvatn) H 30; see also Vatn, H 29
Skridinsenni, mountain on Inn-Strandir Gr 14
Skroppa, Thorstein Oxnabrodd's nurse H 26; Skroppa's Gill (Skroppugil), on Hvalfiardarstrond H 26
Skuf, a shepherd in Hundadal Gr 27
Skutileyiar, islands in Breidafiord Gi 25
Skutilsfiord, north-western Iceland Gi 7
Sledaas, ridge north-east of Thingvoll Gr 16, 32
Sleita, mother (or father?) of Gaut Gr 27
Sleitu-Helgi Gr 30 (see Strife-Helgi in *The Book of Settlements*, chs 168, 183)
Slettahlid, settlement in Skagafiord Gr 70
Slysfiord, in Sunnmøre, western Norway Gr 19
Snæbiorn, son of Eyvind the Easterner Gr 3
Snæfellsness, western Iceland Gr 42, (43); see Ness, the
Snækoll, a berserk Gr 40
Snorri *Godi*, son of Thorgrim (d. 1031) Gi 18, 37; Gr 49, 51, 59, 68, 76 (see Thorgrim Thorgimsson; the name Snorri is related to *snerrir*, 'turbulent person'; cf. *Eyrbyggja saga* ch. 12; also *Laxdæla saga*)
Sodulkolla, Svein of Bakki's mare ('saddle-head') Gr 47; Sodulkolla verses (Söðulkolluvísur) Gr 47
Sokkolfsdal, in Dalir Gr 68
Sokndal (Sóknadalr), in Rogaland, south-west Norway Gr 7
Sol, name of a goddess, in kenning for woman (daughter of Thorir of Gard) Gr 63
Solmund (Eilifsson) Gr 31
Solmund, son of Thorbiorn Iarlakappi Gr 10

Solmund, son of Thorolf Smior H 24
Solvi, king in Gautland Gr 3
Solvi, son of Hrolf the Geitlander H 11
Solvi the Splendid (inn prúði), son of Asbrand Thorbrandsson Gr 44
Sotanaut, name of the sword that had belonged to Soti H 17, 21, 36, 38, 39; name of the ring that had belonged to Soti H 34, 36, 37, 39, 40
Sotaness, in Ranriki, east of Oslo fiord (now Sotenäs) Gr 1
Soti, a dead viking H 14, 15, 19, 39; Soti's grave-mound (Sótahaugr) H 14
South (of Iceland), men of the Gr 12
Spear-marsh (Spjótsmýri is the modern name of a meadow near Thoroddsstadir, Hrutafiord) Gr 49
Spes, noblewoman in Constantinople Gr 86 (heading), 87–92
Spying-Helgi (Njósnar-Helgi) see Helgi
Stad, a headland, western Norway (Stadlandet) Gr 38
Stein the Great Traveller (mjöksiglandi), son of Thorir Autumndark Gr 77
Stein, son of Kolgrim H 23
Stein, priest at Eyiardalsa Gr 64, 65, 67
Stein Gi 20, 21 see Saka-Stein
Stein, a sea-captain Gr 12
Stein, son of Thorgest, lawman or lawspeaker 1031–3, Gr 77, 84
Stein Gr 70, see Tungu-Stein
Steingrimsfiord, Inn-Strandir, north-west Iceland Gi 7
Steinkjer (Steinker), Trøndelag, Norway Gr 22
Steinmod, son of Konal Gr 3
Steinmod, son of Olvir Barnakarl Gr 3
Steinolf, son of Olvir Barnakarl Gr 3
Steinolf Thorleifsson of Hraundal Gr 60, 61
Steinsholt, farm in southern Iceland Gr 6
Steinsstadir, farm in the Tunga area in Skagafiord Gr 70
Steinunn, daughter of Hrut of Kambsness Gr 61
Steinunn (Steinud) the Old Gr 12 (see *The Book of Settlements*, ch. 394)
Steinvor, wife of Thorstein the White at Sandhaugar Gr 64, 67
Stifla, in Fliot, east of Skagafiord Gr 72
Stigi, north-west Iceland Gr 5
Stokkaholm, island off Nordmøre, Norway Gi 1
Stokkar, farm in Surnadal (Stokke, Valsøyfjord, Nordmøre) Gi 2, 3
Strandafloi, a large bay in northern Iceland (the western part of Húnaflói) Gr 9
Strandir, the Strands, the eastern side of the north-west peninsular of Iceland (Hornstrandir) Gr 9, 25, 27; H 33
Strond see Bardastrond
Strond ('the strand'), i.e. Hvalfiardarstrond H 23, 32; the Strond-dwellers, men of Strond H 23
Sturla Thordarson, lawman and historian (1214–84) Gr 49, 69, 93 (his version of The Book of Settlements was made *c.*1260)

Sturlungs, a prominent family in thirteenth-century Iceland (*c.*1200–60), descended from Hvamm-Sturla Thordarson (1115–83), to which Snorri Sturluson and Sturla Thordarson the historians belonged Gr 84
Stykkisvoll, farm in Bryniudal H 24
Styrkar, son of Raud Gi 2, 3
Styrmir the Wise (inn fróði), son of Kari, priest, lawspeaker and historian, prior of the monastery on Videy, author of a version of *The Book of Settlements* (died 1245) H 41
Sudur-Strandir, the western side of Strandafloi (= Inn-Strandir) Gr 9
Sugandafiord, Western Fiords Gr 5
Sugandi see Hallvard Sugandi
Sulki, king of the men of south Rogaland Gr 2
Sunnmøre, district in western Norway Gr 17; cf. Møre
Sur see Thorbiorn Sur; sons of, see Gisli and Thorkel
Surnadal, Nordmøre, western Norway Gi 1, 2, 3; Gr 7; (men of, Sýrdœlir) Gi 5, 6
Svan of Hol, son of Biorn of Biarnarfiord Gr 12
Svart, a herdsman at Indridastadir H 29
Svart, Ingiald's slave Gi 25, 27
Svartfaxi (black-mane), name of Signy's horse H 3, 4
Svarthofdi, son of Biorn Gullberi H 1
Svein, enemy of Gisli Gi 36
Svein, farmer at Bakki Gr 47
Svein Hakonarson, earl in Norway (d. *c.*1015) Gr 19, 22, 24, 37
Svidu-Kari (singeing-Kari), son of Solmund Gr 10 (*Njáls saga*)
Svinadal, north of Hvalfiord H 26, 29, 30
Svinasand, on Hvalfiardarstrond H 29
Svinasund, sounds on Balagardssida, Finland H 17
Sweden Gr 32
Sylgsdalir, in Sweden (unidentified; perhaps around Lake Siljan in Dalarna) Gr 32
Syr, a name for Freyia, whose tears are gold Gr 83
Talknafiord, Western Fiords Gi 5
Thingeyr, Dyrafiord Gi 12
Thingeyrasveit, district round Thingeyrar in northern Iceland Gr 13
Thingness, in Borgarfiord Gr 47
Thingvoll, the site of the Althing in south-western Iceland
Thiorsa, river in south-western Iceland Gr 6; H 19
Thiostolf, son of Biorn Gullberi H 1
Thora, daughter of Olaf Thorsteinsson Gi 5
Thora, daughter of Raud of Fridarey Gi 2, 4
Thoralf of Eyr Gr 52
Thoralf Skolmsson Gr 58 (see *Orms þáttr Stórólfssonar*)
Thorarin Fylsenni (foal-brow), son of Thord Gellir Gr 26
Thorarin, son of Hafr Thordarson Gr 72

Thorarin, Norwegian Gi 7
Thorarin Spaki (the Wise) at Lækiamot in Vididal Gr 28, 31
Thorarin (Thorgilsson) from Akrar Gr 60, 61
Thorbiorg, daughter of Grimkel H 8–12, 18, 19, 21, 29, 31, 32, 37–41
Thorbiorg, wife of Hogni of Hagavik H 2
Thorbiorg Katla H 24, 25, 39, 40; see also Katla
Thorbiorg the Stout, daughter of Olaf Peacock Gr 52
Thorbiorn of Arnarholt (son of Arnbiorn) H 1
Thorbiorn, son of Arnor Hynef, known as Oxen-might Gr 30, 36, 42–45, 47–49, 51; see under Hafli
Thorbiorn, assumed name of Bolli, Orm's slave H 27
Thorbiorn Ferdalang (far-traveller) Gr 30, 36, 37, 42, 43
Thorbiorn, called Glaum (Merryman) Gr 69, 72, 74, 79, 80, 82
Thorbiorn, son of Griotgard H 12–14, 18
Thorbiorn Iarlakappi Gr 10
Thorbiorn Koll (top), (son of Valthiof) H 28
Thorbiorn Laxakappi (salmon-champion) Gr 10 (according to *The Book of Settlements*, ch. 379 the nickname should be Iarlakappi (earls' champion), as further down in Gr 10)
Thorbiorn Laxakarl (salmon-man) Gr 3, 6
Thorbiorn Selagnup (seal's crag) Gi 5
Thorbiorn of Skalmarness H 10
Thorbiorn Sur (whey; the nickname is probably derived from the name Surnadal), son of Thorkel Skerauki Gi 1–4, 19, 28, 38; sons of (Súrssynir) Gi 5; see also Sur
Thorbiorn Thordarson, known as Ongul (hook) Gr 70, 72, 73, 75–86; see also Thord Hialtason, sons of
Thorbrand, son of Harald Ring Gr 44
Thorbrandsstadir, farm in Bryniudal H 24
Thord, name of two brothers at Breida in Skagafiord Gr 70, 72
Thord Cat (köttr) H 23–25 (probably not the same as the Thord Cat, son of Thord, of *Laxdæla saga* and other sagas)
Thord the Coward (inn huglausi), Gisli's slave Gi 13, 17, 20
Thord, kinsman of Eyiolf Gi 36
Thord Gellir ('yeller'), son of Olaf Feilan, father of Eyiolf Gi 15; Gr 26, 77
Thord of Hofdi, son of Biorn Gr 26, 70
Thord Hialtason of Hof Gr 70; sons of (Hialti and Thorbiorn Ongul) Gr 70, 72
Thord Knapp, son of Biorn, Icelandic settler Gr 72
Thord Kolbeinsson, poet on Hitarness Gr 58–60 (see *Bjarnar saga Hítdælakappa*)
Thord, son of Kolgrim H 41
Thord Skalp Gr 70
Thord, son of Solvi H 11
Thordis, daughter of Asmund under Asmundargnup Gr 13

Thordis, daughter of Asmund Hærulang, wife of Glum Ospaksson Gr 14
Thordis, Signy's nurse H 4, 6, 8
Thordis, wife of Thorbiorn Seal's crag Gi 5
Thordis, daughter of Thorbiorn Sur (Súrsdóttir), sister of Gisli Gi 2, 3, 7, 16, 18, 19, 37
Thordis, daughter of Thord Hialtason Gr 70
Thordis, daughter of Thorgrim of Gnup, second wife of Onund Wooden-leg Gr 11
Thordis, daughter of Thorstein Thorskabit Gi 5
Thordisarholt, farm in from Borgarfiord, western Iceland H 8
Thordisarstadir (Eyr, Snæfellsness) Gi 37
Thorelf, daughter of Alf of the Dales Gr 27
Thoreyiargnup, farm in Vestrhop, northern Iceland Gr 31, 34
Thorfinn, workman of Flosi Gr 11, 12
Thorfinn, son of Kar the Old Gr 18–20, 22–24, 28
Thorfinn of Lækiarbug Gr 60
Thorfinn (of Reykiahlid), son of Arnor Gr 80 (see *Ljósvetninga saga*)
Thorgaut, a foreign shepherd Gr 33
Thorgeir, son of Finn H 2
Thorgeir of Fiskilæk, son of Thord Bialki (see *The Book of Settlements*, chs 235, 250) Gr 38
Thorgeir Gyrdilskeggi (belt-beard, i.e. whose beard came down to his belt) H 23, 24, 28, 29, 32, 33
Thorgeir Havarsson, hero of *Fóstbræðra saga,* foster-brother of Thormod Gr 25–27, 50, 51
Thorgeir, son of Onund Wooden-leg, called 'Bottle-back' (flöskubakr) Gr 11–13
Thorgeir Orri (heath-cock) Gi 18
Thorgeir, son of Thord of Hofdi Gr 70
Thorgeir (probably both references are to the son of Thorhadd of Hitardal) Gr 60
Thorgeir, son of Thorir of Gard Gr 38; see Thorir of Gard, sons of
Thorgeir, son of Thorir at Skard Gr 30, 43; see Thorir at Skard, sons of
Thorgeirsdrapa, a poem by Thormod Kolbrun's poet about Thorgeir Havarsson Gr 27. See *Fóstbræðra saga*, in which fifteen verses of this poem are preserved, including the one here; cf. Gr 25
Thorgerd, daughter of Alf of the Dales Gr 27
Thorgerd (in some manuscripts Thorunn), mother of Gest Oddleifsson Gi 23, 24
Thorgerd Horgabrud, legendary figure represented as the object of worship in a number of sagas (see Snorri Sturluson, *Edda,* p. 112, Thorgerd Holgabrud) H 19
Thorgerd, wife of Ingiald Gi 24, 25
Thorgest, son of Stein the Great Traveller Gr 77
Thorgils, son of Ari Masson Gr 27, 49–51
Thorgils Ingialdsson Gr 60
Thorgils Maksson Gr 25, 26, 27

Thorgils at Mel, brother of Kormak Gr 15, 29, 30
Thorgrim of Gnup, father of Thordis Gr 11
Thorgrim *Godi*, son of Thorstein Thorskabit; Thordis's first husband Gi 5–7, 9–20, 37; called Giant-bane Grim Gi 18; one of the two Thorgrims, Gi 11, 13
Thorgrim Karnsargodi (*godi* at Karnsa in Vatnsdal; now Kornsá) Gr 13
Thorgrim Nef (neb) Gi 11, 13, 14, 18, 19, 21, 26; one of the two Thorgrims, Gi 11, 13
Thorgrim, Norwegian (*austmaðr*) Gi 19, 20
Thorgrim, son of Onund, known as 'Hoary-top' (hærukollr) Gr 11–13
Thorgrim, son of Thorgrim Thorsteinsson, see Snorri *Godi* Gi 18
Thorgrima Smith-woman (smiðkona) H 3, 19, 21, 30, 40
Thorhall, son of Asgrim Ellida-Grimsson Gr 53
Thorhall, son of Fridmund Gr 32
Thorhall, son of Grim Thorhallsson Gr 32, 33, 35
Thorhall, son of Kolgrim the Old H 23
Thorhall the Winelander (i.e. who had been to North America), son of Gamli Gr 14, 30
Thorhallsstadir, farm in Forsæludal Gr 32–35
Thorir Autumndark (haustmyrkr), son of Vigbiod Gr 77
Thorir, kinsman of Eyiolf Gi 36
Thorir of Gard, son of Skeggi Gr 38, 46, 51, 56, 57, 59, 62, 63, 67, 77, 82, 84; sons of (Thorgeir and Skeggi) Gr 38
Thorir Haklang (long-chin), son of Kiotvi (Snorri Sturluson, *Heimskringla* II 63) Gr 2
Thorir, a Norwegian Gi 7
Thorir Red-beard, an outlaw Gr 56, 57
Thorir at Skard, son of Thorkel at Bordeyr Gr 30, 43; sons of (Gunnar and Thorgeir) Gr 43, 44
Thorir Thomb ('paunch'), a berserk Gr 19, 20
Thorir of Thorisdal, half-giant Gr 61
Thorisdal, valley (perhaps only legendary) between the glaciers in western central Iceland Gr 61, 67
Thorkel Annmarki ('blemish'; the nickname is probably derived from the farm-name) Gi 18
Thorkel (Thrastarson) at Bordeyr Gr 30
Thorkel Eiriksson, friend of Gisli Gi 4, 10, 12, 15, 20, 21; one of the two Thorkels, Gi 12, 15, 21
Thorkel, son of Eyiolf the Grey, son of Thord Gellir Gr 62 (see *Laxdæla saga*)
Thorkel of Gervidal Gr 52
Thorkel Krafla, son of Thorgrim Karnsargodi Gr 13, 16, 25
Thorkel Kuggi, son of Thord Gellir Gr 26
Thorkel Mani (moon), lawspeaker 970–84 (i.e. later than the time of the supposed events in which he is involved in *The Saga of Hord* and *The Saga of Grettir*) Gr 12; H 10

Thorkel the Rich (inn auðgi), son of Thord; friend of Gisli Gi 4, 5, 6, 10, 12, 15, 16, 21; one of the two Thorkels, Gi 12, 15, 21
Thorkel at Salten Gr 20, 21, 22
Thorkel Skerauki ('rock-increment', a word known on the west coast of Norway, used for the lower of two adjacent rocks that is covered at flood-tide while its higher companion stays uncovered at all times) Gi 1
Thorkel, son of Thorbiorn Sur (Súrsson) Gi 2–7, 9–15, 17–20, 23, 24, 28–30, 38
Thorlak the Saint, bishop, son of Thorhall (d. 1193) Gr 34
Thorlaug, daughter of Sæmund the Hebridean Gr 31
Thorleif, workman of Halldor at Hof Gr 81
Thorleif of Hraundal, son of Steinolf Gr 60, 61
Thormod of Brekka H 11, 23, 24
Thormod Kolbrun's poet, son of Bersi, hero of *Fóstbræðra saga,* foster-brother of Thorgeir Gr 25–27, 50, 51
Thormod Skapti (shaft) Gr 3, 6, 10
Thorodd, son of Arnor Hynef, known as Poem-bit (the origin of this nickname is unknown; it may be that Thorodd had once composed, or had composed about him, a fragment of a poem that was never completed) Gr 30, 48, 49, 51, 83
Thorodd, nephew of Bork (son of Thordis daughter of Thorstein Thorskabit) Gi 5, 19, 20
Thorodd *Godi*, son of Thorvor and Eyvind, father of Skapti Gr 6, 12, 32
Thorodd, Icelandic settler Gr 30
Thorodd, son of Snorri *Godi* Gr 68, 69
Thorodd, son of Thorgrim Thorsteinsson Gi 7
Thoroddsstadir, farm in Hrutafiord Gr 30, 48
Thorolf Mostrarskegg Gi 5
Thorolf Smior (butter, see *The Book of Settlements*, chs 5, 232; son of Thorstein Skrofa) H 24
Thorolf Starri (stiff) H 39
Thorskafiord, north-west Iceland Gr 50; Thorskafiord Heath Gr 52; Thorskafiord Assembly Gi 28
Thorsness (Snæfellsness, western Iceland) Gi 5, 19, 21, 25; Thorsness Assembly Gi 5, 19, 20
Thorstein, son of Asmund Hærulang and Rannveig, half-brother of Grettir; called Dromund (a very large warship used on the Mediterranean; Greek *drómōn,* Old French *dromont*) Gr 13, 23, 24, 39–41, 85–93
Thorstein (Gislason) Gr 59
Thorstein *Godi*, son of Thorvie Gr 6
Thorstein Gullknapp (gold-button) H 23, 26, 27, 34, 36–38
Thorstein, son of Ketil Raum Gr 13
Thorstein Oxnabrodd (oxen-goad) H 11, 24, 26, 32
Thorstein Red, son of Aud the Deep-minded and Olaf the White Gr 26
Thorstein of Reykianess Gr 12

Thorstein, son of Solmund H 24
Thorstein, son of Thorkel Annmarki Gi 18, 19
Thorstein, son of Thorkel Kuggi; known as Thorstein Kuggason Gr 26, 27, 48, 49, 53, 57, 67, 68 (see *Laxdæla saga*; his disputes with Snorri *Godi* are mentioned in *Eyrbyggja saga*, ch. 65)
Thorstein Thorskabit (cod-biter) Gi 5; sons of (Thorgrim and Bork) Gi 5
Thorstein from Upplond, brother of Rannveig Gr 13
Thorstein the White of Sandhaugar Gr 64
Thorvald, son of Asgeir of Asgeirsa (not actually the brother of Kalf) Gr 15, 25, 26, 35, 44, 51, 83, 84
Thorvald Blaskegg (dark-beard) H 23, 24, 33; cf. Blaskeggsa(r)
Thorvald of Drangar (father of Eirik the Red) Gr 9
Thorvald Kodransson, missionary and poet Gr 13 (see *Þorvalds þáttr víðförla*)
Thorvald at Reykir in Skagafiord Gr 69, 75
Thorvald Spark (gneisti) Gi 12
Thorvald of Vatnshorn H 3, 19
Thorvard of Holt Gi 12
Thorvie, daughter of Thormod Skapti Gr 6
Thorvor, daughter of Thormod Skapti Gr 6
Thrand (Mioksiglandi, the Great Traveller), son of Biorn Gr 2–6, 10
Thrand, son of Thorarin of Akrar Gr 60, 61
Thrandarholt, farm in southern Iceland Gr 6
Thrott, a name for Odin, whose storm is battle Gr 48
Thund, name of Odin, in kenning for warrior Gr 24; in kenning for shield, part of kenning for warrior Gr 47; his darling (wife) was Iord, Earth, in a kenning for Grettir Gr 52
Thurid, daughter of Asgeir Ædikoll Gr 26
Thurid, daughter of Grimkel H 1, 11
Thurid, daughter of Hrafn Gi 4
Thurid, nurse of Thorbiorn Ongul Gr 78
Thurid, daughter of Thorhall Grimsson Gr 32
Thver, river in Gnupveriahrepp (Þverá) Gr 6
Thver, river in Vestrhop in northern Iceland (Þverá) Gr 44
Thverfell, farm in the southerly Reykiardal H 4
Thyril, name of a farm and a mountain in Hvalfiord H 23, 36, 38
Tind, son of Hallkel H 13, 41
Tittlingsstadir, farm near Reykiaholar, Breidafiord Gr 50
Torfi, son of Valbrand H 2–4, 8–10, 12, 17, 20–22, 24, 28–30, 32–34, 36; Torfi's foster-brother, see Sigurd
Torfi, son of Vebrand Gr 80
Torfustadir, farm in Midfiord Gr 15
Trekyllir, name of a ship, = wooden bag Gr 12
Trekyllisvik, the Vik (Víkin, the Bay), a bay on Strandir Gr 11, 12
Trøndelag, district in Norway (Þrándheimr) Gi 3; Gr 22, 37, 38; H 23

Trondheimsfiord, Norway, entrance to (Þrándheimsmynni) Gr 22
Tunga, farm in Hrutafiord (Hrútatunga) Gr 30
Tunga, farm in southern Iceland (Bræðratunga) Gr 53, 54
Tunga, farm in Sælingsdal, Dalir (Sælingsdalstunga) Gr 49, 68
Tunga in Vatnsdal Gr 33, 34
Tungua, river east of Skagafiord Gr 72
Tungu-Stein, son of Biorn (of Tunga in Skagafiord) Gr 70, 72, 81
Tunsberg, a town in Oslofiord, Norway (Tønsberg) Gr 23, 39, 40, 85
Tveggi, a name for Odin in a kenning for a seafarer Gr 17
Two-days moor (Tvídægra; in the western part of central Iceland) Gr 16, 31, 47
Tyr, a god in Norse mythology, used in kennings for man H 28
Ulf the Boss-eyed (skjálgi), son of Hogni the White Gr 27
Ulf, son of Grim the Halogalander H 11
Ulf, son of Ulfham the Shape-shifter H 17
Ulfham the Shape-shifter (inn hamrammi) H 17
Ulfham, son of Ulf H 17
Ulfhedin, son of Ulfham H 17
Ulfheid, daughter of Eyiolf Gudmundarson Gr 34
Ulfliotsvatn, farm by a lake of the same name south of Olfusvatn H 19
Ull, a god, in a kenning for warrior Gr 18
Una, daughter of Steinolf Gr 3
Unn, a name for Odin, used in a kenning for battle H 38
Upplond, district of central Norway (Oppland) Gr 1, 2, 13
Uppsalir, farm in the northerly Reykiardal H 21, 22
Vadil, farm on Bardastrond (Haugavaðall) Gi 23
Vadsteinaberg, rock on Hergilsey Gi 26
Vågan, a place in Halogaland (Lofoten islands), northern Norway (Vágar) Gr 20, 22
Valbrand, son of Valthiof, of Breidabolstad H 2, 3, 4, 6, 30, 32
Valgerd, daughter of Thorodd Poem-bit Gr 83
Valhall, Odin's hall (Valhöll) Gi 14
Valthiof the Old, son of Orlyg H 2
Varangian guard, Varangians Gr 86, 87, 88, 90; the Greek emperor's household guard, traditionally manned by Scandinavians. It was first fully organised under Basil II (d. 1025). By about 1100 the Guard was chiefly composed of English soldiers (cf. Snorri Sturluson, *Heimskringla* II 162).
Vatn, i.e. Skorradalsvatn, lake in Skorradal H 29
Vatnsdal, northern Iceland Gr 13, 16, 25, 32–36; Vatnsdal chieftaincy (*godord*) Gr 16; men of (i.e. the descendants of Ingimund the Old, such as Asdis) Gr 13, (16), 17, 48
Vatnsfiardardal, valley in the Western Fiords Gr 52
Vatnsfiord, farm in the Western Fiords Gr 52
Vatnshorn, farm in Skorradal H 3, 22
Vatnsness, in Húnaflói, northern Iceland Gr 15, 29 (men of), 44

Vatnsskard, pass in northern Iceland, between Langadal and Skagafiord Gr 69
Vebrand, father of Torfi Gr 80
Veidileysa (Veiðileysufjörður), a fiord on Strandir, northern Iceland Gr 9
Vellir, farm in Borgarfiord (= Hvitarvellir) Gr 47
Vermund the Slender (inn mjóvi) Thorgrimsson Gr 52 (see *Eyrbyggja saga, Fóstbræðra saga*)
Vestar, son of Hæng Gr 3
Vestein, a Norwegian Gi 4
Vestein, son of Vestein; brother of Aud Gi 4, 5, 7–15, 17, 19, 21, 28, 29; sons of (Berg and Helgi) Gi 38
Vestgeir, son of Biartmar Gi 4, 21
Vestmar, a viking Gr 4
Vestrhop, area west of the Hop lagoon in northern Iceland Gr 15
Viborg (Vébjörg), Jutland Gi 8, 10
Vididal, northern Iceland Gr 11, 13, 15, 28, 34; men of (Víðdælar) Gr 15
Vidrir, a name for Odin, in kenning for shield Gr 63
Vidvik, farm in Skagafiord Gr 70, 79, 81, 82
Viga-Bardi (warrior-, slayings-) see Bardi Gudmundarson
Viga-Styr Thorgrimsson Gr 52
Vigbiod, a viking Gr 4
Vik, the, see Oslofiord
Vik, the (the Bay), see Trekyllisvik; men of (Víkrmenn) Gr 11, 12
Vikar, workman of Hialti Thordarson at Hof Gr 82
Vikarsskeid, near the estuary of Thiorsa (actually more likely that of Olfusa) H 19
Vilborg, daughter of Gizur the White H 11
Vilborgarkelda (*kelda* = spring), west of Olfusvatn, on the eastern side of Mosfellsheiði H 11
Vindheim, farm on Haramarsey Gr 18, 19
Warflame (Gunnlogi), a sword Gi 2
West, the, i.e. the British Isles Gr 1–3, 6, 38, 49
Western Fiords (Vestfirðir), north-west Iceland Gr 49, 52, 54; Western Fiords *Quarter* (Vestfirðingafjórðungr) Gr 27; (vestr í Fjörðu) H 8
Wetherfiord (Veðrafjörðr) = Hrutafiord (*hrutr* is Icelandic for wether) Gr 48, 57
Wooden-leg (Tréfótr) see Onund; Wooden-leg's Mound (Tréfótshaugr), near Kaldbak on Strandir Gr 11
Ygg, a name for Odin, whose drink is poetry, in kenning for poet (Grettir) Gr 47